Subscriber Loop Signaling and Transmission Handbook

Analog

Telecommunications Handbook Series
Whitham D. Reeve, Series Editor

The *Telecommunications Handbook Series* is designed to provide the engineer and technical practitioner with working information in the three basic fields of telecommunications: inside plant, outside plant, and administration and regulatory. This integrated series of handbooks provides practical information on the link between field experience and formal telecommunication industry standards and practices. These books are essential tools for engineers and technical practitioners who require day-to-day engineering and technical information on telecommunication systems.

Other proposed and forthcoming books include coverage on:

- Subscriber loop signaling and transmission: digital
- Introduction to telecommunications
- Grounding methods and measurements
- Telecommunication protection
- Power system design
- Fiber-in-the-loop design
- Telecommunication construction methods
- Satellite earth station design
- Terrestrial radio system design
- Telecommunications regulatory
- Personal communications
- Switching and networking

If you are interested in becoming an author, contributor or reviewer of a book in this series, or if you would like additional information about forthcoming titles, please contact:

Whitham D. Reeve
Series Editor, Telecommunications Handbook Series
Reeve Consulting Engineers
PO Box 190225
Anchorage, Alaska 99519-0225

Subscriber Loop Signaling and Transmission Handbook

Analog

Whitham D. Reeve

Reeve Consulting Engineers

 A volume in the Telecommunications Handbook Series, Whitham D. Reeve, *editor*

 IEEE PRESS

 Reviewed and endorsed by the IEEE Communications Society

The Institute of Electrical and Electronics Engineers, Inc., New York

© 1992 by the Institute of Electrical and Electronics Engineers, Inc.
345 East 47th Street, New York, NY 10017-2394

Printed in the United States of America

10 9 8 7 6 5 4 3 2 1

ISBN 0-87942-274-2
IEEE Order Number: PC0268-3

Library of Congress Cataloging-in-Publication Data

Reeve, Whitham D.
    Subscriber loop signaling and transmission handbook : Analog /
Whitham D. Reeve.
    p.   cm.
    Includes bibliographical references and index.
    ISBN 0-87942-274-2
    1. Telephone switching systems, Electronic. 2. Telecommunication —
Standards. I. Title.
TK 6397.R44 1992   91-19685
621.382 — dc20   CIP

Contents

6   Loop Design   125

7   Transmission Impairments   143

8   Transmission Improvement   179

Preface

The subscriber's loop continues to evolve as more and more *digital loop carrier* (DLC) and optical fibers are introduced into the *public switched telephone network* (PSTN).* But the loop's traditional use for carrying regular voice telephone calls on an analog basis over copper cable is still, by far, the most common. This will continue for a long time, perhaps until the year 2000, when optical fibers and *integrated services digital network* (ISDN) will play an equal, if not more important, role in the loop's function and use. Of course, this transition will not be instantaneous but will indeed take place as the evolution continues. Meanwhile, the loop will continue to be used much as it exists today.

The emphasis in this book is the practical application of telecommunication industry signaling and transmission practices and standards as they apply to voiceband subscriber loop design, construction and use. It tells what the loop does, how it is used and connected, and how it is designed in the sense of current applications.

Any person interested in the technical and qualitative aspects of the loop and its application — engineers, managers, construction experts, telecommunication system users and students — will find *Subscriber Loop Signaling and Transmission Handbook* informative and up to date. Some effort has been made to cover those areas over which the designer, builder or user has some control in a practical sense.

A considerable amount of diverse, but related, information appears in this book, much of which has never before been available in one volume. Chapter 1 covers the details of loop interface while Chapter 2 details loop signaling. These two chapters include practical information on terminal equipment. Unlike other, more common, discussions, this chapter goes beyond the so-called "500" set to include information on modern electronic instruments, key telephone systems and private branch exchanges.

---

* Listings of telecommunication terms and definitions are available [1,2].

The physical aspects of the loop, or outside plant facility, are covered in Chapter 3. It includes discussions on the various cable constructions, how to choose the proper cable for a particular application, as well as practical application information on such characteristics as standard gauge cable pair voltage and current ratings and premises wiring. Chapter 4 backs up Chapter 3 with a discussion of loop termination and protection methods, including comparative cost information.

Transmission is the basic reason for the loop. Therefore, it is covered extensively in Chapter 5. Included are the transmission rules for regular subscriber loops as well as loops used in many special and private line services.

The proper design of loops is generic to any telecommunication application. Therefore, various loop design methods are given substantial treatment in Chapter 6. The design tools presented in this chapter can be used to obtain the transmission requirements described in Chapter 5. Chapter 6 discusses several methods used throughout the telecommunication industry and not just those used by a particular company or group of companies. Since any transmission system is subject to degradation from noise and other impairments, Chapter 7 provides considerable practical information on such impairments.

Transmission improvement methods are covered in Chapter 8. This includes descriptions of conditioning methods used to reduce the negative effects of the impairments covered in Chapter 7. An example is practical information on applying sealing current and noise mitigation devices. In many situations, passive transmission improvement devices are used in subscriber loops to compensate for losses or other problems caused by bridged taps and unavoidable impedance mismatches. An example of such devices is the bridge lifter. These and other devices are discussed in Chapter 8.

Chapter 9 covers the fundamentals of pair gain devices such as digital loop carrier and analog subscriber carrier. A more in-depth discussion of these devices, and digital transmission in general, is reserved for another volume. For those interested in the relatively mysterious subject of coin line services, Chapter 10 provides a practical overview of coin line signaling methods used in the PSTN. This information can be considered an adjunct to Chapters 1 and 2 as applied to coin services.

Detailed theoretical treatments of signaling and transmission are avoided in the main body of this book. However, for those interested in the mathematical derivation of the secondary transmission parameters for non-loaded and loaded cables, mathematical analyses of loop insertion loss and bridged tap loss, transmission level point and other selected topics, appendices are provided.

To bridge the gap between practical applications covered in this book and the standards and practices upon which they are based, many technical references are cited. An appendix is provided with the complete address for all references.

Although this book describes the loop as it relates to the public networks, including the PSTN, most of the discussion is applicable to private networks, too. In fact, many private networks use loops for interconnecting network nodes or as tail circuits. The effective application of loops in private networks is dependent on an understanding of the loop's characteristics; this book will promote the necessary understanding.

The effect optical fibers and ISDN will have on the loop is carefully avoided. That is because this book is intended to cover loop use and performance and analog methods up to about 4,000 Hz. An additional volume is being prepared to extend this bandwidth to at least that required by ISDN primary access (1.544 Mbps), and it will emphasize digital applications.

The various parameters stated in this book to describe transmission and signaling standards or characteristics are not always universal. Variations will exist between different operating companies, standards organizations or users in general. In many cases, these variations are discussed. It is interesting to note, however, that these variations have not been significant from an overall system perspective because all interconnected telecommunications systems in the United States have worked together successfully for a long time. But the telecommunications industry has changed drastically as a result of divestiture of the old Bell System, and this change will continue. With so many new products and services becoming available, it is necessary to reflect on the impact that even minor variations will have in the area of signaling and transmission. It is for this reason that standards organizations such as American National Standards Institute (ANSI), Institute of Electrical and Electronic Engineers (IEEE), Electronic Industries Association (EIA) and many others are vigorously working to prepare universally accepted standards.

A number of conventions of terminology are used in this book. To those familiar with the telecommunication industry, these conventions will also be familiar. On the other hand, the jargon may not be familiar at all to others and it is defined here.

Distance measurements for metallic cable plant historically have been measured in miles or kilofeet. That convention is used in this book. *Subscriber, customer, end user* and *party* are used interchangeably. All use a telecommunication system. The subscriber and customer use the PSTN, whereas the end user or party use the PSTN or private networks. An end user does not necessarily have to be a customer or subscriber.

Local exchange carrier (LEC) and *exchange carrier* (EC) are used interchangeably. The Bell Operating Companies (BOCs) are a subset of the ECs; they are ECs divested from AT&T by the August 24, 1982 Modified Final Judgment (MFJ). The term telephone company, as used in this book, is an organization that either has a franchise or is otherwise authorized by a state public service commission to provide LEC service.

Customer premises equipment (CPE) and *terminal equipment* are used interchangeably. A subset of these are telephone instrument, station set and "500" set. *Network interface device* (NID) and *protector* are used interchangeably except when the discussion separates the two. These are collectively called the *network interface* (NI). *End-office, central office* (CO) and *switching* systems perform the same function with respect to subscriber loops, and the terms are used interchangeably.

Subscriber loops, subscriber lines, lines and *access lines* are all used to indicate the facility that interconnects terminal equipment with the network. The terms network and PSTN are used interchangeably, although a network does not always have to be the public network.

A switched service line (access line) provides a communication channel between two end users on demand. This channel is switched and available for the duration of the call and no longer. Private lines, leased lines or dedicated lines, on the other hand, provide full period service and are available at any time without competition from other end users (at least as far as the network is concerned). The term *leased line* denotes a channel rented from a telecommunication common carrier, which may be an EC.

Finally, *station wiring, inside wiring, customer premises wiring* (or just *premises wiring*), and *premises distribution system* are used interchangeably. All provide the same function of connecting the terminal equipment with the network interface.

The author would like to receive comments from readers on the contents of this book as well as suggestions for its improvement in later editions. Readers can write to the author at the following address:

Whitham D. Reeve
Reeve Consulting Engineers
P.O. Box 190225
Anchorage, Alaska 99519-0225

REFERENCES

[1] Langley, G. *Telephony's Dictionary*. Available from Telephony Publishing Corp.
[2] IEEE Std. 100-1984, *IEEE Standard Dictionary of Electrical and Electronic Terms*. New York: Institute of Electrical and Electronics Engineers. Available from the IEEE Service Center.

Subscriber Loop Signaling and Transmission Handbook

Analog

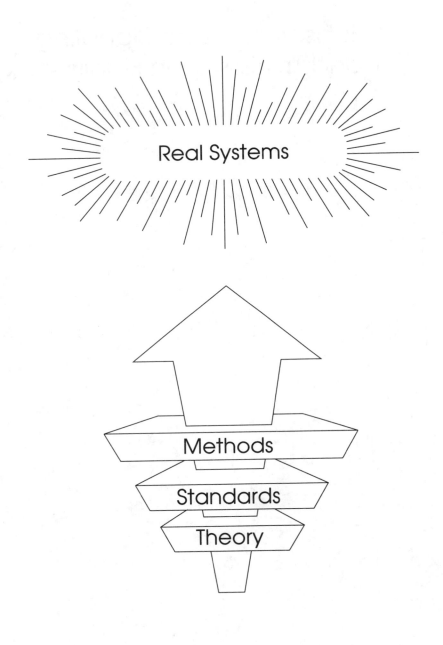

1

Loop Interfaces

The subscriber loop and the equipment inexorably connected to it at each end are functionally defined in this chapter. The most familiar terminal equipment — the ubiquitous telephone instrument — is considered in some detail. Other types of terminal equipment, such as private branch exchanges (PBXs) and key telephone systems, are also considered. Loops used in switched service account for perhaps 90 percent of all loop applications. The next chapter establishes the signaling criteria associated with these loops.

1.1 Loop Function

What is a loop and what does it do? The loop is a transmission and signaling channel or path between a telephone subscriber's terminal equipment and the serving central office or another piece of terminal equipment. "Transmission" implies transfer of information while "signaling" implies the actions required to control the transmissions. Terminal equipment includes:

- Telephone instruments
- Facsimile machines
- Private branch exchanges
- Key telephone systems
- Voice mail systems
- Modems

- Computers
- Alarm systems
- Radio control systems
- Telephone answering machines

as well as many other devices. These are generally referred to as *customer premises equipment* (CPE), which can be defined as any equipment connected by premises wiring to the subscriber side of the *public switched telephone network* (PSTN) interface. Such devices interface voice as well as data signals to the subscriber loop.

The *network interface device* (NID), which serves as the PSTN interface, is described in Chapter 4. The subscriber (that is, telephone customer) can be an individual with one loop or a very large business with thousands of loops.

Put in a more rigorous way, the loop:

- Normally carries power from the central office (switching system or other network equipment) to the terminal equipment
- Transmits bidirectional speech or data signals between the calling and called parties
- Carries bidirectional control signals (supervision) between the calling and called parties and the central office
- Carries call progress tones to the calling party (dial tone, busy tone, ringback tone)
- Carries ringing current to the called party

The foregoing lists the normal signal voltages and currents carried on the loop. It also carries voltages and currents due to maintenance activities as well as those due to the environment, such as induced voltages from nearby power lines, lightning, and other phenomenon. These are discussed in detail in later chapters.

Most loops, shown pictorially in Fig. 1-1, simply consist of a telephone line or outside plant cable pair. Some applications may require a much more complex set of systems, including the cable pair, to make up the overall loop. For example, a foreign exchange circuit, where dial tone from an exchange in one city is provided to a subscriber in another exchange in another city, may include a cable pair, carrier equipment and optical fiber and satellite transmission systems as shown in Fig. 1-2. The loops connected to the terminal equipment at each end are called "tail circuits" or "end links."

The loop can be considered the exchange access portion of an overall telecommunication channel or circuit. This is illustrated in Fig. 1-3 where the exchange access is shown connecting subscriber terminal equipment to a central office. When the subscriber loop is connected to a central office switching system, it is called an access line. Between central offices is the inter-exchange access portion.

Although this book emphasizes the exchange access portion, it is important to realize the loop is designed, built and used to work well within any given exchange and also to work well outside of that exchange through the inter-exchange access portion. This is not necessarily an easy task, as will be seen.

As previously noted, the terminal equipment is connected at one end of the loop, and the central office (CO) is connected at the other end. Of course, the loop does not have to be connected to a central office line circuit and switched as implied here; it can be hard wired to another loop to provide a point-to-point transmission path, it may be bridged to

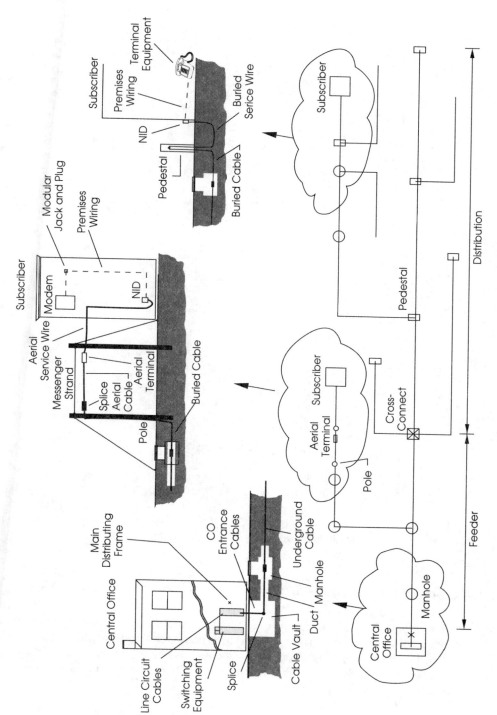

Figure 1-1 Subscriber's Loop

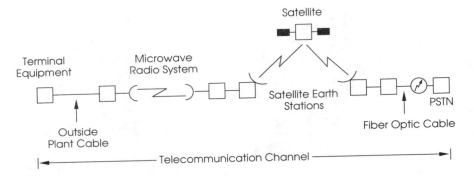

Figure 1-2 A more complex loop

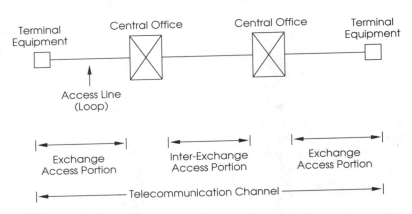

Figure 1-3 Exchange access

other loops (generally through special transmission equipment) to provide a point-to-multipoint transmission path, or it may terminate in some special equipment, such as a computer or specialized signaling system.*

For the very large proportion of cases, the loop and the interface connections are as shown in Fig. 1-4. Each part will be discussed in detail in this and later chapters.

1.2 The Central Office Line Circuit

For purposes of discussion in this section, the central office is considered in its most common way — that of terminating loops on a line circuit and providing a switching function. The central office is a node where loops converge as shown in Fig. 1-5. In this context, the central office is part of a wire center.† A wire center can contain more than one central office switching system.

* The term "bridged" is telephone terminology to indicate a parallel electrical connection.

† A wire center can be said to serve an exchange area, which is a geographical area determined either by the dialing prefix or political boundary.

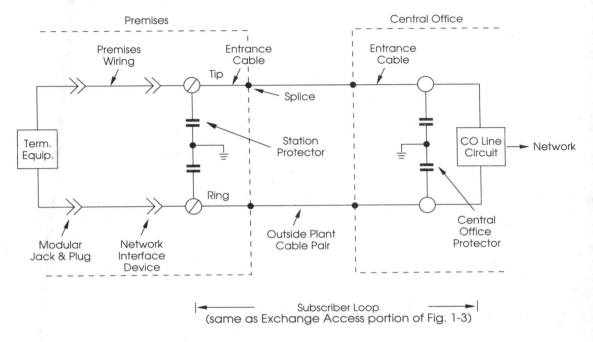

Figure 1-4 Loop and interface connections

The line circuit can be considered a physical part of the subscriber loop when the loop is an access line. The line circuit is the loop's gateway to the PSTN, and it is always located at the end of the loop opposite the terminal equipment. The line circuit:

- Terminates the loop with a balanced 900 Ω (or otherwise standard) termination
- Supplies direct current to the loop from central office battery and ground through balanced feed resistances having a total resistance around 400 Ω
- Supervises the loop currents to determine on-hook and off-hook conditions
- Receives dialed address information from the terminal equipment
- Isolates foreign potentials on the loop from the central office transmission and signaling circuitry.*
- Applies ringing voltage to the loop as well as other call progress tones
- Converts the two-wire loop transmission path to a four-wire (or equivalent) path used internally by the switching system (if the switching system is digital or four-wire — most analog central office switching systems are two-wire and do not make this conversion)
- Provides analog-to-digital and digital-to-analog conversion of the transmission signals (digital central offices only)
- Provides test access for loop and line circuit testing

* A foreign potential is any undesired voltage on a circuit.

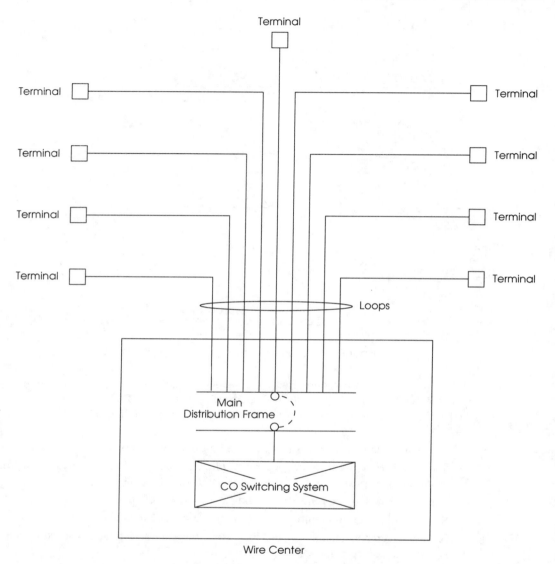

Figure 1-5 Loops converge at a central office

The central office line circuit, as is the subscriber loop, is inherently bidirectional. Even so, the line can be arranged to work in one direction only, if necessary. This means it can be arranged to only terminate calls or only originate calls, but not both. The line circuit functions are colloquially summarized with the acronym BORSCHT (Battery, Overvoltage protection, Ringing, Signaling, Coding, Hybrid, and Test).

1.3 The Telephone Instrument

This and later sections discuss the functions and characteristics of a typical telephone instrument, but not all transmission characteristics are included. Later chapters discuss the transmission requirements under which all terminal equipment must operate.

The largest proportion of loops are permanently associated with the telephone instrument. The transmission properties of both must be designed such that the combination will meet telephone industry objectives. These objectives are, in turn, set to provide satisfactory telephone service to the subscriber.

At one end of the typical loop is the most familiar type of terminal equipment: the telephone instrument. It is the most common means by which the subscriber transmits to or receives signals from the central office. Figure 1-6 shows a simplified schematic of a typical instrument with a tone dial. Telephone instruments are sometimes generically referred to as "500 Sets".*

Virtually all new terminal equipment connected to the PSTN since the early 1980s must be registered with the Federal Communications Commission under Part 68 — "Connection of Terminal Equipment to the Telephone Network" — of its Rules and Regulations [2]. These rules "provide for uniform standards for the protection of the telephone network from harms caused by the connection of terminal equipment and associated wiring thereto . . . ."†

Part 68 does not guarantee the terminal equipment will function adequately, only that it will not harm the network. The difference is worth noting. Some of the regulatory aspects of loop interface and signaling are covered at the end of this chapter.

The basic signals from a telephone instrument may be classified as:

- Forward (from the calling party), consisting of:
  Off-hook (seizure)
  Dialing, and
  On-hook (or clear forward)
and,
- Backward (from the called party), consisting of:
  Off-hook (answer) and
  On-hook (or clear backward)

Dialing may be in the form of dial pulses (sequential on-hook/off-hook) or tones. The central office interprets the forward and backward signals through the switching system line circuit to appropriately set up or drop a connection.

---

* The 500 set was first produced in 1950 by the Western Electric Company [1]. Initially, it was only produced with a rotary dial but was later produced with a tone dial. The set with a tone dial is generally called a "2500 set."

† Par. 68.1 of FCC Part 68.

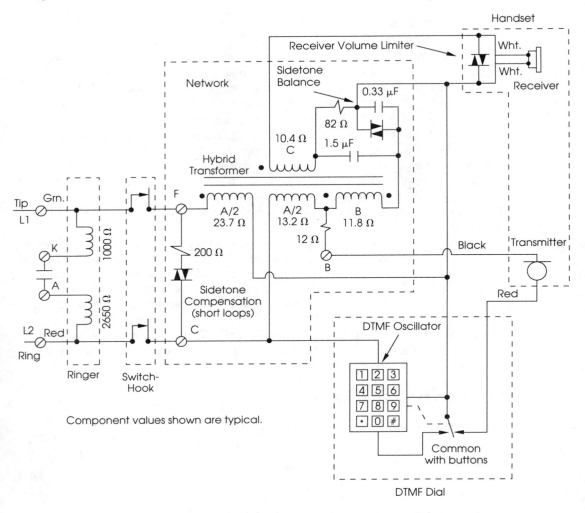

Figure 1-6 Typical telephone instrument schematic

The telephone instrument itself consists of a:

- Dial
- Network
- Transmitter
- Receiver
- Switch-hook
- Ringer*

* The word "ringer" is used to denote any electro-acoustical device to alert the called party. It does not have to be one with metallic gongs.

The switch-hook provides on-hook supervision by opening the loop when the handset is hung up. Conversely, it provides off-hook supervision by closing the loop when the handset is lifted. The transmitter converts voice or other forms of acoustical energy to a varying electrical current while the receiver converts varying electrical signals back to acoustical energy.

The network consists of several components as shown in Fig. 1-6. Its main function is to couple the transmitter and receiver to the loop and supply sidetone to the receiver.* In electromechanical instruments, it is a hybrid transformer and a balance network that converts the two-wire loop to a four-wire transmit and receive circuit. Many modern telephone instruments use an electronic equivalent of the transformer. The network serves other functions, such as limiting the signal level at the receiver and adjusting the sidetone level to an almost constant and acceptable level while working with a wide variety of loops.

The receiver level is limited to protect the listener's ears during high-level signals or noise impulses. Adequate sidetone is necessary so the talker does not shout or talk too softly because of low or high sidetone. If there is too much sidetone coupling, background noise entering the transmitter will interfere with weak signals at the receiver.

The network and transmitter combination is considered to have about 200 Ω dc resistance in an electromechanical type rotary dial instrument, but this can be quite variable. The actual dc resistance of any instrument is equal to the voltage across the instrument divided by the current through it. The relationship is nonlinear because of the nonlinear elements used in the network.

Instruments (including tone dial types) can have an off-hook resistance up to 400 Ω if they are designed according to Electronic Industries Association Standard EIA-470 [3]. According to the EIA, the dc resistance characteristic of an instrument may vary with several conditions. These are:

1. DC resistance must be less than 300 Ω during the on-hook to off-hook transition, during the make interval of rotary dial pulsing (described later), and for at least 1 s after answer,

2. DC resistance may increase to 400 Ω during *dual-tone multifrequency* (DTMF) signaling (described later), after called party answer, and after the talking connection has been made for at least 1 s,

3. DC resistance may be greater than 400 Ω at loop currents less than 20 mA (adequate operation of an instrument is not specified below 20 mA loop current).

The instrument's off-hook resistance must meet certain minimum requirements, too, to ensure proper operation of instruments intended for parallel use (for example, extensions). This is to prevent "current hogging" by an instrument with a relatively smaller resistance. For these instruments,

1. DC resistance must be greater than 100 Ω from 0 to 30 mA loop current.

2. DC resistance can linearly decrease to 80 Ω between 30 and 50 mA loop current.

---

* Sidetone is the acoustical signal resulting from a portion of the transmitted signal being coupled back to the receiver of the same handset. A sidetone circuit is sometimes called a "talkback" circuit.

3. DC resistance can linearly decrease from 80 Ω at 50 mA with a negative slope such that the resistance at 120 mA is greater than 33 Ω.

The above requirements are summarized in terms of a voltage-current relationship in Fig. 1-7. Also shown in this figure are the measured voltage-current curves for three typical instruments. One has an electronic network, and two have a conventional transformer-type network. In certain regions, the instruments are indistinguishable.

The ringer, of course, rings when the called party is to receive a call from the calling party. The ringing may be a warbling tone, tweet, bell sound, or it might be a flashing light. The ringer shown in Fig. 1-6 is connected as a bridged ringer. It is not always connected this way. Other wiring variations, such as connection from tip or ring to ground, which is called "divided ringing," are commonly used.* The actual connection depends on the telephone company's policy, its engineering philosophy or party-line requirements.† Ringing methods are discussed in detail later.

The rotary or tone dial provides address signals to the central office, where the address is that of the called party. Additionally, the push-button tone dial may provide control signals to more sophisticated switching systems or terminal equipment at the other end of the connection. For example, most large stock brokerage firms have toll-free numbers their customers can call to get stock or mutual fund information. Once connected, the customer uses pushbutton tones to control the call's routing to a recording that describes the fund or stock of particular interest. Similarly, many companies use "automated attendants" that instruct the caller, through prerecorded announcements, to dial the wanted department or "hold the line" for a live operator.

The typical electromechanical "500" set is not polarity sensitive. That is, it can be connected to the tip and ring leads without concern for possible tip-ring reversal. Tip-ring reversal can be caused by mistakes during outside splicing operations or premises wiring installations. This condition is easily detected by testing the polarity of the loop at the telephone set connections; the tip lead should be positive with respect to the ring lead when the tip and ring leads have the proper polarity.

Telephone sets that use a DTMF dial or have other line powered functions (such as an electronic telephone set) require proper polarity to function. To preclude possible malfunction on initial installation, or at some later time, the set is equipped with a polarity guard, which is nothing more than a common diode bridge. The polarity guard, shown in Fig. 1-8, allows instruments equipped with them to be connected to the network without regard for tip-ring polarity.

1.4 Private Branch Exchanges and Key Telephone Systems

Private branch exchanges (PBXs) and key telephone systems (key systems) provide additional telecommunication services at the customer premises that normally would

---

* Tip and ring are the two wires of a twisted pair or other telecommunication circuit. They are labeled as such to indicate their sense or polarity. The terms are historical.

† A party line is a given loop or central office line circuit that serves more than one subscriber.

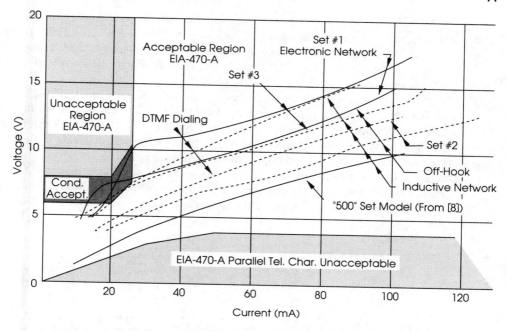

Figure 1-7 Voltage-current relationships for telephone instruments

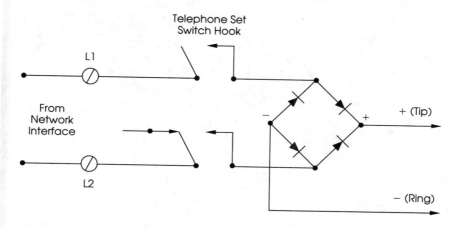

Figure 1-8 Telephone instrument polarity guard

not be available from the single-line telephone instrument previously described. The differences between PBXs and key telephone system applications at one time were quite apparent. The PBX was used in applications requiring approximately 25 or more stations, and key systems were used in smaller applications. The PBX provided a clear switching function requiring station addresses. Also, the PBX concentrated switched traffic into trunk groups.* A key system provided neither of these features.

---

* A trunk is a shared communication channel between switching systems.

The differences, however, have become blurred due to technological advances and associated economies in the design of each system. Now, a PBX may find an application in a smaller environment, and key systems are available for larger applications. In these situations, the two may have indistinguishable features. Figure 1-9 shows how PBXs and key systems fit into the overall network.

At this point, it should be noted that a group of subscriber loops are used to provide service from the central office switching system to the PBX. In this context, the loops are called PBX trunks or direct outward dialing (DOD) trunks. DOD trunks can be used for two-way service by providing central office dial tone and direct access to the PSTN by the user on outgoing calls and ringing to an operator or attendant on incoming calls.

Another application of a group of loops is for direct inward dialing (DID) trunks. Here, the trunks are used for one-way (incoming) service only by allowing a caller in the PSTN to directly dial a particular PBX extension without operator or attendant intervention.

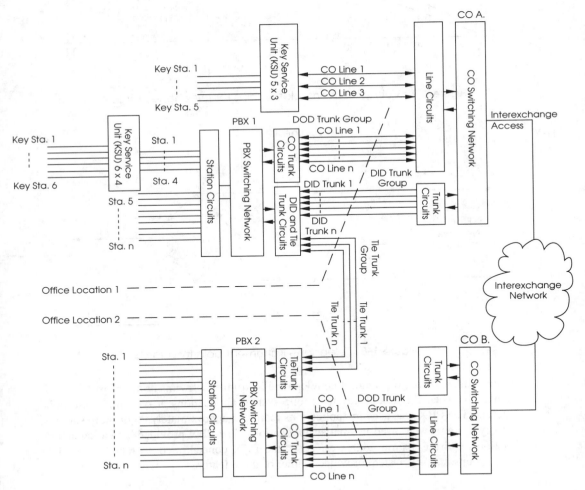

Figure 1-9 PBX and key telephone system network connections

It should be apparent from the previous discussion that a trunk is a common channel or line that is shared by a number of end users. This means trunks are a number of similar lines grouped together from a common functional standpoint. An end user may use any of the lines on any particular call, and the end user has no direct control over which line in the group is used on that call.

The term trunk is also used outside of the context of subscriber loops. In this case, a trunk interconnects switching systems (central offices). Even though the interoffice trunks may use the same facilities as loops, the signaling and transmission requirements for interoffice trunks vary considerably from that used with subscriber loops.

Although the distinction between PBXs and key systems has become blurred in larger systems, key systems can still be categorized as such for most common applications. The key system provides [4]:

- Appearances for multiple directory numbers on a single instrument
- Appearance of a single directory number on multiple instruments
- Status indication on each instrument of each directory number appearing on that instrument
- Ability to bridge multiple instruments onto a busy line
- Busy line hold capability
- Intercom capability

The modern PBX essentially provides the functions of a key system on a single instrument, but it also provides a switching function through [5]:

- Interconnection of instruments at two different locations
- Interconnection of instruments and an attendant (operator) position
- Interconnection of instruments or an attendant position with the PSTN via PBX trunks
- Interconnection of instruments or an attendant position with other PBXs and private facilities via PBX tie trunks

In addition to the blurred distinction between some PBXs and key systems, there may be little difference between PBXs and central office switching systems. Indeed, several PBXs and central office switching systems have been adapted quite successfully to the other role. The major differences have always been, however, the protocol and numbering plans used for on-network and off-network access. Also, the central office line circuit is designed to work in a much more severe environment than the PBX station circuit. The required electrical characteristics of key systems and PBXs are specified in Electronic Industries Association publications [6,7].

1.5 Tariff Aspects

The services and features available on the loop from the PSTN depend on tariffs established by state public service commissions, marketing methods, as well as the technical capabilities of the central office switching systems. The three service categories are illustrated in Fig. 1-10.

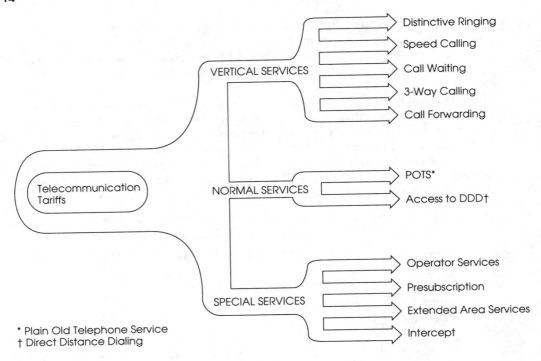

Figure 1-10 Service categories

The normal services are those available upon application for regular telephone service — popularly called "POTS" for "plain old telephone service." These are "basic" services meaning the ability to use the PSTN without significant restriction or engineering but with no added features. Vertical services, on the other hand, are enhanced capabilities that are marketable within the regulatory environment. These usually make the PSTN easier to use and access and provide additional conveniences, such as the ability to conference more than two callers together.

Special handling are those services requiring operator assistance, access to alternate inter-exchange carriers or any other call handling outside the scope of POTS.

1.6 Federal Regulatory Requirements

Part 68 of the FCC rules and regulations governs the connection of any terminal equipment to the telephone network, which consists of the PSTN and certain private lines. Knowledge of certain aspects of part 68 is necessary to the understanding of any such connection. The stated purpose of the FCC rules is to prevent harm to the network. To do this, the rules spell out in detail a number of tests the terminal equipment must pass before it can become certified as suitable for connection to the network. These tests cover external environmental conditions such as temperature, humidity, shock and vibration and voltage surges as well as the failure modes of the equipment under these conditions.

There are a number of other required tests concerning the voltages, currents, signal power levels and load applied by the terminal equipment to the loop (as opposed to the previously described conditions, which are applied to the terminal equipment).

Generally, the terminal equipment must be designed such that the open circuit (no load) voltage at any of its connection points does not exceed 70 V for more than 1 s unless the voltages are used for network control or signaling and are consistent with the telephone company's standards (for example, ringing). When the terminal equipment consists of a PBX, key system or similar system, it cannot apply more than 56.5 V dc or supply more than 140 mA of dc current to the loop for off-premises stations. Other voltage and current limitations are discussed in Chapter 3.

In addition to operational-type voltages mentioned in the previous paragraph, the FCC limits low-level signal type voltages, also. These limitations cover a surprisingly large bandwidth: from approximately 200 hertz (Hz) to 6 megahertz (MHz). All tests for signal power specify the bandwidth over which it must be measured, and all tests are made with loop simulator circuits, shown in Fig. 1-11, or a standard 600 Ω termination.

The loop simulator and standard termination are the only practical way to make such tests. As will be shown in Chapter 5, there is no such thing as a standard subscriber loop, and the simulator promotes standardized evaluation of equipment. It is necessary to limit the signal power over such a wide bandwidth because of multiplexing and signaling equipment used in the network. This equipment makes use of the spectrum up to around 6 MHz, and extraneous signals can disrupt it.

Generally, the signal power applied to the loop simulator by the terminal equipment in the band from 200 Hertz to 4 kiloHertz (kHz) must be limited to −9 dBm under all conditions when averaged over a period of 3 s.* This limitation does not apply to live voice signals. The level of voice signals is discussed in Chapter 5. Signals from certain data communication equipment (DCE), such as most modems, must not exceed −13 dBm over any 3 s interval.

From 4 kHz to 6 MHz, signal power is no longer specified in dBm. Instead, "metallic" voltage, which includes signal voltage plus any other voltages across tip and ring, is specified using a particular impedance at the loop simulator. All voltage levels are specified over an 8 kHz bandwidth.

The metallic (or differential) voltage applied by the terminal equipment to the termination tip and ring conductors must be no greater than 200 mV (−14 dBV) at 4 kHz, decreasing to no more than 100 mV (−20 dBV) at 12 kHz for more than 0.1 s.

The allowable voltage levels continue to decrease at a constant rate up to 90 kHz where the level must be no more than 1.78 mV (−55 dBV) over any 0.1 s interval, and so on as shown in Fig. 1-12. Other specified voltage limitations are shown in this figure, too. These concern longitudinal (common mode) voltages, which must be lower in magnitude than the metallic voltages by approximately 7–16 dBV.

There are certain narrow frequency bands that require special consideration when terminal equipment is being tested. These are 2,450 to 2,750 Hz and 3,995 to 4,005 Hz. The 2,450 to 2,750 Hz band provides signaling functions in the network. These are called

---

* See Appendix A for a discussion of the decibel (dB).

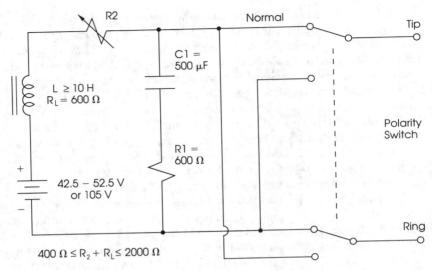

Figure 1-11a FCC two-wire loop simulator circuit

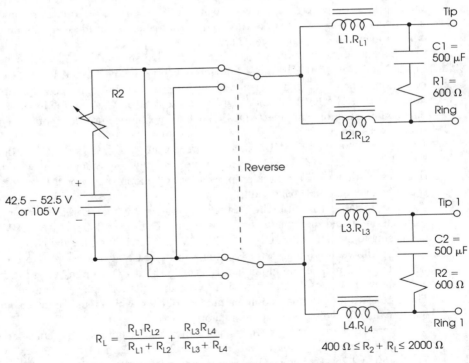

$$R_L = \frac{R_{L1}R_{L2}}{R_{L1} + R_{L2}} + \frac{R_{L3}R_{L4}}{R_{L3} + R_{L4}}$$

$400 \ \Omega \le R_2 + R_L \le 2000 \ \Omega$

Figure 1-11b FCC four-wire loop simulator circuit

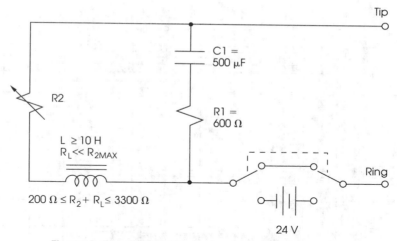

Figure 1-11c FCC Off-premises loop simulator circuit

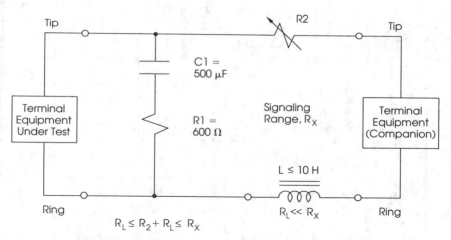

Figure 1-11d FCC private line loop simulator circuit

SF or single-frequency signaling and are used for address transmission and supervision as well as loopback.* Signal levels must be limited to −8 dBm in the SF signaling state and −20 dBm in the idle (on-hook) state. If the terminal equipment does not use SF signaling, the energy in this band must be accompanied by an equal amount of energy in the 800 to 2,450 Hz band. This allows network signaling equipment to differentiate between real and extraneous signals.

The band from 3,995 to 4,005 Hz is one-half the sampling rate for digital loop carrier systems (which is 8 kHz). Unwanted signals in this band can cause serious disruption of digital networks and must be at least 18 dB below the signals in the 200 Hz to 4 kHz band.

---

* SF and loopback usually apply only to four-wire private line circuits. Loopback is a test function that connects the transmit side of a circuit to its receive side at the far (or loopback) end.

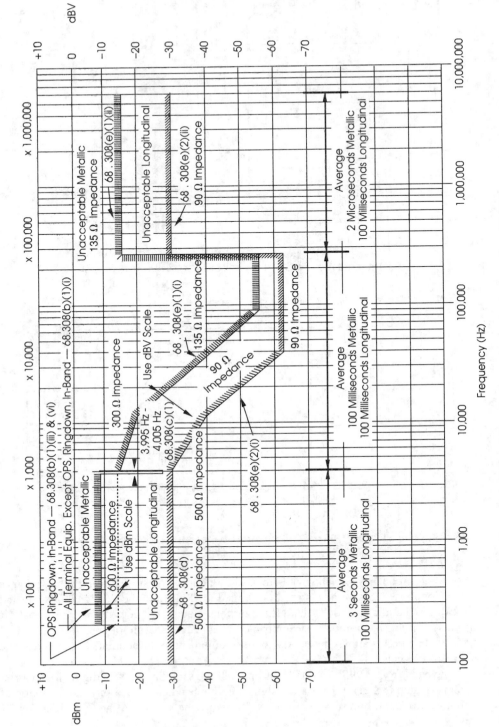

Figure 1-12 FCC signal power limitations, Par. 68.308

18

The load the terminal equipment places on the idle loop is determined by its *ringer equivalence number* (REN), which is defined by the FCC in Part 68 and described in detail in Chapter 2. A "standard" ringer has a ringer equivalence of 1.0. The maximum ringer equivalence that can be placed on a loop is 5.0. High ringer equivalence may prevent terminal equipment from functioning properly on long loops. The FCC defines the frequency characteristics of ringers by an alphabetical code.

Terminal equipment must provide at least some on-hook load to the loop. This allows the telephone company to test the loop for connected equipment. The minimum load is 40 kΩ or approximately 0.2 ringer equivalence.

The FCC specifies a minimum insulation breakdown voltage for premises wiring of 1,500 Vrms. Of equal importance is the requirement by the National Electrical Code, Article 800, which requires the premises wiring have a voltage rating of 300 V.

Until mid-1990, the actual connection of terminal equipment to the network was required by the FCC to be through standard plugs and standard telephone-company jacks. These are the familiar "modular" plugs and jacks, which are described in Chapter 4. The telecommunication industry interpretation of the previous FCC requirements was controversial and confusing.

In CC Docket No. 88-57 in orders adopted June 8, 1990 and August 10, 1990, the FCC modified, and in some respects clarified, the demarcation point requirements. The resulting changes to Part 68 relax the requirement for a plug and jack demarcation point. Now, a simple splice at least 12 inches from the premises wiring side of the telephone company protector is acceptable as a demarcation point. Jack and plug arrangements are still acceptable. With the FCC ruling, the subscriber has more interconnection device choices and presumably can make better use of premises wiring.

The matter of demarcation points is further confused by the fact that, in many states, the public service commissions (PSCs) have specified the demarcation point as the standard plug and jack arrangement that is integral to the telephone-company provided network interface device. Where the network interface device does not have a plug and jack or does not exist, the demarcation point has been considered by PSCs to be the telephone-company provided protector of some other jack located on the premises. The PSC requirements sometimes conflict with FCC requirements. In almost all cases, however, FCC requirements preempt state PSC requirements.

REFERENCES

[1] *Engineering and Operations in the Bell System. AT&T Bell Laboratories*, Murray Hill, NJ, 1983. Available from AT&T Customer Information Center.

[2] *Federal Communications Commission Rules and Regulations. Volume VII, Part 68–Connection of Terminal Equipment to the Telephone Network.* September 1987. Available through Superintendent of Documents.

[3] *EIA Standard 470-A-1987–Telephone Instruments with Loop Signaling.* Available from EIA.

[4] *Compatibility Information for Telephone Exchange Service, Technical Advisory TA-NPL-000912.* BELLCORE, February 1989. Available from BELLCORE Customer Service.

[5] Ibid.

[6] *EIA/TIA-464-A–Private Branch Exchange (PBX) Switching Equipment for Voiceband Application.* Available from EIA.

[7] *EIA Standard RS-478–Multi-Line Key Telephone Systems (KTS) for Voiceband Application.* Available from EIA.

[8] *Transmission Systems for Communications*, Bell Telephone Laboratories, Inc., 1982. Available form AT&T Customer Information Center.

2

Loop Signaling

The subscriber loop was functionally defined in the previous chapter. Since most of the loops are used in switched service, this chapter describes this application and considers the associated signaling aspects in some detail. In those cases where the loop is used in private line service, other signaling requirements may prevail; these are described where appropriate. Later chapters establish the transmission criteria for the loop.

2.1 Call Establishment

A call is established according to the basic sequence shown in the flow chart of Fig. 2-1. The details of each step are explained in the following sections. A call from one subscriber in a central office to another subscriber in the same central office is considered. Calls beyond the central office follow a sequence according to the network requirements and are beyond the scope of this book. The flow chart of Fig. 2-1 does not apply to loops used in private line service.

Call establishment performance is of considerable importance to telephone companies. This performance is measured on an overall basis by [4]:

1. The speed and accuracy with which the desired connection is established, which includes:
   a. Dial tone delay
   b. Call setup time
   c. Proportion of calls cutoff prematurely
   d. Proportion of calls blocked or ineffective

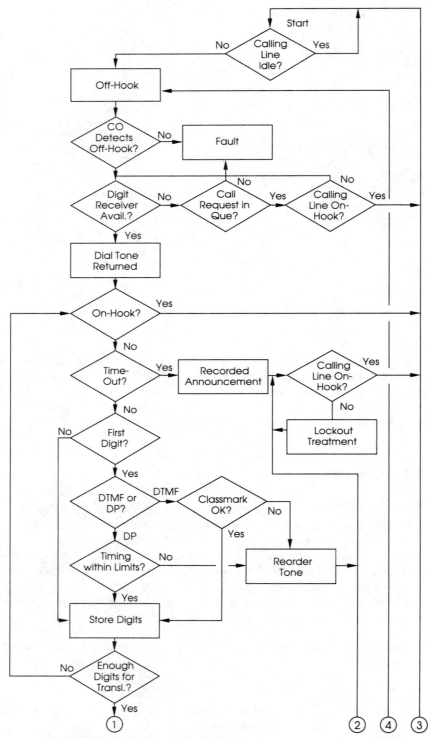

Figure 2-1 Call establishment flow chart (cont. next page)

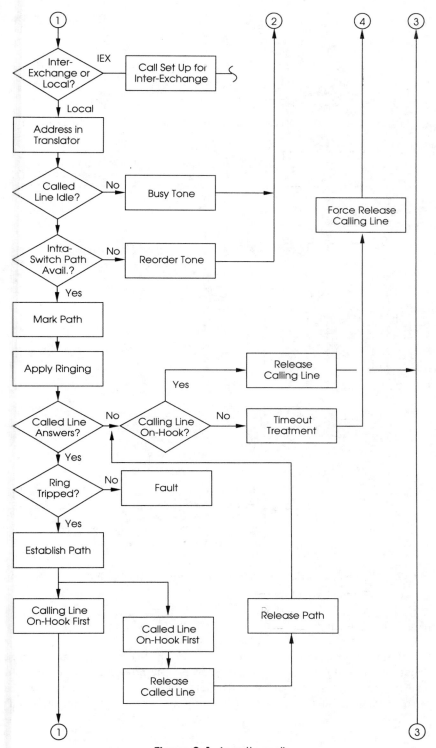

Figure 2-1 (continued)

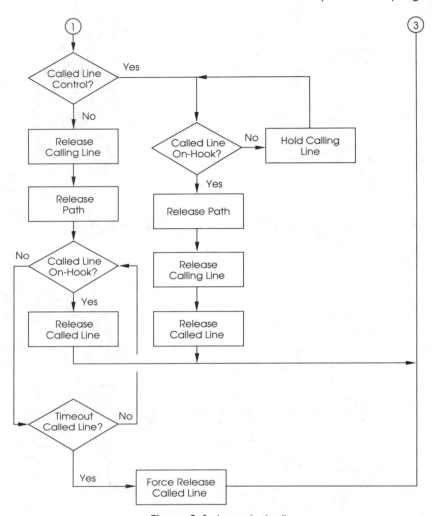

Figure 2-1 (concluded)

2. The quality of the established connection, which includes:

a. Transmission loss
b. Noise
c. Crosstalk*

With the exception of 1.c and 1.d, these quality measures are discussed at some length in the following sections and chapters. The proportion of unsuccessful calls (1.c and 1.d) is expressed as an objective and is a direct function of the switching systems associated with the loops involved. The objectives are usually expressed as a probability

---

* Crosstalk is any disturbing or extraneous signal, such as a voice signal, coupled from adjacent circuits.

of occurrence. Table 2-1 shows typical values for modern central office switching systems. It should be noted that the loop normally has no effect on unsuccessful call probabilities, but this information is presented for completeness.

Table 2-1   Probability of Call
Problems

Problem	Probability
Cutoff Calls	10^{-6}
Intraoffice Blocking	10^{-2}
Interoffice Blocking	10^{-2}

2.2 Seizing the Line

The first step in initiating a call is to seize the line. Generally, this is done by using loop start signaling (closing the loop as indicated in Chapter 1). Another method, called ground start signaling, is usually employed with private branch exchanges. It is described later.

When a call is to be made, the subscriber lifts the handset, which places a 200 Ω (or so, depending on the type; see Chapter 1) short across the loop. The resulting dc loop current is detected by the central office line circuit, which automatically connects equipment (digit receiver) capable of receiving the dialed address information. Dial tone is returned to the calling party to indicate connection of the digit receiver and that dialing by the calling party may commence.

2.3 Digit Receivers

In most switching systems, digit receivers are shared with many other subscribers, so a slight delay may occur before one is connected and ready to receive the dialed information. The delay is known as *dial tone delay* (DTD). Telephone industry standards require no more than 1.5 percent of all calls experience a dial tone delay of more than 3 s during the *average busy season busy hour* (ABSBH). ABSBH traffic is an average of individual hourly periods during the season when the items of equipment being measured are busiest. Two peak periods are also used: 10 HDBH and HDBH. The term "10 HDBH" refers to the average of the 10 highest busy hours throughout the traffic study period (usually the busy season, although peaks outside the busy season may be used). "HDBH" refers to the highest of the 10 highest busy hours in the study period. See [1] for a good discussion of telecommunication traffic engineering.

Digit receivers are engineered ("provisioned") on a statistical basis to meet the above standard as well as other criteria during peak periods.

Table 2-2 shows the overall provisioning requirements usually applied when delay criteria is used. Other methods are used, too. For example, digit receivers may be provisioned on a loss basis rather than a delay basis. If this is used, for example, the

Table 2-2 Digit Receiver Provisioning
              Criteria

Percent DTD > 3 Seconds		
ABSBH	10 HDBH	HDBH
1.5%	5-8%	20%

required number of receivers may be calculated using a loss formula with a loss of 0.1 percent (B.001) during the ABSBH and 0.5 percent (B.005) during the 10 HDBH. *

Some switching systems do not connect a digit receiver when the line is class marked for dial pulse only operation, in which case the line is ready to receive digits almost immediately upon seizure.

After dial tone is provided by the central office digit receiver, a timing condition is set up whereby the digit receiver waits for dialed digits. If, after a preset interval (usually 15 to 20 s), no digits have been received, the call request is routed to a "permanent signal" tone or recorded announcement and finally to lockout. Lockout is a condition such that the particular line circuit is not considered for further call routing action by the central office switching system.

Similarly, if one or more digits are dialed, but not enough for the central office to determine the address after some preset interval (usually the same as above), the call is given "partial dial" treatment, which is similar to permanent signal.

2.4 Dialing

After dial tone is received by the calling party, a rotary dial can be used to provide called party address information to the central office in the form of dial pulses. Dial pulses are the opening and closing of the loop. The nominal pulse rate is 10 pulses per second (PPS), but a typical rotary dial instrument can vary from 8 to 12 PPS. Some systems will accept dial pulses at up to 20 PPS.

The make/break (off-hook/on-hook) ratio applied to the loop is nominally 40 percent/60 percent; that is, the loop is closed 40 percent of the time and opened 60 percent. The break period is the important parameter, and it is allowed to vary from about 58 percent to 64 percent. Because of pulse distortion by the loop, the digit receivers or dial pulse detectors in the central office must be able to properly respond to a break interval of 55 percent to 65 percent. The minimum time between dial pulse digits is 200 ms. Figure 2-2 shows the dial pulse sequence and timing criteria for the number "53 . . . ."

Tone dials provide address information, too, but in a different form. Tone dials contain a dual tone multifrequency (DTMF) signal generator with a four-row by three-column pushbutton pad, although the military and others sometimes use specialized instruments with a four-by-four pad. As the name implies, each pushbutton corresponds to two tones in a two-of-eight scheme.

---

*   The Erlang B Loss Formula is frequently used.

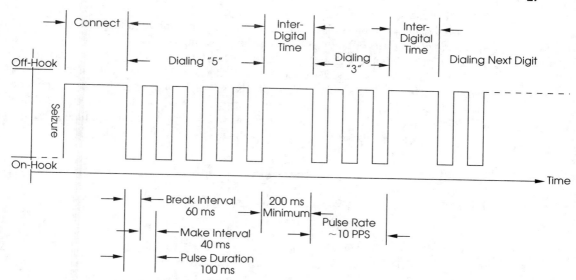

Figure 2-2 Dial pulse sequence for the digits "5, 3 . . ."

Figure 2-3 shows the tone frequencies corresponding to each key or pushbutton number. Sixteen key combinations are shown; all 16 are inherent to the DTMF signaling scheme, but the last column is not used on the four-by-three pad. Also, there are more tone combinations on a four-by-three pad than numbers (12 combinations versus 10 numbers). The "#" and "*" keys are usually used to control ancillary functions, such as cancel timing on a special function call, with central offices equipped to recognize them, or other custom calling features. These are discussed later.

The tone frequencies are chosen in such a way that their harmonics and distortion products will not interfere with other DTMF, call progress or signaling tones. The signal levels applied to the loop at the telephone instrument are +4 to −14 dBm per frequency with a maximum "twist" (level difference between the two tones) of 4 dB. Frequency tolerance must be better than 1.5 percent.

The timing specifications for the DTMF generators in the telephone itself require a minimum pulse duration of 50 ms and minimum interdigital interval of 45 ms. As with dial pulses, the DTMF signals are distorted by the loop due to its inherent transmission characteristics. To compensate for this distortion, DTMF receivers in the central office are usually designed to receive levels from +5 to −22 dBm with a twist of 6 dB. Usually, each dual tone combination must be received by the central office for at least 40 ms, and the interdigital time interval must be at least 50 ms.

The foregoing timing and detection specifications may not be universally accepted. Measurement standards for dial pulse and tone signaling, however, are well established [2,3].

Early studies have shown the average caller requires slightly under 14 s from receipt of dial tone to completely dial a 7-digit number with a rotary dial. Each additional digit requires 1.5 s. The average caller with a tone dial requires slightly over 8 s for seven digits and 0.8 s for each additional digit. These averages can vary considerably depending on the type of traffic being offered to a central office. For example, the mix of 7- and 10-digit dialing during the traffic study period, and the relative use of speed dialing or automatic dialers, will obviously affect the average.

Speed dialing equipment is available that reduces the dialing time considerably. This equipment can be part of the telephone instrument, central office switching system, or a standalone unit. It is programmed to interpret a 1- or 2-digit dialed code as any number up to 15 or more digits long. There are many modems with automatic dialing capability connected to loops. These modems can outpulse a 7-digit number in about 1 s using tone dialing. If everything else is equal, fewer digit receivers are needed when their holding time (dialing time) is short. It is easy to imagine the savings in equipment time in a large central office if every subscriber used tone dialing, and especially speed dialing.

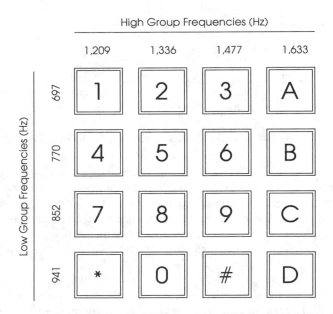

Example: The digit "5" consists of 770 Hz and 1,336 Hz.
Only special instruments have digits "A" through "D."

Figure 2-3 Dual-tone multifrequency scheme

2.5 Call Progress Signaling Tones

After the central office analyzes the dialed digits, it makes a connection through the switching network. If the called line is not busy, the calling party receives ringback tone. Otherwise, the calling party receives busy tone, reorder tone (also called overflow tone), or possibly a recorded announcement or other intercept treatment. A busy tone indicates the called line is busy. It is a tone interrupted 60 times per minute (60 IPM). Reorder tone indicates a network blockage was encountered and is a tone interrupted at 120 IPM. The blockage can occur anywhere—within the switching system itself or because of no available trunks between switching systems (here the tone is known as "all trunks busy" tone or "ATB" tone).

All modern systems in the United States use standard call progress tone levels, frequencies and interruption rates as specified by the *Precise Tone Plan*. The Precise

Tone Plan is a standard tone plan that has strict tolerances on levels, frequencies and distortion. Many older tone plans exist, too, but they are not implemented in new systems. Table 2-3 shows the characteristics of commonly heard call progress tones, both old and new.

As noted from Table 2-3, all level measurements are made in dB with respect to 1 mW except for receiver-off-hook tone. In this case, VU, or volume unit, is used. VU, which is discussed more in Chapter 5, is a measure used to describe actual voice signals. It is measured with a specially calibrated meter designed to have a slow response time and damping slightly less than critical. For complex waves, such as speech and music, the VU meter will read somewhere between average and peak of the complex wave.

Table 2-3 shows two tones not previously explained: "high tone" and "receiver off-hook tone." High tone is used in modern systems to indicate or to signal completion of ancillary functions (for example, programming a line for call forwarding). It also may be used to provide coin return signals to the operator during a coin line call or as a permanent signal indication.* In the table, all tones are with respect to the *zero transmission level point* (0 TLP). For a discussion of the TLP, see Appendix B.

Table 2-3 Common Call Progress Tone Plans

Tone	Precise Tone Plan Frequency	Other Tone Plan Frequency	Level per Frequency (Precise)	Interruption Rate (Precise)
Dial Tone	350 + 440 Hz	600 + 120 Hz 600 + 133 Hz	−13 dBm	Continuous
Busy Tone	480 + 620 Hz	600 + 120 Hz 600 + 133 Hz	−24 dBm	60 IPM
ATB	Same as busy	Same as busy	Same	120 IPM
Ringback Tone	440 + 480 Hz	420 + 40 Hz	−19 dBm	2 s on 4 s off
High Tone	480 Hz	500 Hz	−17 dBm	Cont. or Interrupted
Low Tone	480 + 620 Hz	Same as busy	−24 dBm	Various
Receiver Off-Hook Tone (ROH)	1,400 + 2,060 + 2,450 + 2,600 Hz	Same	+5 VU or +3 to −6 dBm	Cont. or Interrupted

All tones are with respect to the 0 TLP.

* In addition to the "no digits dialed" condition previously explained, permanent signal also includes the condition whereby one party of a call hangs up and the other does not hang up within the allowed disconnect time.

Receiver off-hook (ROH) tone is a loud, somewhat obnoxious, combination of tones placed on the line when the handset is accidentally knocked off-hook or an extension is left off-hook for some predetermined time interval after completing a call. The ROH tones signal the subscriber that the instrument should be hung up. Some systems do not use ROH tone at all but simply lock out the line (after some time interval) until the handset is placed on-hook. ROH tone largely replaces the old "howler," which was a swept level tone with the same function. The howler level approached +40 VU. Such high-level tones are somewhat controversial because the level may be high enough to cause ear damage. Also, they are not compatible with modern digital loop carrier systems.

Other tones, not shown in Table 2-3, are used, too. For example, the call-waiting tone in modern digital switching systems may be two −13 dBm, 440 Hz tone bursts: 0.5 s on, 0.5 s off. A "class of service" low tone is a combination of 480 and 620 Hz tones at −18 dBm per frequency. The familiar "bong" tone used as a prompt with calling card service consists of an initial burst of 941 and 1,477 Hz followed immediately by exponentially decayed 440 and 350 Hz tones at a level of −10 dBm each. Other frequencies and cadences may appear in different systems.

Recorded announcements are call intercept functions used to inform the calling party of a misdirected call which may have occurred because the party dialed the wrong number, was trying to reach a disconnected number, or for other reasons. Some calls are given special intercept treatment by connecting them directly to an operator.

Of course, there is one other condition that the calling party may encounter. It is the "no-ring, no-answer" or dead-end. The call goes nowhere. There are many reasons for this condition. It may be the result of inadequate switching system maintenance or a statistical call misdirection somewhere within the network. All telephone systems are designed to avoid the dead end, but it will be encountered in a small percentage of calls.

If the called party is not busy, ringing forward and ringback tone backward may continue indefinitely in most systems until the call is either answered or the calling party hangs up, whichever occurs first. Many modern systems automatically disconnect all network connections and route the calling party to reorder tone after a certain number of minutes of unanswered ringing.

Due to system design, there can be up to 4 s delay between the time the called line is seized and ringing voltage is applied to it. This explains why an outgoing call sometimes collides with an incoming call that had not yet had time to ring.

2.6 Loop Start and Ground Start Signaling

When the condition of an incoming call colliding with an outgoing call is encountered, it is called *glare*. It is encountered most often with PBXs but can occur with any terminal equipment. If glare occurs frequently, which is very possible on a busy PBX, overall network efficiency is reduced, to say nothing of annoyance to the users.

To eliminate glare on central office lines connected to PBXs, an optional method called *ground start signaling* is used (as opposed to loop start signaling previously discussed). The actual type of signaling is a function of the respective line circuits at the central office and PBX.

Ground start signaling is the preferred signaling method when the terminal equipment includes a switching system, such as a PBX. Its advantages are [4]:

- Greatly reduced likelihood of glare occurring during the silent ringing interval
- Positive indication of line seizure whether or not ringing voltage is present
- Provides a start-dial indication to the terminal equipment without it having to detect dial tone
- Usually provides a positive indication of network disconnect if the terminal equipment remains off-hook after the network returns to idle

With ground start signaling, a ground is applied to one of the conductors of the two-wire loop to seize the line [5]. When the call is from the central office to the PBX, the central office immediately grounds the tip conductor to seize the line. Ringing voltage is also applied but, as previously explained, there can be several seconds delay. The PBX immediately detects the grounded tip conductor and will not allow an outgoing call from the PBX to use this circuit, thus avoiding glare.

Similarly, if a call originates in the PBX and is outgoing to the central office, the PBX immediately places a ground on the ring conductor to seize the line. The central office recognizes this condition and prevents other calls from attempting to terminate on the circuit. It then grounds the tip conductor and returns dial tone after it connects a digit receiver. In the rare situation when the PBX and central office seize the circuit at exactly the same time, one or the other is programmed to back down and allow the other call to proceed.

Figures 2-4 and 2-5 are signaling state diagrams for loop start and ground start signaling. Figures 2-6 and 2-7 show a simplified schematic of the interfaces associated with the two signaling methods.

2.7 Signal Timing

Timing is a critical factor in loop and ground start signaling. For example, the terminal equipment should not enter the addressing signaling stage until loop battery voltage appears across the tip and ring and a minimum time interval has elapsed. This is to ensure the loop condition is not transient in nature. This minimum time interval is 275 ms. Also, the central office line circuit may provide open intervals to the loop during call setup and disconnect. In modern systems these open intervals do not exceed 350 ms.

Other timing criteria for both ground start and loop start not already discussed are shown below [4]. The timing requirements shown below are not absolute quantities and can vary with system manufacturer and telephone company requirements. In modern systems, they are programmable.

- Trip ringing: 200 ms after connect signal (objective)
- Cut-through: no more than 300 ms after connect signal (objective)
- Flash timing: between 300 ms and 2 s
- Disconnect timing: 10 s to several minutes depending on the switching system
- Terminal equipment recognition of idle condition: at least 100 ms and ready to accept a new call in 150 ms
- Guard timing: 1 s

- Remove dial tone; 500 ms after receiving first address digit
- Partial dial timeout: 5 to 30 s between digits
- Permanent signal timeout: 5 to 30 s after loop seizure
- Start addressing: between 70 ms and permanent signal timeout

CO Originates

PBX Originates

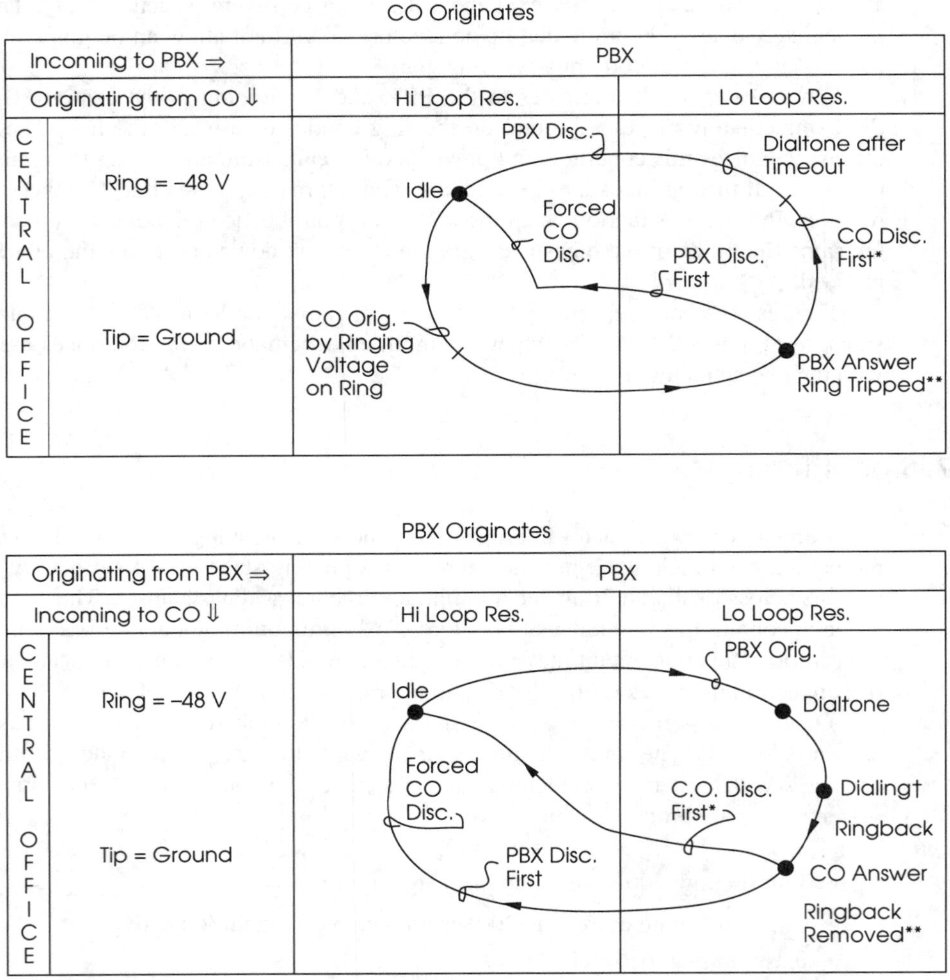

*No disconnect signal passed to trunk.
**CO may reverse tip and ring at this point.
†Tone dialing assumed. If dial pulse, state pulses between Hi and Lo res.

Figure 2-4 Loop start signaling state diagram

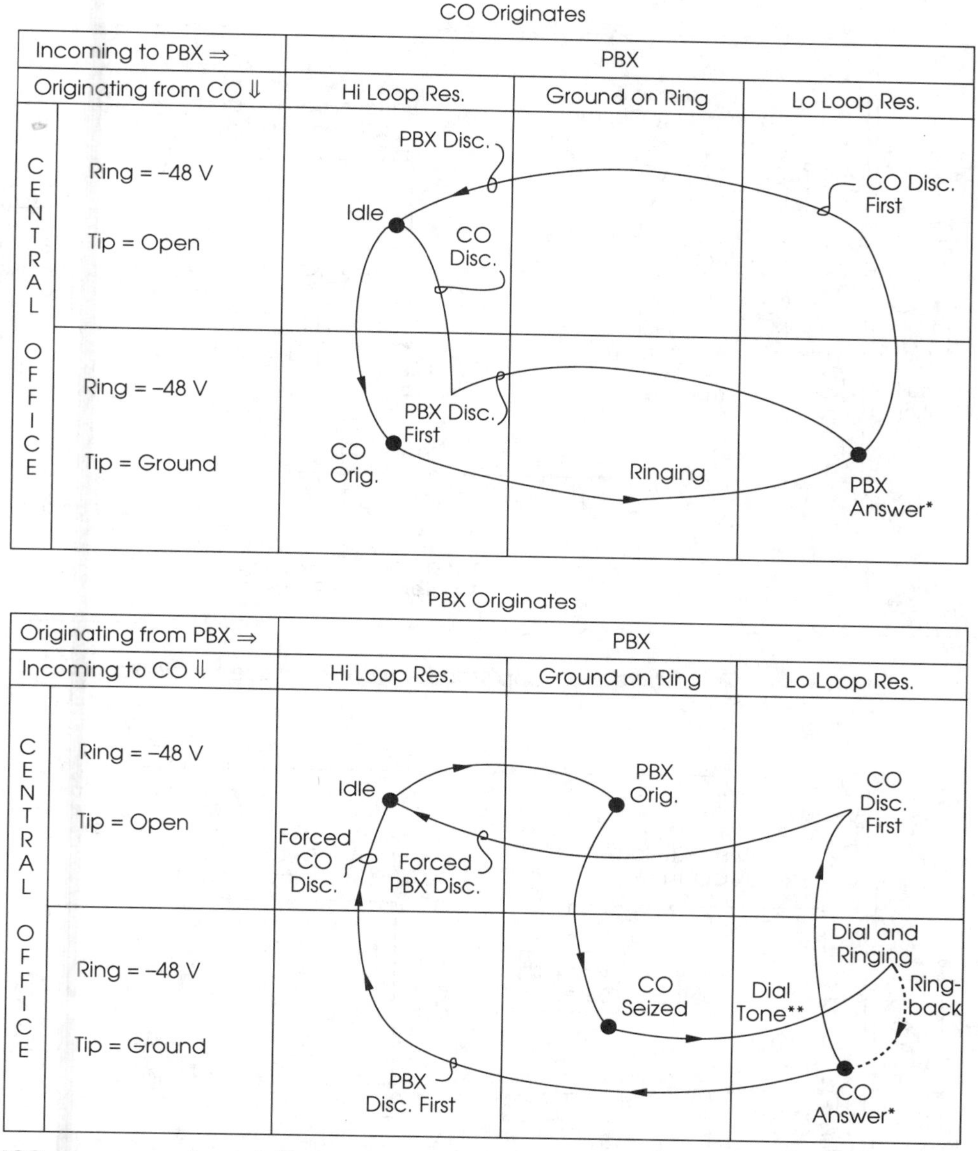

CO Originates

Incoming to PBX ⇒		PBX		
Originating from CO ⇓		Hi Loop Res.	Ground on Ring	Lo Loop Res.
C E N T R A L O F F I C E	Ring = –48 V Tip = Open	PBX Disc. Idle CO Disc.		CO Disc. First
	Ring = –48 V Tip = Ground	CO Orig. PBX Disc. First	Ringing	PBX Answer*

PBX Originates

Originating from PBX ⇒		PBX		
Incoming to CO ⇓		Hi Loop Res.	Ground on Ring	Lo Loop Res.
C E N T R A L O F F I C E	Ring = –48 V Tip = Open	Idle Forced CO Disc. Forced PBX Disc.	PBX Orig.	CO Disc. First
	Ring = –48 V Tip = Ground	PBX Disc. First	CO Seized Dial Tone**	Dial and Ringing Ringback CO Answer*

*CO may reverse tip and ring on answer, depending on type of CO equipment.
**Tone dialing assumed. If dial pulse, state pulses between Hi and Lo loop res.

Figure 2-5 Ground start signaling state diagram

2.8 Ringing

The next step in the call is ringing. The ringing voltage applied to the called party's loop at the central office line circuit depends on the ringing frequency. The frequencies normally used for ringing range from 16 Hz to 66 2/3 Hz. They are arranged in discrete

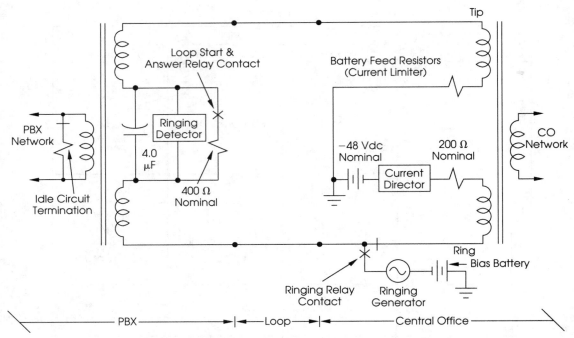

Figure 2-6 Loop start network interface block diagram

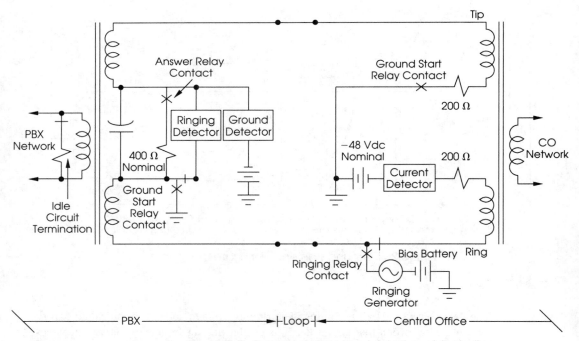

Figure 2-7 Ground start network interface block diagram

relationships, depending on the system, and are given such names as "harmonic," "decimonic," "synchromonic," and "single-frequency" as shown in Table 2-4.

Table 2-4 Common Ringing Schemes

Ringing Scheme	Frequencies Used (Hz)
Decimonic	20, 30, 40, 50, 60
Harmonic	16 2/3, 25, 33 1/3, 50, 66 2/3
Synchromonic	16, 30, 42, 54, 66
Single-Frequency	20 (or any above)

The choice of a particular frequency scheme can depend on many things, such as the cost of various ringer types and central office ringing equipment, and the type and length of loops to be served. For most situations, one scheme will work just as well as another, although harmonic ringing is generally avoided due to false ringing problems. Also, 60 Hz ringing is also avoided because the frequency is the same as the power line frequency, and it is susceptible to false ringing, too.

The multifrequency schemes are generally used where multi-party service is offered. Single-frequency is generally associated with single-party systems. The preferred frequencies for single-frequency systems are 20 or 30 Hz. Some central office switching systems have two ringing buses — a single-frequency bus (with, say, 20 or 30 Hz ringing) and a multifrequency bus (with, say, synchromonic ringing).

As indicated in Chapter 1, ringers may be connected in a bridged or divided manner. This is further illustrated in Fig. 2-8, parts a through d, depicting various ringer connections. There are a number of possible variations such as ac-dc, superimposed and variations within these two categories. The choice of any particular method is dictated by service requirements. For example, consider an eight-party party line. Since there are only five frequencies available in any particular multifrequency scheme, bridged ringing does not offer enough combinations to serve eight parties. The solution is to use four-frequency, divided ringing. That is, ringers tuned to 20, 30, 40 and 50 Hz might be connected one each at parties 1 through 4 from tip to ground. On parties 5 through 8, similar ringers would be connected from ring to ground. Divided ringing has other advantages, such as the ability to ring more ringers over longer distances than bridged ringing.

Divided ringing has disadvantages, though. Multi-party lines with divided ringing will have noticeably lower transmission quality. This is due to longitudinal unbalance, which is an asymmetric relationship of the tip and ring conductors to ground. Degradation in longitudinal balance can be as high as 10 dB with divided ringing unless steps are taken to prevent it. This is why it is very important with divided ringing that the same number of ringers are connected to the tip as are connected to the ring, even if it means using a dummy ringer. A dummy ringer is a ringer identical to the one connected to the other side of the line but with the gong disabled.

Another method of maintaining loop balance is to use ringer isolators on loops with divided ringing. Ringer isolators effectively isolate the ringer from the loop except when ringing voltage is applied. Modern ringer isolators are simple electronic switching devices. These are not generally applied to loops less than 300 Ω where ringing pre-trip can be a problem. Older ringer isolators were electromechanical devices with a gas-filled

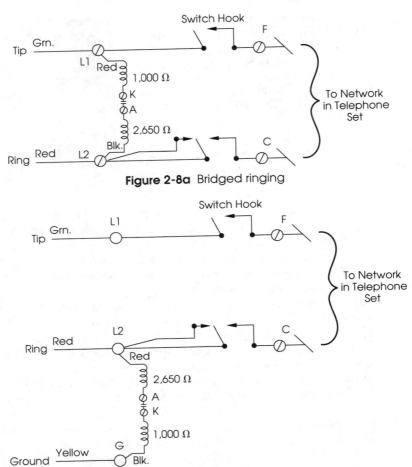

Figure 2-8a Bridged ringing

Figure 2-8b Divided ringing (ring party — no identification)

electron tube and relay. Both the solid-state and electromechanical types are illustrated in Fig. 2-9, parts a and b. The connections shown in this figure are for a ringer connected from ring to ground. A tip side connection would be similar except the ringer would be connected tip to ground.

Bridged ringing avoids the inherently unbalanced operation of divided ringing. When bridged ringing is used with multi-party lines, each ringer is tuned to a different frequency and connected tip to ring. A good source of information on choosing a ringing method is [6].

Related to ringing schemes, but not covered by multifrequency systems, is coded ringing. This scheme places a different ringing cadence on the loop depending on the party being called. The ringing voltage and frequency are the same for all parties. For example, 54 Hz ringers could be connected for bridged ringing in each of the two parties on a two-party line. The first party would be signaled by one long ring and the second party could be signaled by two short rings. Coded ringing is not used in modern systems with multi-party service. Its only modern application is with some enhanced line circuit features such as Centrex.

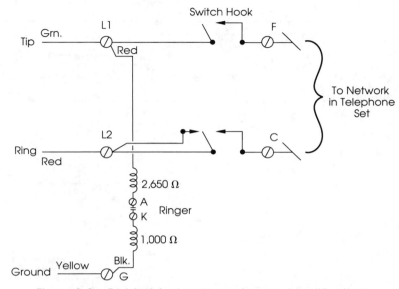

Figure 2-8c Divided ringing (tip party — no identification)

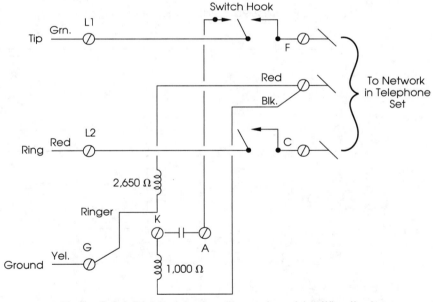

Figure 2-8d Divided ringing (tip party — identification)

For all the complications, it is a relief that multi-party service is relatively limited in the United States as a whole (much less than 1 percent of total lines).

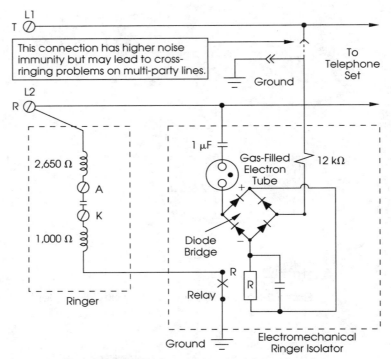

Figure 2-9a Electromechanical ringer isolator

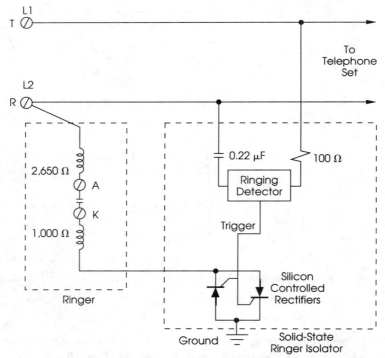

Figure 2-9b Solid-state ringer isolator

The ringing voltage applied to the loop by the central office line circuit varies from a nominal 105 Vac at 16 Hz to 140 Vac at 66 2/3 Hz.* The ac ringing voltage is biased by a dc voltage (usually a nominal 48 Vdc, but it may be as high as 105 Vdc) to allow the central office to detect called party answer by sensing a dc current. A 48 Vdc bias is the most common ringing bias category, and it is called ac-dc ringing as shown in Table 2-5. In some systems the polarity of the bias voltage is used to select a particular party on a multi-party line. The ringers are isolated with a diode, which acts as a polarized switch. This method is called superimposed ringing.

Table 2-5 Ringing Bias Categories

Bias	Type
–48 Vdc	ac-dc
±105 Vdc	Superimposed

To provide reliable ringing on long loops equipped with electromechanical ringers, the ringing voltage should be applied for at least 1.3 s. This requirement precludes short cadences in a nonstandard ringing scheme. The normal cadence is 2 s on and 4 s off. Other cadences may be used with special line features as previously mentioned.

There are many different types of ringers available. They are generally classified as tuned (or resonant) and untuned (straight-line). Tuned ringers are frequency sensitive and comparatively voltage insensitive. Untuned ringers are voltage sensitive and comparatively frequency insensitive. Different types may be used on long loops (greater than 2,000 Ω) or multi-party lines. For example, a tuned ringer will work better on a long loop than a straight-line ringer. Also, a tuned ringer is generally needed on multi-party lines (although not always on two-party lines if divided ringing is used). A straight-line ringer is generally used on single-party lines.

The choice between ringer types is somewhat complicated by the large number of types available, such as electromechanical, electronic, tuned, straight-line, and long loop. Of course, when the telephone instrument is subscriber owned, as is now the case, telephone companies have little control over what type of ringer is installed (except with multi-party service). This places the burden on the subscriber of purchasing terminal equipment with the proper ringer.

The "B" type ringer (defined in FCC Part 68, Par. 68.312, Table 1 and shown in Table 2-6) covers the widest frequency range and can be used in all applications suitable for an untuned ringer. If frequency selective ringing is needed, Table 2-6 can be consulted to pick the appropriate ringer type.

The ringing voltage available at the telephone instrument (as opposed to the voltage applied to the loop at the central office as discussed above) depends on the number and type of ringers attached, the loop length, and other factors, such as line leakage and earth potential differences (for divided ringing).

Each ringer presents an ac coupled load of approximately 5,000 to 10,000 Ω to the loop, although this can be quite variable as discussed later. Ringing voltage drop can be a serious problem on a long loop with a large number of ringers attached; the loop gets loaded down. Voltages as low as 40 V can be expected.

---

* The exact voltages used at any particular frequency are not standardized among all systems. It is possible that the voltage could be less than 100 V.

The foregoing generalization of ringer loads does not take into account the ringer equivalence number (REN) prescribed by the FCC in Part 68. The REN is used to describe the on-hook impedance of the terminal equipment, and it is actually a dimensionless ratio that reflects consideration of the dc and ac loads imposed on the loop by the terminal equipment. These loads do not necessarily have to be due to a ringer; they apply to any load placed on the loop during the on-hook condition.

A ringer equivalence of 1.0 for a given item of terminal equipment is defined as the larger of:

1. 25 MΩ on-hook dc resistance for all applied voltages up to 100 Vdc; or

2. 150 kΩ on-hook dc resistance for all applied voltages from 100 to 200 V; or

3. 0.6 mA of dc current flowing between tip and ring during simulated ringing; or

4. Either 5,000, 7,000 or 8,000 Ω of ac impedance (depending on the ringer type; the latter is most common) during simulated ringing.

Other ringer equivalences are determined by taking the ratio of measured values to those above. The voltages and currents used to determine ringer equivalence take into account testing the telephone company may perform on subscriber loops, some of which are discussed in Chapter 7.

An REN of 1.0 means the terminal equipment loads the loop the same as a standard load used in the definition of REN. A ringer or device with an REN of 2.5 loads the loop 2.5 times as much.

Table 2-6 FCC Ringing Types

FCC Ringing Type	Freq. Range (Hz)	Ringing Scheme	Nominal Freq. (Hz)
A	20±3	SF, Decimonic	20
A	30±3	SF, Decimonic, Synchromonic	30
B	15.3-68.0	Any	Any
C	15.7-17.4	Synchromonic, Harmonic	16 or 16 2/3
D	19.3-20.7	SF, Decimonic*	20
E	24.3-25.7	Harmonic	25
F	29.3-30.7	SF, Decimonic, Synchromonic*	30
G	32.6-34.0	Harmonic	33 1/3
H	39.2-40.9	Decimonic	40
J	41.0-43.0	Synchromonic	42
K	49.0-51.0	Decimonic	50
L	52.9-55.1	Synchromonic	54
M	58.8-61.2	Decimonic	60
N	65.4-68.0	Synchromonic, Harmonic	66, 66 2/3
P	15.3-34.0	Any	16, 16 2/3, 20, 25, 30, 33 1/3
Q	20±3	SF, Decimonic	20

* For frequency selective applications.

Ring trip, which is simply the disconnection of ringing voltage from the loop when the called party answers, also is a problem on long loops due to the lower loop current. Adequate loop current is required by the central office to reliably detect answer. Under normal conditions, up to six long-loop, tuned, bridged ringers will function properly on a 4,300 Ω, 24 gauge loop. Straight-line ringers have a much smaller range, but up to five of them can be rung on a 1,300 Ω loop. Good sources of information on ringing ranges on various loop configurations are [6,7].

2.9 Answering the Line

When the called party answers, off-hook, or answer, supervision is returned to the central office. Answer supervision is nothing more than current flow in the loop because the telephone instrument network and transmitter are now connected across the cable pair by the switch-hook. Current flow is detected by the central office, which operates a ring-trip relay (either electromechanical or electronic), disconnecting ringing voltage from the loop. Simultaneously, the calling and called parties are "cut-through" (connected), and conversation may take place.

The called party's voice may be used to indicate answer ("Hello") or, on a data call, a modem may return answer tone, which is detected by another modem on the other end of the call. Some central offices provide "reverse battery answer supervision" to the calling party. This means the battery relationship on the two loop conductors (tip and ring) is reversed on answer. Normally, on an idle circuit (before answer) the tip conductor is positive (grounded) with respect to the ring conductor; after answer, the tip is negative (battery). The answer condition remains as long as the called party is off-hook.

Many central offices do not provide reverse battery answer supervision without extra equipment or a special line circuit. If reverse battery supervision is required, it may be an extra-cost feature. Some companies tariff this item as "hotel/motel reverse battery supervision" or simply as "reverse battery supervision."

Other forms of answer supervision can be provided. For example, a third conductor that is switched from battery voltage to ground (or ground to battery voltage) upon answer is sometimes available. Many companies can provide tones or other indications as determined by their tariffs. Answer supervision can be used for many purposes; for example, it may be used to operate a counter to count calls (called peg count), start and stop a timer in an automatic call detail recorder, or initiate data transfer on a computer data circuit.

2.10 Loop Signaling During Call Progress

Intermediate sequence signaling can take place once the call has been established and is in the "talking" state. These signals take the form of switch-hook flashes or tone dial commands. A form of tone dial commands was previously discussed for the brokerage firm. In other situations the "#" and "*" keys have special uses. The actual application of the "*" and "#" keys is not universal among all central offices or PBXs.

The "*" or "asterisk" key is used in many modern systems as a prefix digit to indicate to the central office the digits following are service oriented; that is, the digits following indicate the desired service feature package such as custom calling (call forwarding, call waiting, three-way calling and speed calling) and Centrex features.

The "#" or "pound sign" or "octothorpe" key, when used as a prefix, indicates that the digits following are facility oriented; that is, the digits following indicate the desired capability of the transmission channel. This can be the selection of a long distance carrier or call routing details. When the "#" key is a suffix to digits, it indicates the end of dialing.

The switch-hook flash plays an important role in all modern switching systems. The flash can be made by manually and momentarily placing the switch-hook on-hook (for example, by pushing it down). Many telephone instruments are equipped with a "flash" key that provides a properly timed on-hook regardless of the time the key is held down.

The flash serves an ancillary signaling function such as indicating the desire to establish a three-way call (conference call) with an existing two-way call. Similarly, it can indicate the answer of a waiting call. The switching system equipped with these features is able to distinguish the desired action from the existing call status as well as the features available to the line making the flash.

The flash must be long enough to be interpreted by the switching system as a deliberate on-hook and not a transient. On the other hand, it cannot be so long that it is interpreted as a "hang-up" or permanent on-hook. The minimum flash time is normally around 0.3 s (300 ms). The maximum time is normally between 1 and 2 s.

2.11 Disconnect Sequence

The disconnect sequence upon call completion can vary. The usual practice is to allow either party to initiate the disconnect sequence. That is, if either party hangs up (goes on-hook), the switching system will drop the connection within its network for both parties, thereby freeing the path for another call.

In some cases, it is desirable to allow the called party to control the disconnect sequence. This occurs, for example, on lines with call trace or call identification requirements, such as with schools and emergency and public safety organizations. In these cases, the called party can "hold" the connection as long as desired (for example, the time required to make manual identification of the calling party) and then drop the call at its convenience. Calls to an operator are another example of the called party having control over the disconnect sequence.

In any case, the disconnect sequence takes place according to some preset timing condition. For "either party control," the line hanging up first will be immediately released for another call. If the other party continues with an off-hook, the switching system will wait a preset interval (usually 10 or 15 s) and then treat the line condition as a permanent signal as discussed above.

REFERENCES

[1] Bear, D. *Principles of Telecommunications Traffic Engineering*. Peter Peregrinus Ltd., 1988.

[2] IEEE Standard 742-1986, *IEEE Standard Functional Requirements for Methods and Equipment for Measuring the Performance of Tone Address Signaling Systems.* Piscataway, NJ: Institute of Electrical and Electronics Engineers, 1986.

[3] IEEE Standard 753-1983, *IEEE Standard Functional Methods and Equipment for Measuring the Performance of Dial-Pulse (DP) Address Signaling Systems.* Piscataway, NJ: Institute of Electrical and Electronics Engineers, 1983.

[4] *Compatibility Information for Telephone Exchange Service*, Technical Advisory TA-NPL-000912. BELLCORE, February 1989. Available from BELLCORE Document Registrar.

[5] ANSI T1.401-1988, *American National Standard for Telecommunications, Interface between Carriers and Customer Installations, Analog Voicegrade Switched Access Lines Using Loop-Start and Ground-Start Signaling.* New York: American National Standards Institute, 1988.

[6] *REA Telephone Engineering & Construction Manual Section 212–Ringing Systems.* Rural Electrification Administration, November 1970, Addendum No. 1, May, 1973.

[7] *Telecommunications Transmission Engineering*, Vols. 1-3. Winston-Salem, NC: Western Electric Company, Inc., Technical Publications, 1975. Available from AT&T Customer Information Center.

3

The Outside Plant Facility

This chapter describes the types of physical outside plant facilities that make up the subscriber's loop. Of particular interest are the types and characteristics of cables used in subscriber loop applications. In addition, a description of the premises wiring is provided so the complete physical connection to the terminal equipment can be envisioned.

3.1 Cable Pairs

The main and most important part of a conventional two-wire loop is an outside plant cable pair (two twisted conductors), which provides a bidirectional signaling and transmission path. Some loops, in particular those associated with dedicated or private line circuits, consist of two cable pairs to provide a four-wire circuit with independent transmit and receive pairs. Associated with each cable pair of either the two-wire or four-wire loop are ancillary devices for protection and termination, which are discussed in Chapter 4.

3.2 Exchange Cables

Exchange cables are those cables used for exchange services such as regular subscriber or private line services.* Exchange cables are categorized according to their

---

* Many times, trunk and exchange services are combined in one cable; however, descriptions of trunk systems are beyond the scope of this book.

service classifications as shown in Table 3-1. These classifications are universal. It should be noted that it may be possible to use a given cable type in several classifications. For example, filled cable is normally considered for direct buried applications, but it is also used in aerial and underground service. Exchange cables are considered to have a life of 25 to 35 years.

Table 3-1 Exchange Cable Service Classifications

Class	Application
Indoor	Risers in the central office building
Aerial	Lashed to separate messenger or self-supporting on an above-ground structure
Buried	Buried directly in the earth
Underground	Installed underground in duct or conduit

Depending on the gauge, exchange cables are available in standard pair counts from 6 through 4,200 pairs. When cables up to around 1,200 pairs are manufactured for direct burial and aerial applications, the core may be filled with a jelly- or rubber-like substance to prevent insulation damage and higher attenuation from moisture. Alternately, these cables may be built with an air core and then pressurized after installation with dry air to prevent moisture ingress. All larger cables are pressurized. Moisture in a cable increases its capacitance; the increased capacitance can increase the attenuation as much as 40 percent over dry values.

It is virtually impossible to keep moisture out of unpressurized air-core cables installed in an outdoor environment over a long time period regardless of the service classification. If pressurization is not available, or the cable is relatively small, filled cables provide much better long-term service than unpressurized air-core cables in all service classifications. Contrary to fairly common practice among some companies, unpressurized air-core cables should never be placed underground or directly buried.

3.3 Color Coding

Many pairs are combined together to form a cable. The individual pairs are formed into units, and the units are then assembled or cabled into cores (much like a rope). The basic unit contains 25 pairs which are color coded for identification as shown in Table 3-2. Each conductor has a solid and tracer color, which is opposite to allow identification of tip and ring. For example, the tip conductor of pair 1 has a solid white color with a blue tracer. The ring conductor has a solid blue color with a white tracer. Note, also, the repetitive color code for the tracer every five pairs. When necessary, the basic unit is divided into sub-units of 12 or 13 pairs to attain cable roundness and the desired pair count.

In cables larger than 25 pairs, the units are wrapped with a colored tracer ribbon (unit binder) according to a similar color coding scheme. For example, a 100-pair cable contains 4 units of 25 pairs each. The first unit (pairs 1 through 25) would be wrapped with a binder colored white-blue, the second unit (pairs 26 through 50) would be colored white-orange, and so on. Since there are 25 basic colors in the color code, up to twenty-five 25 pair units can be identified this way. Only 24 are used, however, which takes care of cables up to 600 pairs. Beyond 600 pairs, "super unit binders" are used. This color code is shown in Table 3-3.

The telephone color code shown in Table 3-2 is not the only one used. For example, the most common station wire, also known as *quad* or *inside/outside* (I/O) wire, consists of four conductors with the color code shown in Table 3-4. Other types of multi-pair station wire will conform to the color code shown in Table 3-2. In addition, various other color codes are used for wiring electronic equipment, some of which may be used in telecommunication systems.

Table 3-2 Telephone Color Code

Pair No.	Color (Tip-Ring)	Pair No.	Color (Tip-Ring)
1	White-Blue	14	Black-Brown
2	White-Orange	15	Black-Slate
3	White-Green		
4	White-Brown	16	Yellow-Blue
5	White-Slate	17	Yellow-Orange
		18	Yellow-Green
6	Red-Blue	19	Yellow-Brown
7	Red-Orange	20	Yellow-Slate
8	Red-Green		
9	Red-Brown	21	Violet-Blue
10	Red-Slate	22	Violet-Orange
		23	Violet-Green
11	Black-Blue	24	Violet-Brown
12	Black-Orange	25	Violet-Slate
13	Black-Green		

Table 3-3 Super Unit Binders

Super Unit	Binder Color
Pairs 1-600	White
Pairs 601-1,200	Red
Pairs 1,201-1,800	Black
Pairs 1,801-2,400	Yellow
Pairs 2,401-3,000	Violet
Pairs 3,001-3,600	Blue
Pairs 3,601-4,200	Orange

Table 3-4 Quad Station Wire
Color Code

Pair. No.	Color (Tip-Ring)
1 2	Green-Red Black-Yellow

Note: The yellow conductor (or yellow
and black conductors together) is used
as a ground lead when divided ringing
is required.

3.4 Insulation

All modern cables use conductors insulated with a polyolefin (plastic) formed by an extrusion process. Older cables use a paper (or pulp) insulation. Polyolefin insulated cable (PIC) is a general term used to describe all modern plastic insulated cables. The actual insulation type may be classified as solid (polyethylene or polypropylene) or expanded foam (dual expanded polyethylene or expanded polyethylene – PVC). Expanded foam cables have found widespread use since about 1980. In many applications, material only costs for expanded foam are less (by about 10 to 15 percent) than solid insulation type cables. Expanded foam cables are always filled.

3.5 Crosstalk

As previously noted, each cable pair consists of two twisted insulated conductors. The twist is used to decrease electromagnetic interference (EMI) due to crosstalk between adjacent pairs in a cable. The twist also helps keep the conductors of the pair balanced with respect to the shield and other pairs. Neighboring pairs in a given 25-pair unit have a different twist length to further reduce crosstalk between them. The twist length (or pitch) is usually left-hand (counter-clockwise), and it varies from 2 to 6 inches. It is optimized to reduce crosstalk at higher frequencies (hundreds of kilohertz) since it is in this region where crosstalk can become a problem.

The requirement for adequate crosstalk performance in all exchange cables is highly stressed during their design and construction. Crosstalk due to cable pair irregularities is managed by tightly controlling capacitance unbalance (pair-to-pair, pair-to-shield and pair-to-ground) and resistance unbalance during the manufacturing process.

3.6 Shielding

All outside plant cables are shielded with corrugated aluminum or copper tape. To increase corrosion resistance, the aluminum is bonded to a thin plastic (copolymer). A corrugated rather than smooth surface is used to increase shield strength and flexibility.

The shield isolates the enclosed conductors from outside sources of electromagnetic interference, such as induction from power line harmonic frequencies. The ability of a shield to isolate the cable pairs from such interference is determined by its shield factor.

Shield factor is a function of the end-to-end shield resistance, the mutual impedance between the shield and cable pairs, frequency and the ground system impedance. Cable shields with a low resistance and low mutual impedance have a higher shield factor. Larger cables have both these features and so offer a better shield factor than smaller cables. Tables are available to simplify the calculation of shield factor for telecommunication cables [1].

The thin aluminum or copper shield used in conventional telecommunication cables does very little to isolate the pairs from power line interference at the fundamental frequency (60 Hz). Since the telephone instrument, and other terminal equipment, is designed to have little response at 60 Hz, this usually is not a problem. The shield is more effective, however, at harmonic frequencies, which are annoying to the subscriber or can cause problems with data transmission.

The shield in a given cable provides almost twice the shielding (induced voltage cut almost in half) at 540 Hz than it does at 60 Hz. Also, a cable with four times the diameter of another cable will provide twice the shielding.

Physically, the shield thickness is generally 0.008 inches (8 mil) for aluminum and 0.005 inches (5 mil) for copper.* Coated aluminum is the preferred shield because it is cheaper and usable in all but the most demanding applications (such as some highly corrosive environments). For reference purposes, a 1,200-pair, 24 gauge, aluminum shielded cable has a shield resistance of around 1 Ω per mile (Ω/mi); a 100-pair, 24 gauge cable has a shield resistance of almost 4 Ω/mi.

The shield is made continuous through splice points, which are found in vaults, manholes, aerial terminals and pedestals, and connected to earth ground at regular intervals (at least four times per mile). Shield continuity and grounding are very important; otherwise, the cable pairs are susceptible not only to noise but to damaging overvoltages during lightning activity, power faults and power system switching transients.

Wrapped between the shield and the cable core of modern exchange cables is a non-hygroscopic dielectric tape, which provides additional insulation to increase the pair-to-shield withstand voltage.

For digital carrier applications, an additional shield is used that separates the cable pairs into two compartments. This is called compartmental core cable, "Z-Screen," "D-Screen" or "T-Screen." The latter indicates the primary application for this type of cable, which is T-carrier. The separation is necessary to eliminate crosstalk between the transmit and receive pairs of the transmission system. The cross-section of a compartmental core cable is illustrated in Fig. 3-1. Compartmental cone cables are frequently installed for analog loops when it is known that the service will be upgraded to digital in the future.

3.7 Armor

In addition to the shield, a steel tape may be used as an armor for increased physical protection and strength. The tape is corrugated and usually 6 mils thick. It is polymer coated to reduce corrosion. Alternately, the properties of both shield and armor can be

---

* One mil = 0.001 inch or 0.0254 mm.

combined in a single corrugated tape. A copper/iron alloy (6 mils thick) or extra thick (10 mil) copper is used in this case.

Armored cables find applications in areas infested by gophers, beavers, squirrels or other chewing rodents. Another application for these cables is where they are installed in a severe physical environment such as direct burial in sharp, broken rocks and where bedding sand is not available.

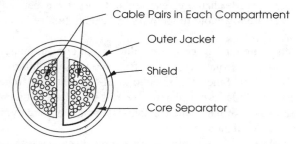

Figure 3-1 Compartmental core cable cross-section

3.8 Outer Jacket

The outer covering (jacket or sheath) on all modern cables is a tough plastic, the thickness of which varies with the size of the cable. It varies from 60 mils for a cable with diameter around 0.75 inches to 110 mils for a cable with approximately 2 inches or larger diameter. The type of plastic varies with the application. A vinyl material is used for riser cables in a central office because it will not support a flame, and its burn products are nontoxic. Low-density, high molecular weight polyethylene (or ethylene copolymer) or high-density polyethylene is used in outside applications.

In aerial applications, the cable is lashed to a supporting messenger, which varies from 3/16 inch to 7/16 inch diameter, depending on the strength required and the material used. In some aerial applications, a self-supporting cable is used. This cable incorporates a supporting messenger along with the outer sheath. Because of its shape, this cable is called *Figure 8*. Due to strength limitations, Figure 8 cable is generally not available in pair counts above 300 pairs (26 gauge), 200 pairs (24 gauge), 100 pairs (22 gauge) or 50 pairs (19 gauge).

Many older cables have a lead sheath that acts as both a shield and outer covering.

3.9 Feeder and Distribution Cables

Referring back to Fig. 1-1 in Chapter 1, feeder cables comprise the loop from the central office to main junction points called a serving area interface (SAI), facility area connector (FAC), cross-connect or control point. The actual name depends on the company, but the function is to provide a point at which feeder cable pairs can be administered and connected to individual distribution cable pairs.

Distribution cables comprise the loop from the main junctions to a distribution terminal such as a pedestal or aerial terminal. In any given area, there are generally more distribution pairs than feeder pairs. This allows efficient use of larger and more expensive feeder cables through easier administration and assignment of subscribers.

Feeder and distribution cables can contain as many as 4,200 pairs (8,400 conductors) or as few as 6 pairs, all within a single sheath. Cables are available with 19, 22, 24 or 26 American Wire Gauge (AWG) copper conductors. The most widely used feeder and distribution cable size is 24 gauge. This is due to economic tradeoffs that take into account the typical loop length.

In the smaller cable sizes, good design practice calls for using cables that are multiples of the basic 25-pair unit (25 and 50). Pair counts of 6, 12, 18 and 37 are avoided unless other factors make their use clearly more economical than 25 or 50 pair sizes. There is very little difference between the installed cost of 6 or 12 and 25 pair cables or 37 and 50 pair cables in most applications.

The extra pairs not only give extra insurance to accommodate unforeseen growth, but they also allow the allocation and use of pairs in the field to be more logical due to the 5-pair and 25-pair color coding scheme. The long-term result, of course, is easier administration and maintenance.

3.10 Service Wires

Service wires make up the final portion of the loop. They are installed between the distribution terminal and the actual serving point or network interface device (for example, at an office building or residential establishment). Beyond the network interface device are premises wiring systems, which are described at the end of this chapter.

Service wires can be one pair up to hundreds or thousands of pairs depending on the establishment to be served. Service wires in the smaller sizes are not always twisted because they are usually short and do not measurably degrade transmission quality. Aerial service wires are usually 18 or 19 gauge, while buried service wires are usually 19, 22 or 24 gauge. High-purity copper is the most widely used conductor material for underground service wires, while copper with special alloying (or other means for strength) is used for aerial service wires.

3.11 Summary of Physical Characteristics

The physical characteristics described above are summarized in Table 3-5 for modern cables. Figure 3-2 illustrates the construction of various cable types. Finally, a matrix and a flow chart are provided in Table 3-6 and Fig. 3-3 that can be used to select the cable characteristics suitable for a particular application.

3.12 Cable Costs

Cable costs vary considerably with gauge, construction and the current cost of copper (and aluminum, if that type of shield is used). Nineteen gauge cable can be twice as expensive as 24 gauge cable for a given pair count. Filled cable is 10 to 25 percent more expensive than air-core cable, depending on the gauge and pair count. Table 3-7 shows a comparison chart with relative material costs for various cable gauges and sizes.

Table 3-5 Exchange Cable Physical
                Characteristics

Insulation	Polyethylene Polypropylene Dual expanded polyethylene Expanded polyethylene — PVC
Gauge	19, 22, 24, 26 AWG, copper
Pair Count	6, 12, 18, 25, 37, 50, 75, 100, 150, 300, 400, 600, 900, 1,200, 1,500, 1,800, 2,100, 2,400, 2,700, 3,000, 3,600, 4,200[a]
Core	Air or filled
Shield	Bonded aluminum (8 mil), copper (5 or 10 mil) or copper alloy (6 mil)
Armor	Bonded steel (6 mil) when separate from the shield
Sheath	Vinyl, HMW polyethylene, HD polyethylene

[a] Not all pair counts are available with all gauges.

Table 3-6 Exchange Cable Selection Matrix

	Alvyn	PIC	PIC Armored	Self-Supporting	Filled	Air Core
Indoor	√					√
Aerial Normal		√		√	√*	√
Aerial Severe			√	√	√	√
Buried Normal		√			√	
Buried Severe			√		√	
Underground Normal	√				√	√
Underground Severe			√		√	√

*Filled, self-supporting cables are not available.

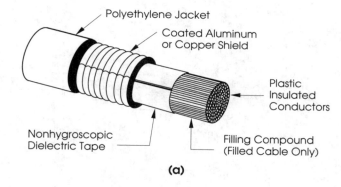

Polyethylene Jacket

Coated Aluminum
or Copper Shield

Plastic
Insulated
Conductors

Nonhygroscopic
Dielectric Tape

Filling Compound
(Filled Cable Only)

(a)

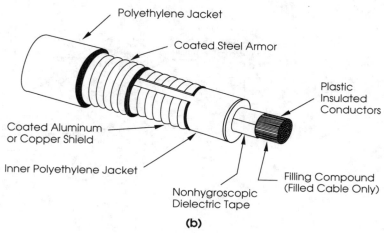

Polyethylene Jacket

Coated Steel Armor

Plastic
Insulated
Conductors

Coated Aluminum
or Copper Shield

Inner Polyethylene Jacket

Nonhygroscopic
Dielectric Tape

Filling Compound
(Filled Cable Only)

(b)

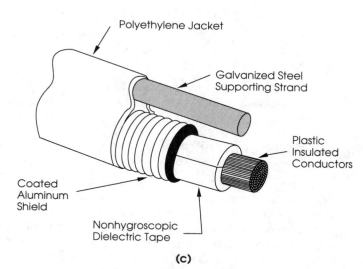

Polyethylene Jacket

Galvanized Steel
Supporting Strand

Plastic
Insulated
Conductors

Coated
Aluminum
Shield

Nonhygroscopic
Dielectric Tape

(c)

Figure 3-2 Exchange cable constructions: (a) normal duty PIC;
(b) severe duty PIC (armored); (c) self-supporting ("Figure 8")

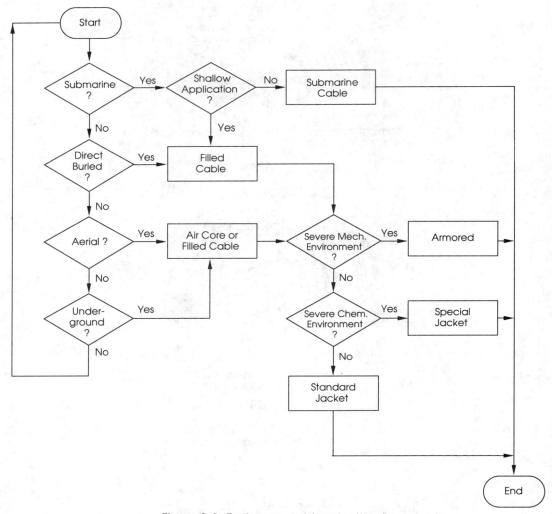

Figure 3-3 Exchange cable selection flow chart

3.13 Voltage and Current Limitations

All cables used in telecommunication applications have voltage and current limitations. The maximum continuous current-carrying capacity of any given conductor gauge depends on many factors such as the ambient temperature, allowable temperature rise, number of conductors in a bundle, and insulation type. Table 3-8 shows the values for various copper conductor gauges, assuming a 25°C ambient temperature and 40°C rise. These are provided to give an idea of the current magnitudes and not as an operating guideline.

The maximum current available from a central office line circuit on a loop is in the range of 130 to 145 mA, although some older systems can supply at least 175 mA. For other signaling and control applications, the telephone company will normally limit the current on loops to 1.3 A, which coordinates with 26 gauge cable. If the loop is connected to subscriber-owned equipment at both ends, then other restrictions apply as discussed below.

Also shown in Table 3-8, for reference, is the fusing current for each gauge, which is the point at which the conductor will fuse open. These are approximations; actual values depend on many variables. Fusing currents and fusing times are inversely related. For example, if the current is increased by a factor of 3, the fusing time will decrease by a factor of about 1/10.

Table 3-7 Relative Costs of Exchange Cable Gauges and Sizes

AWG	Pairs							
	12	25	50	100	200	400	900	1,200
26	0.72	0.73	0.82	0.78	0.77	0.76	0.77	0.76
24	1.00	1.00	1.00	1.00	1.00	1.00	1.00	1.00
22	1.18	1.21	1.41	1.31	1.43	1.40	1.36	1.37
19	1.94	2.33	2.59	2.59	2.56	2.57	n/a	n/a

Table 3-8 Exchange Cable Pair Currents

AWG	Max. Current Capacity (40° Rise)	Fusing Current (0.1 s)
19	8.0 A	600 A
22	5.0 A	300 A
24	2.0 A	190 A
26	1.3 A	110 A

Telecommunication cables are manufactured for an intended application according to a specification prepared by the cable customer. In many cases, these specifications are generic and are in widespread use throughout a segment of the telecommunication industry.* Generally, the specification includes an insulation breakdown voltage, a high-voltage proof test and insulation resistance. The insulation breakdown voltage (or dielectric strength) is the voltage at which the insulation will fail. It is usually specified in volts per mil of insulation thickness. Typical insulation thickness is around 30 mils, but this is quite variable among cable types and manufacturers. Cable specifications normally only show an insulation breakdown voltage, and the manufacturer then applies enough of the particular material to satisfy the requirement.

The high-voltage proof test is at a somewhat lower voltage than the insulation breakdown voltage. It is the voltage at which cables are tested after manufacture and before shipment to the customer. The actual values depend on the cable gauge, whether filled or air-core, and insulation type. All proof tests are made for 3 s. The cable is not expected to withstand these voltages indefinitely.

---

* Examples are the REA specifications, which are used by REA and non-REA borrowers alike; and BELLCORE specifications, which are used by the Bell Operating Companies (BOCs).

Insulation resistance is a measure, in megohm-miles (MΩ-mi), of the leakage between a given conductor and the other conductors and shield in the cable. By inspecting the units, it is clear that the insulation resistance can decrease with increasing length. For example, an air core cable 5 mi long will measure at least 2,000 MΩ (10,000 MΩ-mi/5 mi). Insulation resistance tests are usually made at around 550 V for new cables at the factory, or 250 V for installed cables in the field. The higher the measured resistance, the better. Table 3-9 shows the voltage ratings for typical telecommunication cables.

Table 3-9 Exchange Cable Voltage Ratings

Insulation Breakdown Voltage	300-1,200 V/mil

High-Voltage Proof Test (3 s):
    Conductor-Conductor
    Conductor-Shield
	2-7 kV
	10-20 kV

Insulation Resistance (100-550 V):
    Air Core
    Filled
	10,000 MΩ-mi
	1,000 MΩ-mi

Unlike power cables, outside plant telecommunication cables usually do not have a specified maximum working voltage. Nevertheless, most telecommunication cables are considered to have a working voltage of 300 V across the tip and ring of any given pair and between pairs.*

This does not mean the user can arbitrarily apply 300 V to the loop. As expected, FCC Part 68 has certain maximum voltage and current limitations for terminal equipment in various configurations that preclude such operation.† Basically, the terminal equipment cannot apply more than 56.5 Vdc to a loop connected to an off-premises station or supply more than 140 mA to the loop under any circumstances. During ringing, no more than 300 V peak-to-peak can be applied to the loop.†† The reasons for these limitations are obvious: safety and network harm. Some telephone company tariffs may specify more stringent voltage and current limitations.

The voltage and current limitations imposed by the FCC, and discussed in the previous paragraph, on equipment connected to the loop do not apply to the telephone companies. Although the working voltage of cable pairs is considered to be 300 V, telephone companies will use higher voltages under certain conditions. These are always associated with special equipment located outside the central office. For example, the line repeaters in long T-carrier span lines may be powered by up to 360 V at the central office. This voltage dwindles to much lower values along the span line due to voltage drop across the repeaters and resistive voltage drop in the cable pairs.

* The working voltage considered here is root-mean-square (rms) or dc.
† Par. 68.306.
†† 300 V peak-to-peak corresponds to approximately 106 Vrms, assuming a sinusoidal ringing voltage.

3.14 Premises Wiring

Although not directly a part of the outside plant cabling system, and not necessarily considered a part of the subscriber's loop, premises wiring (also called *station wiring* or *inside wiring*) is a natural and necessary extension of it. Therefore, it would be worthwhile to discuss some attributes of these facilities.

Premises wiring is any wiring that interconnects telecommunications equipment on a particular premises. It is not always connected to the network interface device; however, the discussion in this section will be limited to that part of premises wiring connected to the loop through the network interface device and used in conjunction with terminal equipment.

It usually is not subjected to the same environment (electrical or physical) as outside plant cables, but the wiring inside buildings presents another set of problems to be considered by the designer, builder and users of such systems. These are noise performance and fire hazard problems.

Unlike outside plant cables, for economic reasons, premises wiring systems are not always shielded, and this can lead to problems with *electromagnetic interference* (EMI). It should be noted that premises wiring can be a noise source in addition to noise receptor. With short runs, signals on premises wiring normally have negligible effect on other systems. The reverse is also true. On longer runs, however, the lack of shielding can allow transmission degradation through noise pickup, and premises wiring also can act as a transmitting antenna.

Modern premises wiring systems are carrying a much higher percentage of digital transmission (versus analog or voice transmission), and the transmission speeds are steadily increasing. The use of unshielded twisted pair (UTP) rather than shielded twisted pair (STP) for 16 megabit per second (Mbps) data transmission in office buildings is becoming commonplace. Digital transmissions can cause and are subject to crosstalk interference because of their wide frequency spectrums. Such interference problems can be expected to increase unless the spectrums of these signals are coordinated with other uses.

In addition to the transmission problems facing the users of premises wiring systems, the uncontrolled deployment of polyolefin insulated and jacketed cables inside buildings can lead to safety problems even in minor fires or situations where the cable insulation may burn. Flame spread and burn byproducts (toxicity) are of concern in any building installation.

To reduce the safety hazard, the regulations covering premises wiring systems have become progressively tighter with the last few editions of the National Electrical Code (NEC®).* The application or location of a particular part of the premises wiring determines the type of covering required by the NEC®. The coverings are coded as shown in Table 3-10 in descending order of fire resistance rating. Multipurpose cables shown in this table can be used for communication applications as well as other applications. Communications cables and wiring systems covered by the NEC are required to have a minimum voltage rating of 300 V. A more complete discussion on the various cable types used in communications and communication-related applications in buildings was presented in [3].

---

* See Article 800 [2].

Table 3-10 Premises Wiring Coverings

Cable Type	Covering Type
Multipurpose plenum cable	MPP
Communications plenum cable	CMP
Multipurpose riser cable	MPR
Communications riser cable	CMR
Multipurpose cable	MP
Communications cable	CM
Limited use communications cable	CMX
Undercarpet communications cable	CMUC

The complexity of premises wiring system installations will vary with the application. In simple installations (one, two or as many as four access lines and minimal customer premises equipment), the wiring is almost always arranged in a star pattern as shown in Fig. 3-4. Here the terminal equipment is wired directly to the network interface device. Other arrangements commonly used in simple installations are the "daisy chain" where extensions are multipled (paralleled) with the terminal equipment in the chain preceding it. Standards for simple wiring, such as EIA/TIA 570, are emerging [4].

More complex systems will use a fully engineered premises wiring or premises distribution system (PDS). An example of the architecture of such a system is shown in Fig. 3-5. These are systems of fully integrated components (usually from a single manufacturer) for mechanical and electrical assembly of the wiring from the network interface device to the various terminal equipment.

Premises distribution systems are seldom used with simple installations but are commonplace with private branch exchanges (PBXs) and larger key systems (above around 25 stations), especially when interworking of these devices is required with local area networks (LANs). In this application, the PDS interconnects not only regular telecommunication terminal equipment (telephone instruments, modems, facsimile machines and the like) but also computer and other digital and analog equipment associated with the local area network.

With the integration of digital and analog signal transport for all applications, a considerable cost savings can be achieved not only in the initial installation but in daily administration of the local network.* Premises distribution systems can consist of:

1. Cables with twisted metallic pairs only (STP or UTP)
2. Cables with both twisted metallic pairs and optical fibers
3. Cables with optical fibers only

---

* Because premises wiring can be very labor intensive, it is imperative, from an economic standpoint, that the designer consider the total telecommunication requirement. The requirements would normally include video, data transmission, security, energy management and telecommunications. The bandwidth required could easily approach 500 MHz or more in more complex situations. It is beyond the scope of this book to discuss wiring systems that would serve these wideband requirements. Standards are being prepared that do address these systems [5,6].

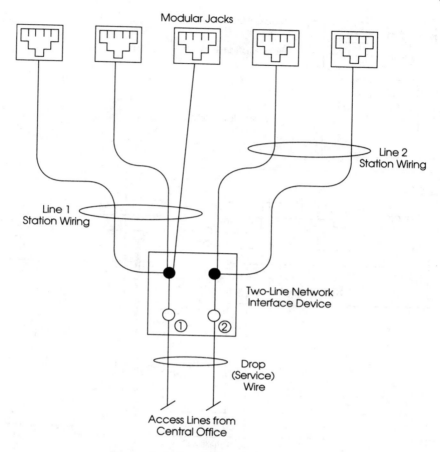

Figure 3-4 Simple premises wiring

4. Coaxial cables

5. Any combination of the above*

In those applications where the PDS interconnects terminal equipment and the loop, a color coding scheme generally is used at interconnection points to indicate the function of the wiring. The terminal blocks used for interconnection (using jumpers) have colored labels and the various cables are marked with color coded tags at each end. There is no universal acceptance of the color scheme used, but a common one is shown in Table 3-11. An explanation of the functions follows. Different PDS manufacturers may have different functions and colors in their product lines.

Central office connections (green) are the cables and terminal blocks associated with the entrance cable from the LEC. House cable terminations (white) are vertical and horizontal cables between the equipment room and telecommunications (satellite) closets or service cabinets within the building. Auxiliary connections (yellow) are cables and terminal blocks that connect to network terminating, signaling and conditioning equipment, paging systems and the like. Information outlets (blue) are cables and connections

---

* Some manufacturers make cable that incorporates all types into a single integral cable, commonly called Siamese cable.

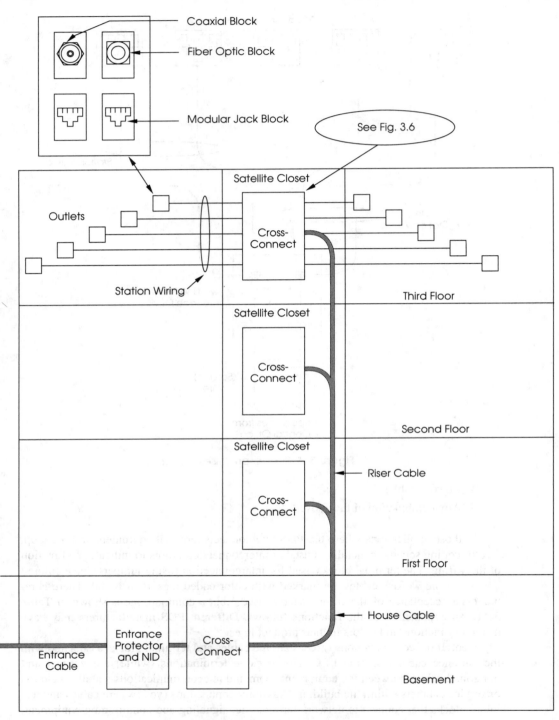

Figure 3-5 Premises distribution system

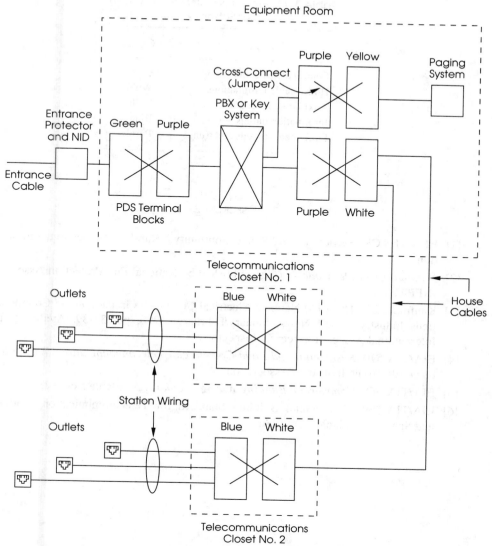

Figure 3-6 Premises distribution system application

from the telecommunications closet or cabinet to the modular connector.* Finally, equipment stations and trunks are the connections from the PBX or key system trunk, line and station circuits. Figure 3-6 shows how the above PDS color code is applied in a typical installation.

---

*   The actual outlet may consist of multiple jacks of different designs for different functions; for example, modular jacks, coaxial connectors and special-purpose connectors.

Table 3-11 Premises Distribution System
Color Scheme

Function	Color
Central office connections	Green
House cable terminations	White
Auxiliary connections	Yellow
Information outlets	Blue
Equipment stations and trunks	Purple

REFERENCES

[1] REA TE&CM Section 451.2, "Shield Continuity." Rural Electrification Administration.

[2] *National Electrical Code — 1990*, published by National Fire Protection Association (NFPA).

[3] Kaufman, S., "The 1990 National Electrical Code — Its Impact on the Communications Industry." IAEI News, January/February, 1990, pp. 34-39. Available from International Assoc. of Electrical Inspectors.

[4] EIA/TIA-570, *Residential and Light Commercial Telecommunications Wiring Standard.* Electronic Industries Association.

[5] EIA/TIA-568, *Commercial Building Wiring Standard.* Available from EIA.

[6] EIA/TIA-569, Commercial Building Standard for Telecommunications Pathways and Spaces. Available from EIA.

4

Protection and Termination

This chapter is concerned with the protection and termination of the subscriber loop. In many cases the two functions are combined, and discussions of both are necessary for a complete understanding. The termination and protection practices of telephone companies vary widely. Even within a given company, the practices will vary with geographical region. A complete discussion of geographical specifics is beyond the scope of this book. Therefore, even though enough information is provided to design and use practical systems, this chapter may be considered indicative instead of exhaustive. The references will provide additional specific information on practices of the larger companies or organizations [1–4].

4.1 Protection Fundamentals

Protection is primarily provided for personnel safety, and its job is to limit the chance of shock or fire. The secondary purpose of protection is to reduce the chance of equipment damage through overvoltage or overcurrent. Also, improperly designed, installed or maintained protection equipment can degrade loop transmission and signaling.

Voltages and currents that constitute a hazard (to either personnel or equipment) and are not required for operation are abnormal in any telecommunication system. Any such voltages or currents are called *foreign potentials*. There are five fundamental ways of protecting loops (or, in general, telecommunication cables) from foreign potentials:

1. Aerial shield wires
2. Parallel conductivity
3. Grounding (direct or through a gap)

4. Voltage limitation and equalization

5. Current limitation

Many factors influence the protection scheme used in any particular application. Some considerations are exposure to foreign potentials from:

- Lightning
- Power contacts
- Power line induction
- Ground potential rise

Obviously, areas with considerable lightning, accidental power contacts and switching transients require better protection methods than areas without these problems. A number of good handbooks are available that thoroughly describe protection theory and techniques [4–8].

Depending on the type, telecommunication protectors provide grounding (through a gap or solid-state device), voltage limitation and current limitation, or three of the fundamental methods listed above. For most applications this is quite adequate, and shield wires and parallel conductivity are not needed except in extreme cases of exposure to lightning.

4.2 Exposure

Exposure is a term used to define the vulnerability of telecommunication facilities to foreign potentials. Such facilities are considered to be exposed to foreign potentials from lightning if they are installed where [1]:

1. There are more than five thunderstorm days in a year and the soil resistivity is greater than 100 ohm-meters (Ω-m)*, and

2. The facilities are not shielded by buildings (for example, built-up high-rise environment) and installed in an extensive underground metallic duct system.

In almost all applications, telecommunication services are provided to the same establishments as are power services. Telecommunication facilities are considered to be exposed to power contact from power services if:

1. The telecommunication cables could possibly contact the power lines, and

2. The voltage of the power lines is more than 300 V to ground.

If telecommunication cables parallel power lines for any great distance (more than approximately 1/2 mile), they are exposed to power induction. Whether or not the induction is hazardous, is situational, and any time the resulting power influence is greater than

---

* Both parameters are illustrated in [4] for the contiguous 48 states. Worldwide maps of thunderstorm days are shown in [6] and are available from the World Meteorological Association in Geneva, Switzerland.

50 V, it is considered hazardous. The effects and measurement of power influence are discussed in greater detail in Chapter 7.

Ground potential rise (GPR) is due to power system faults to ground that raise the earth's potential at one location with respect to another location. If grounded telecommunication cables traverse the two locations, the voltage difference between the two ends of the cable could be hazardous. The distance need not be great. The chance of hazardous GPR is greatest near power generating stations or substations. Any cables in the vicinity of these locations are exposed. The determination of what is "in the vicinity" requires calculations of GPR using accepted methods. For an example of such methods, see [9].

Telecommunication facilities connected to cables are exposed if the cables are exposed. The cables are considered to be unexposed if none of the above conditions exist. In some cases the determination of "exposed" or "unexposed" facilities may be subjective. Also, facilities unexposed today may be exposed tomorrow, as conditions change. It is good practice to follow the following simple rule:

If in doubt, consider the cables and associated facilities exposed.

Figure 4-1 summarizes the required steps to determine exposure and provides a simplified method for choosing the station protection type and grounding requirements. Once the decision has been made that a particular cable is exposed or not exposed, the protection scheme can be chosen as shown. If the cable is unexposed, no protection is required; if exposed, protection is required. Other aspects of this chart are discussed in later sections.

4.3 Subscriber Loop Protection

In exposed applications, the cable pair used in a loop is protected at each end by connecting it to carbon block, gas tube or solid-state protectors. The protectors, which are located at the central office and at the subscriber's premises as shown in Fig. 4-2, are primarily for personnel protection, but they also protect the cable pair and central office and terminal equipment. When the protector is located at the subscriber's premises and is legally required, it is called *primary protection*. Protectors are designed to coordinate with the voltage and current limitations associated with telecommunication cables, while taking into account the ability of the human body to withstand electromotive abuse.

The protectors limit the voltage at each end to less than 600 V (usually between 250 and 450 V) by shunting the high voltage to ground. Sometimes "heat coils" or fuses are used in conjunction with the voltage limiting device. Heat coils are used where sustained currents due to foreign potentials may flow on cable pairs and damage terminal equipment or cause a fire hazard. When the current approaches 2 to 5 A, the heat coils divert it to ground and away from the equipment as shown in Fig. 4-3(a). Fuses, on the other hand, actually open the circuit and thereby remove the path through which the current flows as shown in Fig. 4-3(b).

So called "sneak current" fuses are also used at the subscriber's premises, particularly with electronic PBXs and key systems. These fuses have current ratings around 350 mA. They are usually installed on the premises distribution frame associated with a PBX or key system as shown in Fig. 4-4. Supplementary protection equipment installed between the primary protection device and the terminal equipment is called *secondary*

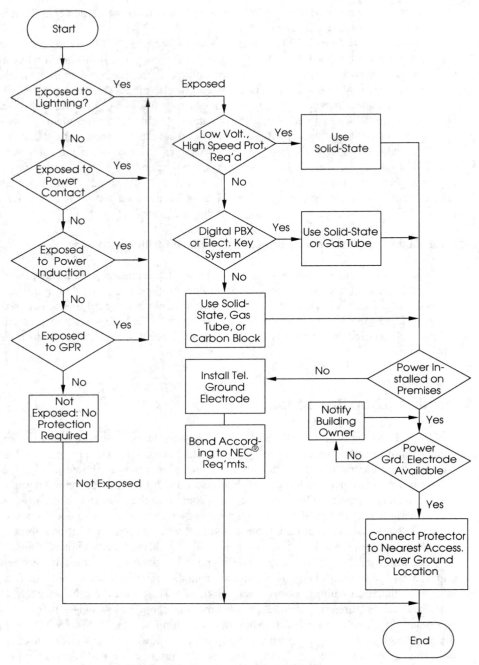

Figure 4-1 Station protection flow chart

protection. Secondary protection usually includes voltage limiting devices similar to primary protection devices. However, secondary protection devices are generally more sensitive than primary protection and, because of this, will usually react first to overvoltages or current overloads on the loop.

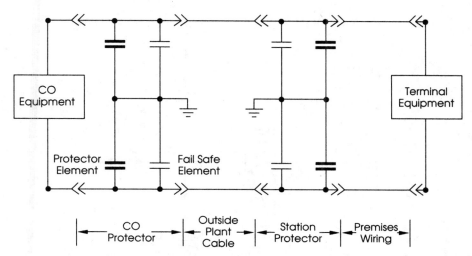

Figure 4-2 Central office and station protectors

Primary protection devices located at the telecommunication service entrance on the subscriber's premises are also called *station protectors*. They are classified as fused or fuseless and are available with carbon or gas tube gaps. Fuseless protectors are recommended for most applications. The current station protection philosophy in the telecommunication industry is to not use fused protectors except under certain conditions as required by the National Electrical Code® (NEC®), Article 800 [10].

Safety is the main reason for avoiding the use of fused protectors unless absolutely necessary. If a foreign voltage is accidentally applied to the loop conductors and the fuse blows, the conductors on the source side of the break may continue to be energized with a potentially lethal voltage. The person replacing the fuse to restore service may not be diligent enough to check for voltage first and may be electrocuted. Fuseless protectors are designed to short the foreign voltage to ground, thereby draining the current safely to earth. The flowchart in Fig. 4-5 can be used to select the proper protector type.

4.4 Carbon Block Protectors

Carbon block protectors are the least expensive and are used in most applications. The much faster gas tube and solid-state protectors are used with sensitive electronic equipment and systems which require a faster acting device.

Carbon block protectors use two carbon buttons separated by a small air gap (typically 0.003 inches, or 3 mils) as shown in Fig. 4-6. When the voltage across the gap reaches its breakdown potential, an arc ignites. The breakdown potential depends on many factors, such as air temperature, humidity and pressure. The arc has a relatively low impedance which shunts the voltage to ground where it is safely dissipated. Carbon protectors are subject to shorting if heavy fault currents flow through them. The shorting may be asymmetrical, which will grossly unbalance the line and subject the conductors to overvoltage. This asymmetry, if sustained after the fault disappears, will also ruin transmission quality. Fusible (fail-safe) elements are provided to shunt sustained heavy fault currents. These are small solder pots that melt and flow together to permanently short the circuit to ground and thus act as a fail-safe device.

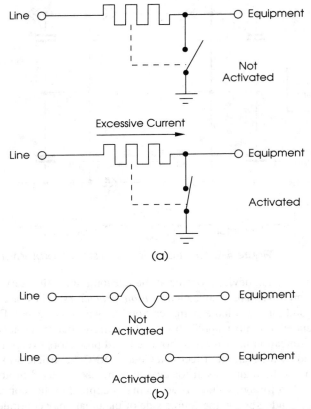

Figure 4-3 Heat coils and fuses: (a) heat coil; (b) fuse

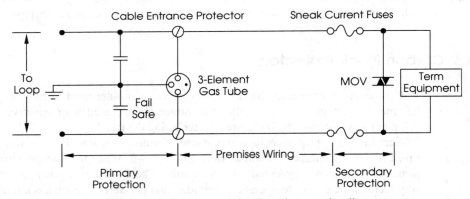

Figure 4-4 Primary and secondary protection

4.5 Gas-Tube Protectors

Gas-tube protectors are faster acting and more reliable than carbon types. Gas-tube protectors contain a spark gap in a sealed enclosure filled with an inert gas as shown in

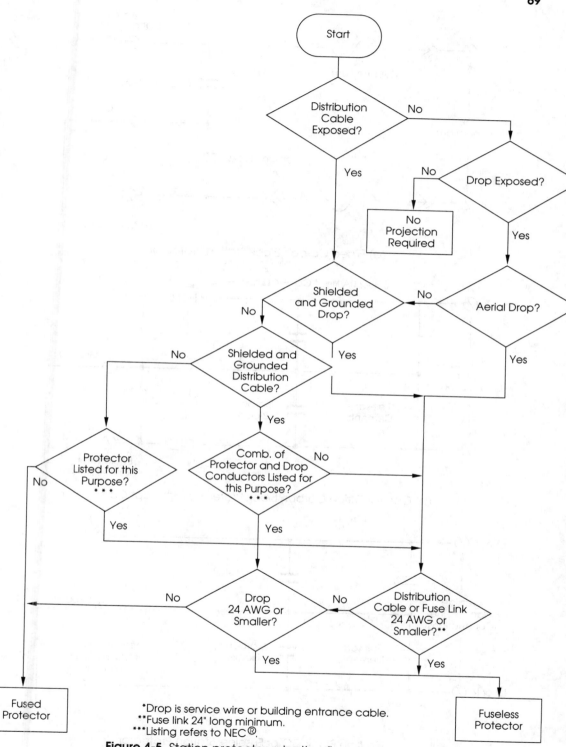

*Drop is service wire or building entrance cable.
**Fuse link 24" long minimum.
***Listing refers to NEC ®.

Figure 4-5 Station protector selection flowchart

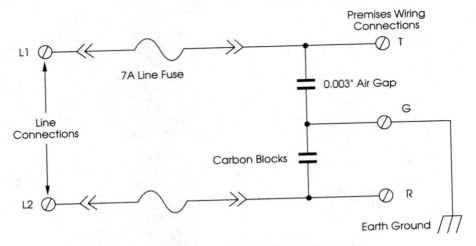

(a) Fused Carbon Block Station Protector

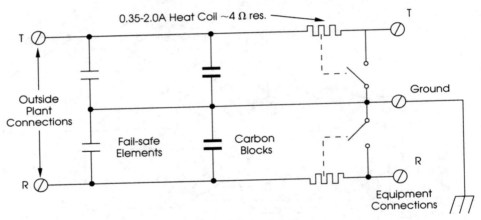

(b) Central Office Carbon Block Protector with Heat Coils

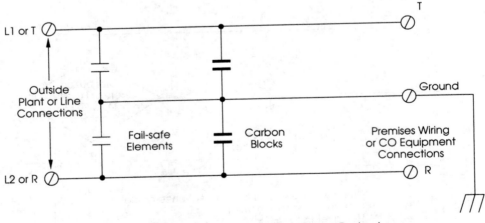

(c) Carbon Block CO or Fuseless Station Protector

Figure 4-6 Carbon block protectors

Fig. 4-7. They are self-restoring unless the fault currents are exceptionally high. In such cases, a fusible pellet will melt, which permanently shorts the circuit to ground as with the carbon block protector.

If a high degree of protection is required when using gas tube protectors, a three-electrode device is needed to ensure that both conductors are shunted to ground during a high-voltage condition on either conductor. This eliminates the possibility of a high-voltage difference between conductors.

4.6 Solid-State Protectors

The solid-state protector provides similar protection but is faster and shunts foreign potentials at a more consistent voltage than a gas tube. It is made with *metal oxide varistors* (MOVs), which are devices whose resistance varies with the voltage applied to them, or silicon avalanche diodes, which are also voltage limiting devices. Present solid-state protectors have a higher capacitance to ground (2 to 4 times) in the unfaulted condition than either carbon or gas tube protectors and, therefore, can potentially contribute to line unbalance. See Fig. 4-8 for a schematic drawing of a typical solid-state protector.

Solid-state protectors in telecommunication applications are relatively new, and the results from only a few field tests are widely available; nevertheless, solid-state protectors hold much promise. All tests have shown solid-state protectors will significantly reduce central office line card failures in high incident lightning areas [11–13].

Of special concern during the early development of solid-state protectors was their current handling capabilities. Compared to gas tubes, early solid-state units had limited capabilities, but present production units have equivalent current handling and provide the same fail-safe mechanisms.

The basic solid-state protector is cost competitive with gas tube types. However, where MOVs or other solid-state elements are combined with gas tubes to take advantage of the characteristics of both types, the combination is more expensive than gas tubes alone. Solid-state protectors are presently available for primary protection applications in central offices and secondary protection of subscriber premises terminal equipment.

Table 4-1 compares the specifications of the three basic types of telecommunication protectors (solid-state, gas-tube and carbon) in typical configurations.

4.7 Relative Cost of Protection Apparatus

Table 4-2 shows the relative cost of various protectors used in central offices.

4.8 Protector Color Coding

Protectors used in central office environments and in many buildings with more than approximately six loops will be of standard physical sizes and configurations. A color coding scheme is used to identify these protectors when they are used in different applications, as shown in Table 4-3.

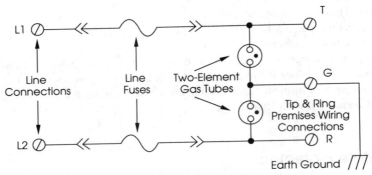

(a) Fused Gas Tube Station Protector

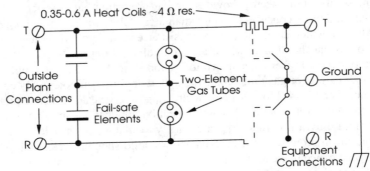

(b) Gas Tube Central Office Protector with Heat Coils

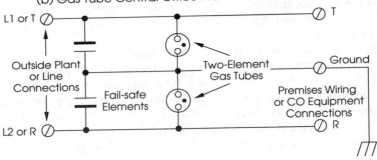

(c) Gas Tube Central Office or Fuseless Station Protector

A three-element gas tube may be substituted
to provide enhanced, balanced protection.

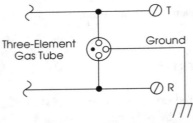

(d) Alternative Configuration

Figure 4-7 Gas tube protectors

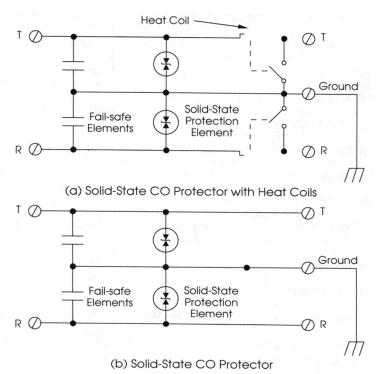

(a) Solid-State CO Protector with Heat Coils

(b) Solid-State CO Protector

Figure 4-8 Solid-state protectors

The *standard* (black) application is any application not covered by other colors. *Special* (red) application is any application requiring special attention by telecommunication personnel. This does not necessarily mean special protection requirements, only special attention. *Continuity only* (gray) does not have any protection; the "line" and "equipment" sides are permanently connected inside the device housing. *PBX battery* (yellow) includes protection and indicates that the PBX (or any other telecommunication device on the premises) feeds battery voltage out to the loop (or into the central office). Finally, the *service denied* (green) protector includes outside plant protection, but there is no continuity between the line and equipment sides of the protector (open circuit).

4.9 Protector Grounding

It is absolutely essential that the protector is adequately earth grounded and that the ground path is able to carry the anticipated fault current.

When protectors are installed in a central office, a No. 6 copper conductor is used to connect the 100-pair protector assembly to the grounding bus. A larger conductor is used to connect the bus to the building ground window or system. The actual size depends on the anticipated fault currents as well as many other factors.

Central office grounding is a complex subject which will not be covered here. On the other hand, grounding of the protector at the subscriber's premises follows a few relatively simple rules which can be addressed quite handily. First, the protector must always be

Table 4-1 Typical Telecommunication Protector Specifications

Parameter	Solid-State	Gas Tube	Carbon
60 Hz Breakdown	215-245 V	300-500 V	300-500 V
Impulse Breakdown: @ 100 V/μs @ 10 kV/μs	265 V 300-400 V	600 V 1,000 V	750-1,000 V 1,000-1,200 V
Leakage Current	2 μA	Not Specified	Not Specified
Dc Holdover Time	150 ms	150 ms	Not Specified
Surge Life[a]: @ 100 A, Std. Pulse @ 10 A rms @ 300 A, Std. Pulse	Unlimited Unlimited Fail-Safe	Not Specified Not Specified >100	Not Specified Not Specified >25
Capacitance	60-100 pF	25 pF	Not Specified
Series Resistance[b]	3.6-4.0 Ω	3.5 Ω	3.5 Ω
Insulation Resistance	100-1,000 MΩ	100 MΩ	Not Specified

[a] Std. pulse is 10 x 1,000 μs.
[b] Units with heat coils only.

Table 4-2 Relative Costs of Standard Telecommunication
Central Office Protectors

Type	Relative Cost
Carbon (350V) w/o Heat Coil	1.00
Carbon (350 V) w/Heat Coil	1.76
Gas Tube (400 V, 2-Electrode) w/o Heat Coil	2.14
Gas Tube (400 V, 2-Electrode) w/Heat Coil	2.82
Gas Tube (400 V, 3-Electrode) w/o Heat Coil	2.89
Gas Tube (400 V, 3-Electrode) w/Heat Coil	Not Avail.
Solid-State (240 or 300 V) w/o Heat Coil	1.93
Solid-State (240 or 300 V) w/Heat Coil	2.60

Table 4-3 Protector color coding

Application	Body Color
Standard	Black
Special	Red
Continuity Only	Gray
PBX Battery	Yellow
Service Denied	Green

grounded (this cannot be overemphasized). Second, if electrical power is provided at the premises, the electrical equipment is always grounded, too, and the telecommunication protector ground must be bonded to it.

In many cases, the telecommunication protector can use the same grounding electrode as the power source. Whatever the case, bonding is always necessary to ensure that there is no potential difference between power and telecommunication equipment ground systems. This is especially important where it is difficult to obtain good earth grounds, such as in frozen soils or rock. This bonding requirement holds even though the telecommunication and power grounds are on opposite sides of the building.

Article 800 of the NEC® [10] covers the minimum requirements for grounding of station protectors. According to the NEC®, the grounding conductor from the protector to the grounding electrode must be No. 14 copper, minimum. Although not specified in the NEC®, larger conductors should be used if multiple protectors are installed. Table 4-4 shows the recommended conductor sizes needed for multiple fuseless and fused protector installations. These are general recommendations to be used when more stringent requirements are not specified. Although the number of circuits that may be grounded with a given conductor size is slightly more for fused protectors, it is good practice to use the recommendations for fuseless protectors for all installations.

Again, the primary requirement is to preserve personnel safety by reducing the chances of fire and shock; the secondary requirement is to prevent cable insulation and equipment damage.

Table 4-4 Protector Grounding Conductor Size[a]

Wire Size	No. of Fuseless Circuits	No. of Fused Circuits
#14 AWG	1	1
#12 AWG	2 to 5	6
#10 AWG	6	7
# 6 AWG	7 or More	8 or More

[a] Adapted from (1).

4.10 Station Protector and Network Interface Device

The station protector may be contained in a regular protector housing or *network interface device* (NID). The type used depends on the company providing telephone service and possibly the age of the service. The protector housing is a small canister, usually mounted on the outside of the building. When properly installed, it provides a grounding means for the protectors as well as termination means for the service wire and premises wiring system. See Fig. 4-9(a).

The NID provides a similar function, but it physically separates (with a barrier) the service wire connections and protectors from the premises wiring. It contains the protectors, grounding stud and modular jack in one compartment and a modular plug and terminals or a 50-position ribbon connector for connecting the premises wiring in another

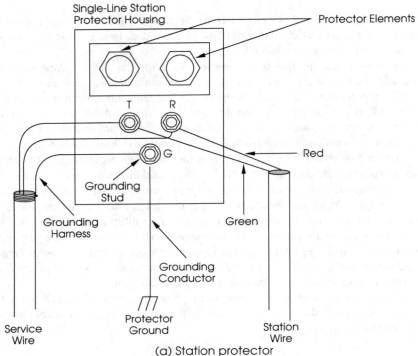

(a) Station protector

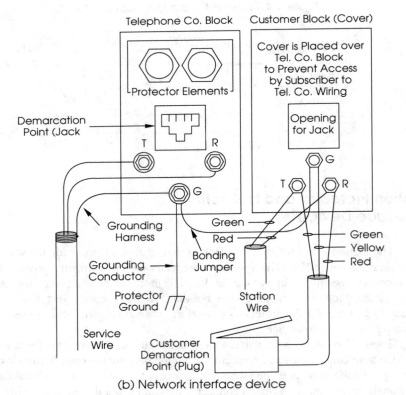

(b) Network interface device

Figure 4-9 Protectors and network interface devices

compartment as shown in Fig. 4-9(b). More sophisticated NIDs contain devices (called responders) for testing the loop under control of the central office.

The NID does not necessarily have to be collocated with the station protector devices. In these cases, the protector is a separate assembly mounted according to protection requirements. The NID is then mounted at some other convenient location. The NID may be a single modular jack or an assembly with hundreds or thousands of modular jacks or 50-position ribbon connectors.

Since the protector or NID can be exposed to voltage and current surges of large magnitudes, they must be designed and installed to minimize the chances of fire or other damage. Devices that carry a label or are listed by an electrical equipment testing laboratory such as Underwriters Laboratory (UL®) or Electrical Testing Laboratories (ETL) have been tested under such conditions.

The NID will eventually be used by all companies on all new installations and possibly retrofitted to many existing installations. It provides a well defined demarcation point between the telephone company's wiring system and the subscriber's premises wiring system.

4.11 Connection Devices

The physical shape and size of the modular jacks and ribbon connectors used to connect terminal equipment to the premises wiring system and to connect the premises wiring system to the network interface device are defined in FCC Rules and Regulations, Part 68.* Some will be discussed here.

The wiring configurations for typical modular plugs and jacks are shown in Fig. 4-10. The most common of these is the six-position plug called an RJ-11W (wall-mounted) or RJ-11C (all others), which can be used to connect any single-line telephone instrument to the premises wiring (Fig. 4-10(a)). Although the RJ-11 has six positions, only two positions are used (tip and ring). An outdoor plug and jack with three positions is called the RJ-15C (Fig. 4-10(b)).

For terminal equipment requiring a series connection with the premises wiring (for example, alarm or call detail recording devices), the RJ-31X is commonly used (Fig. 4-10(c)). This connector has eight positions and is slightly wider than the six-position connector. The RJ-14W and RJ-14C are commonly used for two-line telephone sets (Fig. 4-10(d)). This connector is another six-position device, but four positions are used (T1 and R1, T2 and R2).

The 50-position (25-pair) miniature ribbon connector (jack) is the RJ-21X, which is used anywhere distribution wiring is provided in multiples of 25 pairs. The RJ-21X is commonly used for connecting PBX equipment with the premises wiring system. Older electromechanical key system station sets used this type of connector exclusively.† The common name for this connector is "ribbon connector" or "Amphenol" plug. The latter refers to a manufacturer of the connector.

Other connectors are specified in the FCC Rules and Regulations, but most of these are for special applications such as data communication equipment (DCE) with programmable transmission levels.

---

*   See Subpart F, "Connectors" [14].

†   The older key systems are generically referred to as "1A2" systems.

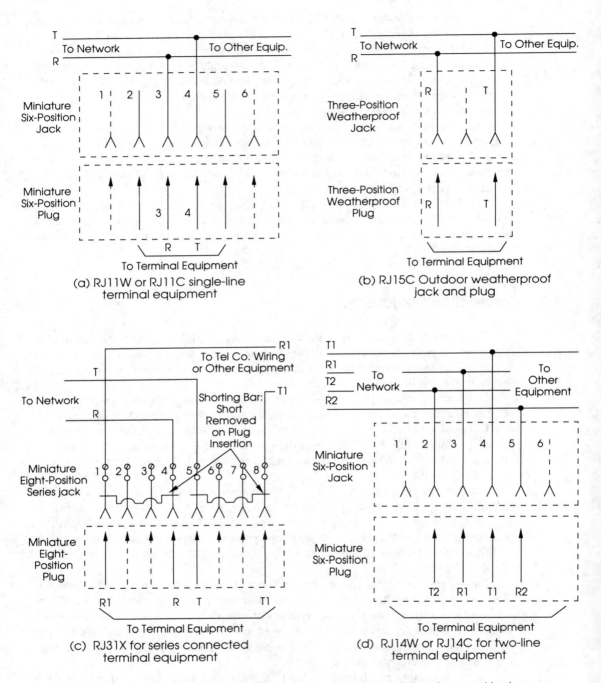

Figure 4-10 Wiring configurations for typical modular plugs and jacks

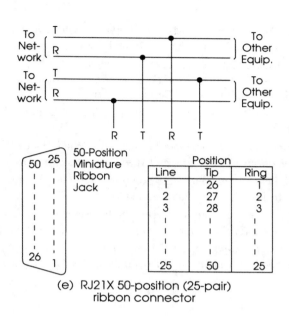

(e) RJ21X 50-position (25-pair)
ribbon connector

Figure 4-10 (continued)

REFERENCES

[1] *Outside Plant Engineering Handbook.* Winston-Salem, NC: AT&T Document Development Organization, January 1990. Available from AT&T Customer Information Center.

[2] *REA Telecommunications Engineering and Construction Manual*, Sections 801, 802, 805, 810, 816, 817, 822, 823, and 825. Available from Rural Electrification Administration.

[3] *Station Installation and Maintenance Handbook.* GTE Automatic Electric Inc. Available from GTE Practices Manager, publication No. CHB-120.

[4] *Telecommunication Electrical Protection.* AT&T Technologies, Inc. 1985. Available from AT&T Customer Information Center.

[5] Hayes, J. B. and D. W. Bodle. *Electrical Protection of Tactical Communication Systems, Technical Report #6.* Available from National Technical Information Service, Order No. AD693300.

[6] MIL-HDBK-419, *Military Handbook, Grounding, Bonding, and Shielding for Electronic Equipments and Facilities.* Washington, DC: U.S. Department of Defense, December 1982. Available from Naval Publications and Forms Center.

[7] Denny, H. W. and J. A. Woody. *Grounding, Bonding, and Shielding Practices and Procedures for Electronic Equipments and Facilities.* Washington, DC: Department of Transportation, Federal Aviation Administration, Report # FAA-RD-75-215, December 1975. Available from NTIS, Order No. ADA022332, ADA022608, and ADA022871. This document is similar to Ref. 6, but the emphasis is toward ground-based navigation and communication equipment associated with FAA facilities.

[8] Hart, W. and E. W. Malone. *Lightning and Lightning Protection.* Interference Control Technologies, Inc., 1979 and 1984.

[9] ANSI/IEEE-Std-367-1987, *IEEE Recommended Practice for Determining the Electric Power Station Ground Potential Rise and Induced Voltage from a Power Fault.* Available from the IEEE Service Center.

[10] *National Electrical Code*®. National Fire Protection Association, 1990. Available from NFPA.

[11] Bagnall, G. J. "Solid-State Protection — Where Does REA Stand?" *REA Telecommunications Engineering and Management Seminar Record*, 1989.

[12] Thrasher, M. "A Solid-State Solution." *Telephony*, June 12, 1989, pp. 46-52. Available from Telephony Publication Corp.

[13] Carr, T. and J. Napiorkowski. "Solid State Protection Changes the Archetype." *Telephone Engineer and Management*, July 1, 1989. Available from TE&M.

[14] *Federal Communication Commission Rules and Regulations, Part 68.* Available from the Superintendent of Documents, U.S. Government Printing Office.

5

Transmission

The emphasis in this chapter is on the transmission characteristics and requirements of nonloaded and loaded cable pairs up to 4,000 Hz. The requirements and characteristics cited are fundamental to loops used in almost all analog applications, including switched and private line services.

5.1 Presentation of Transmission Parameters

A wide variety of parameters is used to describe transmission system performance. The more important ones that apply directly to subscriber loops are loss and noise. These, in turn, can be presented in a variety of ways, depending on the organization providing or specifying the service. Typically, a range or other distribution of a particular parameter is specified.

There should be some predetermined agreement between the design value and the measured value, but the measured value will always show some variability. This variability will be due to:

- Test equipment calibration
- Environmental variations that will affect the circuit components as well as the measuring equipment
- Human factors associated with reading meters or displays
- Position of the test equipment or lead lengths
- Cable splicing techniques
- Cable and equipment manufacturing tolerances

These effects will influence the measurements of a large number of loops so that the results show some type of distribution. Therefore, when the transmission parameters of a loop are determined, they really can be specified only on a statistical basis. The Institute of Electrical and Electronics Engineers (IEEE) has identified three forms for the results of parameter calculations or estimations [1]:

- A cumulative distribution
- A histogram
- An analytical distribution function

Other forms, or variations of the above forms, can be used. The most typical, of course, is the single-value specification; for example, "the loop loss will not exceed 8.0 dB." This provides an upper bound only; the loop in this case could have any loss up to 8.0 dB. Similarly, a cumulative distribution would specify "99 percent of the loop losses will fall between 4.5 and 5.5 dB." If a normal distribution curve is used to specify the parameters, a mean value and a standard deviation are given.

Because of this statistical nature, it would seem that the distribution of individual parameters for several loop segments in tandem could not be combined by simple addition. This is indeed true, and various mathematical techniques are used to describe the entire connection [1]. For field problems, the simple method of ignoring parameter distributions is satisfactory, and simple addition is frequently used.

The parameters for a circuit are often specified by an *acceptance limit* and *immediate action limit*. The acceptance limit is the maximum (or minimum) value or deviation that is allowed when a circuit is placed into service. The immediate action limit defines the threshold beyond which immediate corrective action is to be taken. For example, attenuation distortion between two frequency limits may have an acceptance limit of –0.5 to +2.5 dB and an immediate action limit of –1 to +3 dB. Anytime the distortion exceeds –1 or +3 dB, immediate action is required.

5.2 Bandwidth

Most loops consist of at least one cable pair. The cable pair is a transmission line, and it has predictable electrical characteristics. Like any practical transmission line, the usable bandwidth on a loop is limited. Tests have shown that on voice calls, the subscriber's satisfaction with transmission quality is related to, among other things, the loop's frequency response. It is no surprise that wider bandwidths provide higher satisfaction.

A voice channel is considered to require a nominal bandwidth of 4,000 Hz. For all practical purposes, however, the usable bandwidth of an end-to-end call in the PSTN, including the loop, is considered to fall between approximately 300 and 3,400 Hz (this is called the *voice band*) giving a bandwidth of 3,100 Hz. This bandwidth is entirely acceptable from a voice transmission point of view, giving subscriber satisfaction level above 90 percent [2].

While it is not unduly difficult to provide a 3,100 Hz bandwidth in the loop, the loop and the associated terminal equipment have evolved in such a way that this bandwidth is essentially fixed at this value and will continue to be for analog transmission. This, along with loop signaling methods used now and in the past, ensures backward compatibility. The bandwidth is somewhat restrictive for data transmission when using modems. However, the problem of bandwidth restriction has encouraged a number of innovative solutions in modem design. These solutions will continue to evolve with the loop.

Obviously, on a loop derived entirely from copper cable, the frequency response of the loop itself would extend down to dc (zero frequency). The lower response is lost, however, once the loop is switched or connected to other transmission and signaling equipment, all of which are ac coupled. Where dc continuity is not available or not practical, special tone signaling equipment is used to replace the dc signals. When voice signals or other signals with frequency content approaching zero frequency are placed on the loop, the transmission is considered to be in the baseband.

Similarly, the upper frequency limit is not exactly 3,400 Hz. Depending on how it is specified or the type of cable, the limit may be much higher. In practice, the loop does not generally set the upper limit of a voice channel; the upper limit is mostly due to the design of the equipment that interfaces with the loop.

For voiceband transmission, the bandwidth (or frequency response) of a telecommunication channel is defined as the limiting frequencies where loop loss is down by 10 dB from its 1,000 Hz value [2]. The field measurement of bandwidth usually does not proceed with measurement of the 10 dB points. Instead, simple slope tests are made; these provide an indirect, but reliable, indicator of the transmission channel bandwidth. If the slope, as defined below, is within predetermined limits, the bandwidth of the channel can be assumed to be acceptable.

Slope tests are loss measurements at 404, 1,004 and 2,804 Hz (this is also called the *three-tone slope*). The loss at 1,004 Hz is subtracted from the loss at 404 Hz to give the low-frequency slope, and from 2,804 Hz to give the high-frequency slope. Objective values for slope are given in Chapter 7.

5.3 Transmission Line Primary Constants

Like all transmission lines, cable pairs can be described by their fundamental electrical characteristics, or primary constants. These are series inductance, L; shunt capacitance, C; shunt conductance, G and series resistance, R. All are described in customary electrical units per unit length. Figure 5-1 shows a T-equivalent circuit commonly used to represent telecommunication transmission lines.

Inductance, L, of the typical cable pair depends on the geometry of the conductors and is affected by the magnetic flux distribution within and around them. It is around 1 mH per mile at low frequencies for air core PIC and about 7 to 10 percent higher for filled PIC. Due to skin effect, inductance decreases to about 70 percent of its initial value as the frequency increases from about 50 kHz to 1 MHz and is fairly constant at higher frequencies.*

Capacitance, C, depends on the geometry and dielectric medium between the conductors. It is standardized during manufacture at 66 or 83 nF per mile, although cables with different values are available. Cable with 83 nF per mile capacitance is the most common. Capacitance is independent of frequency for all practical purposes.

Conductance, G, depends on the dielectric medium between the conductors and is negligible at about 0.05 (air core) or 0.16 (filled) microsiemens (μS) per mile at 1,000 Hz

---

* Skin effect is the tendency for higher frequency currents to travel near the outside surface of a conductor rather than distributed evenly throughout the entire cross-section.

for modern cables.* It increases by a factor of 30 (air core) or 20 (filled) for each decade (factor of 10) increase in frequency. The value can vary considerably from those given above due to different insulation types and core filling compounds, but conductance can still be considered negligible at voice frequencies.

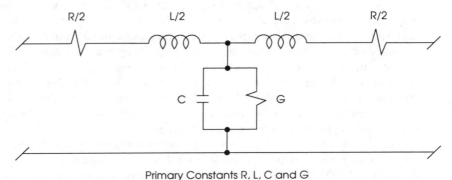

Primary Constants R, L, C and G

Figure 5-1 Transmission line equivalent circuit

Resistance, R (measured in ohms per mile), depends on the resistivity of the conductors and the current distribution within them. It is approximately constant at lower frequencies but is proportional to the square root of frequency at higher frequencies (above about 10 kHz) where skin effect and proximity effect dominate. The resistance of each conductor gauge is different due to the different cross-sectional area. Resistance is temperature dependent, increasing by about 4 percent for each 10°C increase in conductor temperature at voice frequencies (see Chapter 6).

Table 5-1 shows the values of primary constants for typical cable pair gauges. The variation of the primary constants with frequency limits the application of ordinary exchange cable pairs to frequencies below a few MHz.

5.4 Secondary Parameters

The propagation constant ($\rho = \alpha + j\beta$) and characteristic impedance (Z_0) are the secondary parameters used to describe transmission line characteristics.† All are functions of frequency and can be found from the primary constants as shown below.

$$\rho = \alpha + j\beta = [(R + j\omega L)(G + j\omega C)]^{\frac{1}{2}}$$

where

$$\omega = \text{radian frequency, } 2\pi f$$

---

* The unit siemens per mile replaces the historical unit, mhos per mile.

† The secondary parameters are mathematically derived from the primary constants in Appendix C. Simplified analyses of nonloaded cable secondary parameters when the primary constants are known and primary constants when secondary parameters are known are covered quite well in [3]. There are numerous other sources of information on twisted pair transmission characteristics [4–8].

The real portion of the propagation constant, denoted RE(ρ), is called the attenuation constant, α, and the imaginary portion, denoted IM(ρ), is called the phase constant β. Both are quantities per unit length; the attenuation constant is expressed in nepers per unit length and the phase constant in radians per unit length.* The characteristic impedance, on the other hand, is independent of length. It can be found from the primary constants, too.

$$Z_0 = [(R + j\omega L) / (G + j\omega C)]^{\frac{1}{2}}$$

Table 5-1 Exchange Cable Pair Primary Constants[a]

Air Core PIC, 1,000 Hz, 55° F				
Gauge (AWG)	R (Ω/Mile)	L (mH/Mile)	C (nF/Mile)	G (μS/Mile)
19	83.7	0.98	83	0.05
22	167.3	0.98	83	0.05
24	265.5	0.97	83	0.05
26	428.0	0.97	83	0.05

Filled Core PIC, 1,000 Hz, 55° F*				
Gauge (AWG)	R (Ω/Mile)	L (mH/Mile)	C (nF/Mile)	G (μS/Mile)
19	83.7	1.05	83	0.16
22	167.3	1.05	83	0.16
24	265.5	1.03	83	0.16
26	428.0	1.13	83	0.16

[a] Data from Northern Telecom Cable Ltd. "Cable Technical Information" data sheets. The values are typical for outside plant exchange cables.

The equations for the secondary parameters can be simplified somewhat for modern exchange cables as follows:

$$\rho = [-\omega^2 LC + j\omega RC]^{\frac{1}{2}}$$

with

$$\alpha = RE(\rho) \text{ and } \beta = IM(\rho)$$

as before, and

* A more convenient unit than the neper is the decibel such that 1 neper = 8.686 dB.

$$Z_0 = [(L/C) - j(R/\omega C)]^{\frac{1}{2}}$$

In practical applications, due to impedance mismatching of the loop by its terminations, the actual circuit input impedance (as opposed to the theoretical cable pair characteristic impedance shown above) does vary with loop length. An expression for the input impedance of a real loop is:

$$Z_{in} = \frac{Z_0 [Z_T + Z_0 \tanh (\rho l)]}{[Z_0 + Z_T \tanh (\rho l)]}$$

where

Z_0 and ρ = as previously defined
Z_T = the impedance of the load connected to the loop
tanh = the hyperbolic tangent function
l = length

The secondary parameters are shown in Figs. 5-2 and 5-3 for nonloaded, air and filled core cables at voiceband frequencies. These are values that can be used in many analyses, such as insertion loss and impedance matching problems. Depending on the application, however, the insertion loss of the loop may vary from the predicted values shown here. The variations may be ignored when trying to determine first-order transmission effects (that is, rough estimates). For more accurate estimates of loop transmission performance, the measured secondary parameters for the cable in question should be used while taking into account the terminal impedances as noted previously.

As with the primary constants, secondary parameters are temperature dependent. Generally, attenuation is related to temperature such that the higher the temperature, the higher the attenuation. The relationship is nonlinear and is due primarily to changes in conductor resistance. Transmission parameters provided on cable manufacturer's data sheets are usually measured at 55°F (12.8°C) or 68°F (20°C). Current loop design methods require the quoted values to be adjusted (corrected) to the maximum expected temperature of operation. *

5.5 Transmission Requirements

The two basic transmission requirements on any circuit are:

1. The received signal must have adequate level.
2. The received signal level must be sufficiently higher than the noise (high enough signal-to-noise ratio).

For voice transmission, these two requirements are highly subjective and are rated on user satisfaction. The adequacy of a circuit for data transmission is based on error performance. Adequate level is provided by controlling circuit loss. *Signal-to-noise ratio*

* See Chapter 6.

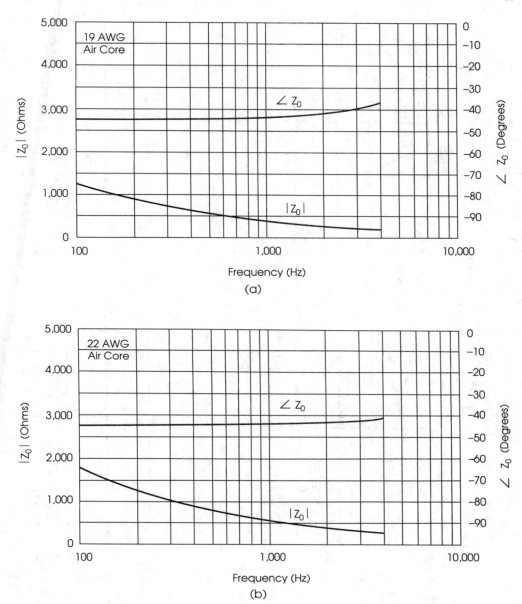

Figure 5-2 Nonloaded cable pair secondary parameters, characteristic impedance, PIC, 55°F (continued on the following pages)

(SNR), on the other hand, is not normally addressed or measured as such on subscriber loops. This is because small amounts of noise may be most noticeable during pauses in speech while relatively large noise levels may not be noticed at all during speech. In other words, the parameter of interest is the interfering effect of noise rather than its absolute power with respect to signal level. With data circuits, the data signal level is set high enough to provide the necessary SNR at the receiver. Therefore, the absolute noise level itself is controlled within certain limits as described in Chapter 7.

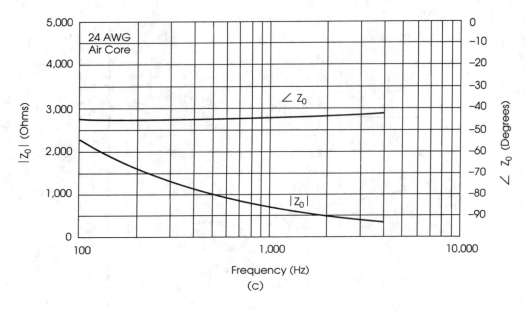

(c)

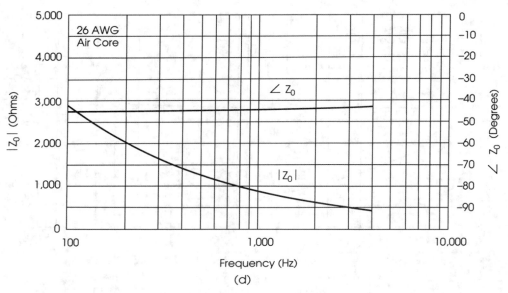

(d)

Figure 5-2 (continued)

For reference, however, it is informative to know what the acceptable signal-to-noise ratios are for various call types. Generally, the SNR should be at least 30 dB for voice calls (based on subscriber satisfaction) and 15 to 20 dB on data calls (based on the specified error rate, coding and modulation method). These figures are end-to-end. Each portion of the transmission system (loops, switching systems, terrestrial and satellite radio systems, etc.) contribute to lowering the SNR. It follows that the SNR for any given part of the overall connection must be higher than the overall requirement.

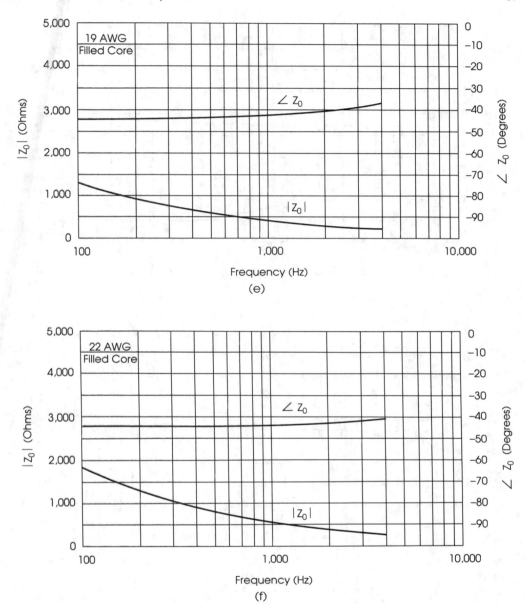

Figure 5-2 (continued)

5.6 Loop Transmission Loss

The telecommunication industry generally agrees that adequate transmission levels will be obtained on regular (switched) subscriber loops as long as the loss (attenuation) of the loop at 1,000 Hz is no more than 8 dB. Some companies may consider 6 dB as maximum acceptable loss, and others may consider anything less than 10 or 10.5 dB as adequate. The 6 dB loss limit is sometimes used on loops served by digital loop carrier systems that introduce an additional 2 dB loss in the receive side of the circuit (prior to four-

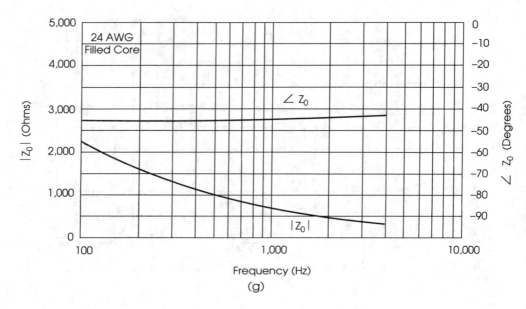

(g)

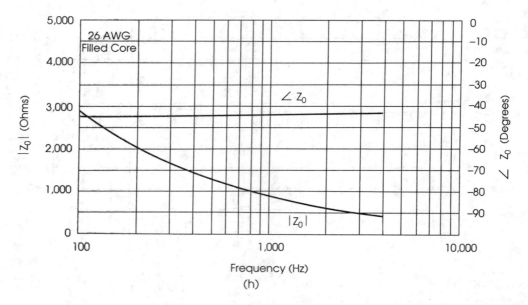

(h)

Figure 5-2 (continued)

wire to two-wire conversion) to increase the return loss. This will give an overall circuit loss, in the receive direction, of 8 dB.

Higher losses on loops will result in "can't hear" or "can't be heard" complaints from subscribers or high error rates on data circuits. Other maximum loss values apply to loops used in non-switched service. These are discussed in Chapter 6.

The loop should have some minimum loss, too. For switched loops, the best performance in terms of customer satisfaction is when the loop has a loss in the 3.0 to 4.0 dB range [2]. It can be expensive to design all loops to meet this criterion; therefore, a range

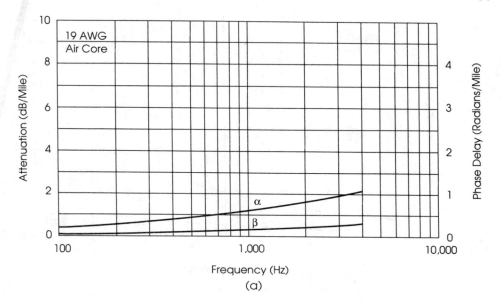

Frequency (Hz)

(a)

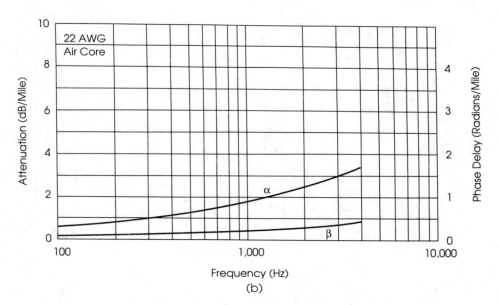

Frequency (Hz)

(b)

Figure 5-3 Nonloaded cable pair secondary parameters, attenuation and phase constants, PIC, 55°F (continued on the following pages)

of 2 to 6 dB or 3 to 5 dB is a satisfactory alternative for a large majority of the loops. For loops used in long-haul circuits, the minimum loss is determined by the desired echo performance, which is discussed in Chapter 6.

From this point forward, *attenuation*, as determined from the secondary parameters, is used interchangeably with *insertion loss* (or just *loss*). This is only strictly correct when

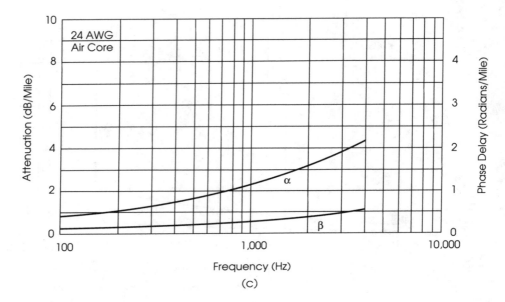

(c)

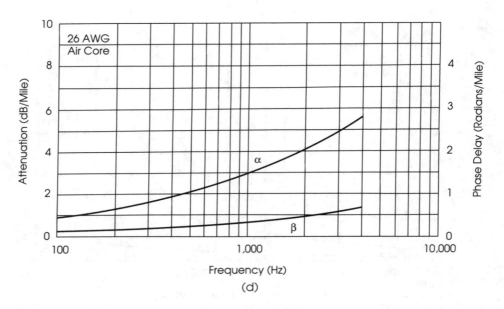

(d)

Figure 5-3 (continued)

the loop is terminated in its characteristic impedance (Z_0). In practice this does not always happen, if ever, but for practical problems it is sufficiently accurate.*

The 8 dB loss corresponds to about 3.5 mi (18,000 ft) of 24 gauge nonloaded cable, which has about 950 Ω loop resistance at 68°F (20°C). For loaded cable (discussed

---

* Appendix D contains a mathematical analysis of the problem where a loop is not terminated in its characteristic impedance. The error can be significant, but for practical terminations (600 and 900 Ω) it is small: less than 1 dB in 10,000 ft of 24 AWG cable.

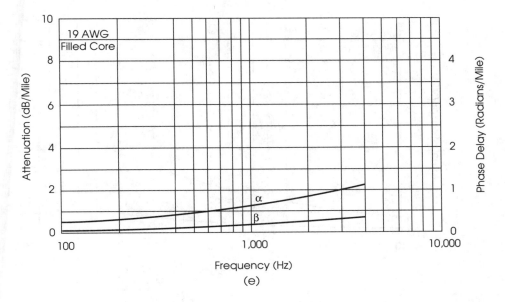

(e)

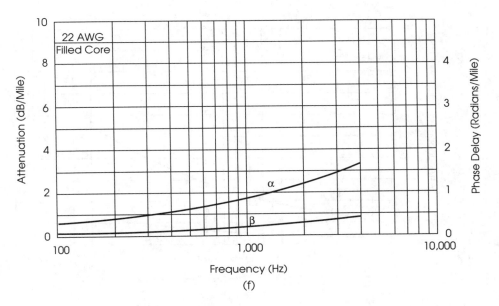

(f)

Figure 5-3 (continued)

later), the 8 dB loss corresponds to about 6.6 mi (35,000 ft) of 24 gauge cable, which has about 1,850 Ω loop resistance (including load coils). As it turns out, this is beyond the signaling range of the typical central office line circuit. See [2] for a detailed description of loop performance requirements. Loop design methods taking into account transmission requirements for various applications are covered in detail in Chapter 6.

   Voice frequency repeaters (VFRs) are used to "treat" high-loss loops by adding gain to the audio signals to improve transmission. The gain added is usually a nonlinear

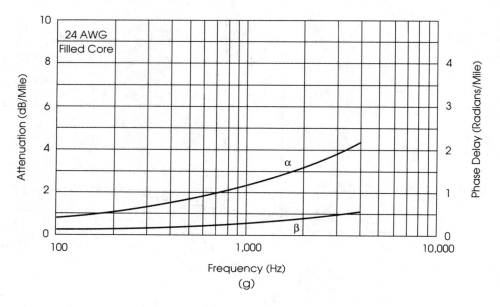

(g)

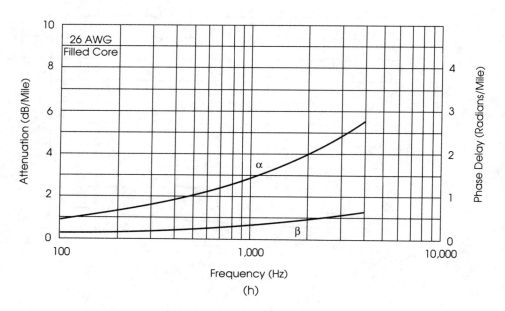

(h)

Figure 5-3 (continued)

function of frequency; this is called *equalization*. The equalization depends on the cable characteristics (gauge and whether loaded or nonloaded). VFRs are generally used on loops with loss greater than 10 dB. The actual criterion is usually a matter of engineering policy for any particular company. See Chapter 6 for additional information on applying VFRs in the loop.

5.7 Transmission Levels

Adequate transmission levels at the receive end of a circuit are essential to providing satisfactory telecommunication service. It is obvious this is not possible unless loop loss is thoroughly controlled, as previously discussed, and enough signal level is provided at the loop input.

Historically, the average voice signal level was measured with a *volume unit* (VU) meter. Although for modern voice measurement studies the VU has been replaced by two new measurements (discussed below), the VU meter is still widely used and, in many cases, is the only voice measurement device available. Therefore, it is worthwhile to examine both methods, with emphasis on VU.

The VU meter is a specially designed meter with specified ballistic characteristics. It is used only with voice or music signals, and measurements of other signals with it are meaningless. There is no direct correlation between a VU measurement and a measurement of the same signal in dBm except for a steady 1,000 Hz tone. With a steady 1,000 Hz tone at 0 dBm, the VU meter will read 0 VU, and 1 dB change in level corresponds to 1 VU change.

A rough measurement used by many technicians is that average voice level measuring 0 VU corresponds approximately to an average reading of −8 to −10 dBm on an analog dBm meter. Using this measurement method is subject to serious errors and requires considerable practice and concentration to grasp the average value of speech on the dBm meter. Meters with digital displays are more difficult to interpret than analog dBm meters.

Figure 5-4 shows an overall connection between two loops with the expected VU levels at each end.

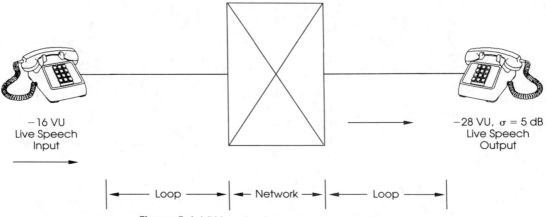

Figure 5-4 VU levels of an end-to-end connection

Early telephone sets produced an output of around −13 to −15 VU with the average talker [3]. If the average loop had 4 dB loss, the input measured at the central office would be around −19 VU. At that time, the central office line circuit was considered a −2 *transmission level point* (TLP), so the input to any trunk transmission equipment would be approximately 17 dB below line-up levels.*

---

* The concept of transmission level point is explained in Appendix B.

Some improvements have been made in telephone sets and transmission equipment since these early measurements, but for purposes of transmission study, the output of telephone sets is still assumed to be in approximately the same range; that is, –16 VU with a 5 dB standard deviation. The input to the line circuit of modern switching systems is now considered to be the 0 TLP. With a 4 dB average loop, the input measured at the central office would be around –20 VU. Therefore, the input to the trunk transmission equipment would be around 20 dB below line-up levels.

The received VU varies with transmission system losses. Tests have shown that a VU level at the receiver between approximately –22 and –34 VU results in satisfactory service [1]. This would indicate total system losses from talker to listener should be limited to around 12 dB for satisfactory service on the large majority of connections (taking into account the distribution of signals about the mean).

An interesting curve, shown in Fig. 5-5, illustrates the "Percent Customer Reaction" to various received levels using the classic "500" set. Note the convergence of the "Good Region" at a received level of –28 VU. This curve also illustrates that a circuit can be rated as "too loud" if the level at the receiver is too high.

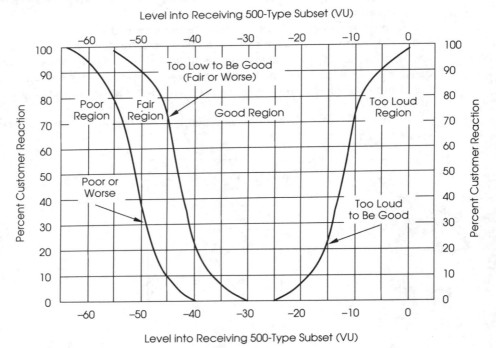

Figure 5-5 Judgment of grade of telephone conversation vs. received volume. (*Source*: Defense Communication Agency Circular 300-175.)

The two newer measurements of voice signals previously mentioned are the *equivalent peak level* (EPL) and long-term conversational level. Both are measured in dBm0 (decibels with respect to a level of 1 mW at the 0 TLP), which allows easy comparison with transmission system characteristics.

EPL is the level below which approximately 95 percent of instantaneous talker power will fall. Studies have shown the EPL is about –12 dBm0, and the average long-term conversational level is about –27 dBm0 on local calls (and not much different on long-distance calls) [6]. Standard deviation for both is around 5 dB, which means that 90 percent of EPL measurements will fall between –4 and –20 dBm0. Corresponding values for average (long-term conversational) levels are –19 and –35 dBm0.

Speech, as measured at the talker, is considered to have a dynamic range of around 40 dB. The above measurements show a much narrower range because they are affected by the telephone transmitter and loop transmission characteristics as well as the way the measurements were made.

Data transmissions are not measured with a VU or EPL meter. The actual instantaneous signal level placed on the loop by a modem is more constant than voice and is readily measured by conventional instruments. The instantaneous data transmission levels do vary, however, with the signal content and type of modulation. A typical modem will have an average transmit level, measured over any 3 s interval, of –9 to –12 dBm if it is used in the PSTN. Therefore, for a short loop, the level could be as high as –9 dBm0 at the input to the line circuit.* For private line applications, the same modem will have an adjustable output of 0 to –15 dBm. Modems usually have a receiver operating range of 0 to –43 dBm, although the error rate at the lower levels may not be acceptable in the presence of any noise.

Too much signal level, whether voice or data, can overload the transmission facilities and cause distortion and crosstalk. The industry uses a long term objective average maximum signal level on any voice channel of –16 dBm0. Any given voice channel may be idle for periods of time, so the long-term objective is slightly relaxed for short-term measurements. The maximum signal power of "live" traffic should not exceed –13 dBm0 during an actual call when averaged over any 3 s interval. As previously shown, unamplified voice signals from telephone instruments will average somewhat below the maximum limits.

When short-term alignment tests are made on voice channels, the above requirements are further relaxed. In this case, the maximum test level is 0 dBm0, but this high a level is unnecessary in all but a few cases. A level of –10 dBm0 is satisfactory for most testing, and some tests require it. Several types of automatic transmission test equipment use a level of –16 dBm0.

If the above maximum levels are observed, crosstalk and equipment overload will not be a problem. For loops connected to any type of digital or analog carrier equipment, the level will be limited to no more than +3 to +5 dBm0 as it is converted from an analog to a digital signal or used to modulate an analog carrier. The limiting action during digital conversion of the excess signal level, however, will cause data errors and voice distortion. Excessive levels on an analog carrier (FDM) channel can lead to undesirable distortion and interference with other channels in the same equipment.

5.8 Impedance Matching

It has been seen that the characteristic impedance of twisted pair cable pairs varies with frequency in the voice band. This variation is called impedance distortion; there is a variation from some reference value.† It might seem desirable to always terminate a cable

---

* The –9 dBm0 level is the maximum allowed by the FCC in Part 68, par. 68.308.

† See Chapter 7 for more information on the transmission effects of impedance distortion. The effects of differing load impedances on loop insertion loss are analyzed in Appendix D.

pair in its characteristic impedance (called an image match). In practice this is not possible because of the wide variation in terminal equipment and exchange cable parameters. An image match is defined as

$$\text{Image Match } Z_0 = Z_L = R + jX$$

where

$$
\begin{aligned}
Z_0 &= \text{line characteristic impedance} \\
Z_L &= \text{load impedance} \\
R &= \text{resistance} \\
X &= \text{reactance}
\end{aligned}
$$

Suppose it were possible to image match the loop. The input impedance of the loop would be easily predictable for all loops regardless of length, as previously shown. Predictability, especially in a narrow range, would ease the problems associated with designing central office line circuits or other devices connected to the loop. Also, sidetone problems would be somewhat eased by the image match for many regular two-wire telephone loops, but sidetone problems would be encountered on those circuits using short loops (for example, when the loop is connected to subscriber carrier equipment located near the subscriber). This is due to the practical design limitations of telephone instruments: it is difficult to economically produce devices that can function perfectly over an almost infinite range of loop characteristics.

For maximum power transfer, the loop should be terminated in the complex conjugate of its characteristic impedance [9]. But this is not always desirable either, because sidetone problems can again be encountered on short loops, and echo and stability (singing or oscillation) also could be troublesome on long-distance calls [10]. The complex conjugate match is defined as

$$\text{Complex Conjugate Match } Z_0 = R + jX \text{ and } Z_L = R - jX,$$

where

$$Z_0, Z_L, R \text{ and } X = \text{as defined previously}$$

Although it apparently is not possible to perfectly match the loop characteristic impedance to a load at all frequencies, mismatches decrease the return loss, which introduces another undesirable effect: echo or signal reflection. Return loss quantifies the magnitude of reflections caused by mismatched source and load impedances and is discussed in greater detail in Chapter 7.

Low return loss will cause problems on long-distance circuits where propagation delays and echoes become significant. On local loops, low return loss can give rise to excessive echo, which in many situations is not distinguishable from excessive sidetone, the effects of which already have been discussed. The harmful effects of low return loss cannot be underestimated. The overall return loss for a typical subscriber loop, terminated in a "500" set (off-hook) will be about 15 dB at 1,000 Hz, decreasing to around 7 or 8 dB at the voiceband edges [11].

In practice, a compromise impedance is used for standardization instead of an image or complex conjugate match. The compromise does not necessarily eliminate sidetone or echo problems on all loops, but it does allow for the common test, design and use of sub-scriber loop circuits with a wide variety of terminal equipment in a nationwide transmission system. It should be noted that most impedance mismatch problems usually occur at two-wire to four-wire conversion points (hybrids), and it is at these points that most reflections (and echoes) originate, as discussed in the next section.

For line circuits used in two-wire central offices, the compromise impedance (that is, the impedance looking into the line circuit) consists of a 900 Ω resistor in series with a 2.16 µF capacitor as shown in Fig. 5-6(a). As would be expected, the actual impedance of this resistor/capacitor combination varies with frequency. For example, at 300 Hz, the impedance is $933 \angle -15.3°$ Ω. At 1,000 Hz and 3,400 Hz, the values are $903 \angle -4.7°$ Ω and $900 \angle -1.4°$ Ω, respectively. In most applications, the reactance added by the capacitor is ignored, and the termination is considered resistive.

With the large-scale installation of digital central office switching systems starting in the late 1970s, it became apparent that additional work was required to characterize the two-wire subscriber loop. Every digital switching system is inherently four-wire, and a hybrid is installed at every subscriber line circuit. To improve the return loss of these circuits, a new set of standard balance networks was developed for the line circuit hybrid. These are shown in Fig. 5-6(b) for nonloaded loops and Fig. 5-6(c) for loaded loops [12].

Some test instruments present a 735 Ω resistive load to the loop as shown in Fig. 5-6(e). This value is the geometric mean of 600 and 900 Ω. Any of the three values (600, 735 and 900 Ω) provide a suitable compromise match for most purposes. For loaded loops (discussed later) used in private line applications, the standard compromise impedance match is 1,200 Ω resistive as shown in Fig. 5-6(f).

Terminal equipment connected to two-wire subscriber loops is considered to have 600 Ω impedance as shown in Fig. 5-6(d). The termination impedances at each end of a four-wire circuit are also considered to be 600 Ω resistive. As with the 900 Ω termination discussed above, this is by historical convention only and does not mean cable pairs used in four-wire circuits have a different characteristic impedance than those connected to two-wire line circuits. For cables used in subscriber loop applications, the impedances are not different, and this termination is another compromise.

The exact reasons for choosing the 600 and 900 Ω compromise impedances are lost in history, but inspection of Table 5-2 gives a possible clue. Nonloaded subscriber loops used fine cable gauges (26 AWG), which have a characteristic impedance around 900 Ω. Four-wire circuits used trunk plant, which in many cases was heavier gauge (22 AWG). The impedance of pairs in this case is about 600 Ω.

When relatively wideband terminal equipment (for example, a high-speed modem) is connected to a private line local loop, it is designed to match an impedance of around 135 to 150 Ω resistive as shown in Fig. 5-6(g). This value is chosen because the loop characteristic impedance decreases to 100 Ω at higher frequencies, and the lower impedance loads the loop in such a way to provide some measure of equalization for relatively wideband terminal equipment. This matching impedance would not apply to terminal equipment used on band-limited facilities (that is, when filters or loading limit the bandwidth to 3,100 Hz).

To complete the discussion of impedance, Fig. 5-7 is provided, which shows the variation of loop input impedance with length when nonloaded loops of the four standard gauges and lengths out to 10 mi are terminated in a 600 Ω resistive impedance. The values shown are for the air core PIC previously described. Filled PIC will give the same values.

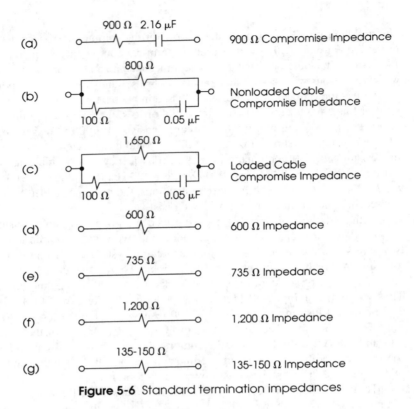

Figure 5-6 Standard termination impedances

5.9 Two-Wire to Four-Wire Conversion

A four-wire circuit always provides better transmission quality than a bidirectional two-wire circuit because each direction can be optimized, and the effects of impedance mismatches (and subsequent low return loss and echo problems) are limited except at the two-wire to four-wire conversion point.

Four-wire equivalence is inherent to all carrier transmission systems used for long distances. Even when carrier systems are not used, four-wire loops provide superior performance over two-wire loops in private line applications. Figure 5-8 shows a conceptual circuit which uses a four-wire loop connected to two-wire loops at each end.

The four-wire loop is converted to two-wire using a hybrid in order to accommodate two-wire terminal or central office equipment. A hybrid transformer, shown in Fig. 5-9, does the conversion.

Of special consideration with any four-wire circuit that includes at least one two-wire conversion is hybrid balance. The hybrid is basically a four-port bridge with the transmit and receive portions of the four-wire circuit connected to opposing ports as shown in Fig. 5-9. These two ports are balanced because the characteristics of the transmit and receive circuits are identical.*

---

* At least in principle, they are identical. Sometimes the transmit and receive circuits will traverse different routes, which will give them different characteristics. This is avoided for obvious reasons.

Table 5-2 Nonloaded and Loaded Cable Pairs, Impedance and Attenuation

Air-Core PIC, 1,000 Hz, 55°F

	Nonloaded		Loaded (H88)			Loaded (D66)	
Gauge	Z_0 (Ohms)	Attenuation dB/mi (dB/kft)	Gauge	Z_0 (Ohms)	Attenuation dB/mi (dB/kft)	Z_0 (Ohms)	Attenuation dB/mi (dB/kft)
19	$401 \angle -44.4°$	1.237 (0.234)	19	$1,022 \angle -05.1°$	0.398 (0.075)	$1,004 \angle -05.3°$	0.410 (0.078)
22	$567 \angle -44.7°$	1.781 (0.337)	22	$1,043 \angle -09.5°$	0.758 (0.144)	$1,025 \angle -09.7°$	0.771 (0.146)
24	$714 \angle -44.8°$	2.259 (0.428)	24	$1,081 \angle -14.2°$	1.163 (0.220)	$1,063 \angle -14.4°$	1.177 (0.223)
26	$906 \angle -44.9°$	2.881 (0.546)	26	$1,165 \angle -20.4°$	1.782 (0.337)	$1,147 \angle -20.6°$	1.797 (0.340)

Filled-Core PIC, 1,000 Hz, 55°F

	Nonloaded		Loaded (H88)			Loaded (D66)	
Gauge	Z_0 (Ohms)	Attenuation dB/mi (dB/kft)	Gauge	Z_0 (Ohms)	Attenuation dB/mi (dB/kft)	Z_0 (Ohms)	Attenuation dB/mi (dB/kft)
19	$401 \angle -42.7°$	1.234 (0.234)	19	$1,023 \angle -05.1°$	0.399 (0.076)	$1,004 \angle -05.3°$	0.410 (0.078)
22	$567 \angle -43.9°$	1.779 (0.337)	22	$1,043 \angle -09.5°$	0.758 (0.144)	$1,025 \angle -09.7°$	0.771 (0.146)
24	$714 \angle -44.3°$	2.258 (0.428)	24	$1,081 \angle -14.2°$	1.163 (0.220)	$1,063 \angle -14.4°$	1.177 (0.223)
26	$906 \angle -44.5°$	2.878 (0.545)	26	$1,165 \angle -20.4°$	1.781 (0.337)	$1,147 \angle -20.6°$	1.796 (0.340)

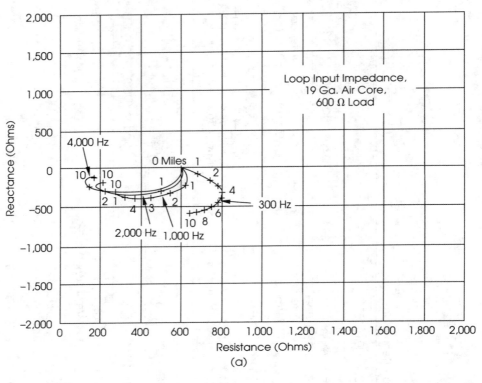

(a)

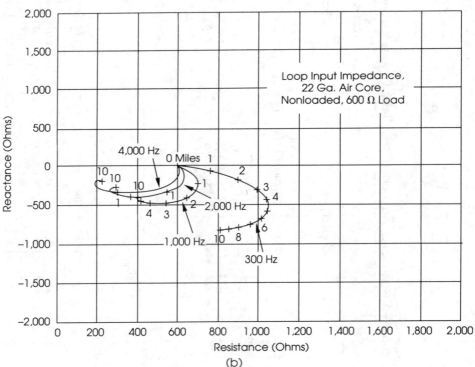

(b)

Figure 5-7 Loop input impedance

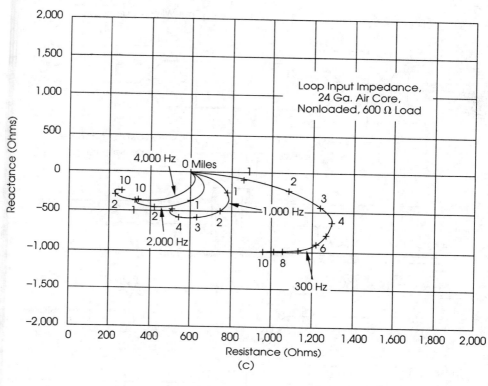

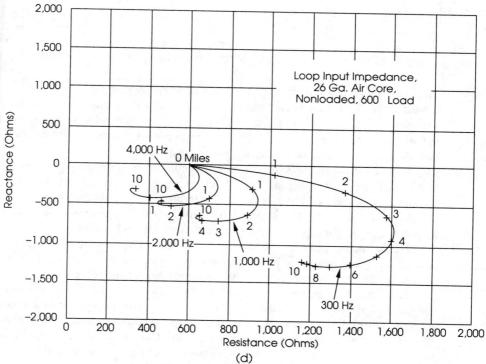

Figure 5-7 (continued)

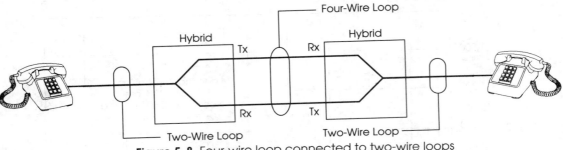

Figure 5-8 Four-wire loop connected to two-wire loops

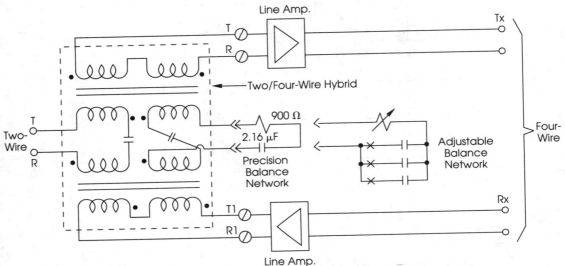

Figure 5-9 Four-wire to two-wire conversion using a hybrid transformer

The two-wire circuit and the hybrid balance network are connected to the remaining (opposite) ports. A loop connected to the two-wire port can be any length and have almost any impedance. In order to balance the bridge and minimize adverse interaction between the transmit and receive circuits (that is, maximize return loss), the balance network impedance must exactly equal the two-wire impedance.

This is not overly difficult if a wide selection of balance impedances are available that would cover all situations. In a practical sense, however, this is not the case, for technical and administrative reasons. Therefore, many hybrids have a selection of compromise impedances (for example, 600, 900, 1,200 Ω or a variable resistor) as well as a limited selection of capacitors as shown schematically in Fig. 5-9.

The balance impedance value is chosen when the circuit is being designed (it can be assigned by prescription), or it can be found by testing the loop and adjusting the balance impedance for maximum return loss between the transmit and receive ports.

The actual balance achieved is called *trans-hybrid return loss*, which is discussed in Chapter 7. This loss includes the inherent loss between the two-wire and the transmit and receive ports (3.5 dB each with hybrid transformers) and the balance return loss between the transmit and receive ports. Balance return loss is simply a comparison of the impedance at the two-wire port and the balance network impedance, and it always should be as high as possible.

$$\text{Trans-Hybrid Loss} = \text{BRL} + 7 \text{ dB}$$

In the above equation, BRL equals *balance return loss*, and the 7 dB includes the 3 dB splitting (or dissipation) loss in each two-wire to four-wire leg, plus 0.5 dB insertion loss in each leg of the transformer itself.

$$\text{Balance Return Loss} = \frac{(Z_{2W} + Z_B)}{(Z_{2W} - Z_B)}$$

where

$$Z_{2W} = \text{two-wire line impedance}$$
$$Z_B = \text{balance network impedance}$$

5.10 Tuning the Loop

The low-frequency equivalent of a loop is a lowpass filter; that is, the loop attenuates higher frequencies more than lower frequencies. It is somewhat poor in this respect, however, because the dropoff rate is a little more than 3 dB per decade at voice frequencies. The dropoff is due mostly to the distributed capacitive reactance of the cable pair.

The cable pair can be reactively tuned to provide better attenuation characteristics for voiceband applications. Ideally, the tuning would be by a distributed inductance of sufficient magnitude to compensate for the capacitive reactance.

Adding more distributed inductance is not practical, so the tuning (or "loading") is done by adding series inductance (load coils) at fixed intervals along the cable route. The process is called *lumped loading*. The result is also a lowpass filter, but attenuation in the passband is smaller and more constant, and the attenuation slope at the band edge is much sharper than without loading.

Loading is used only on loops longer than 18,000 ft (19, 22 and 24 gauge) or 15,000 ft (26 gauge). The overall loading scheme is described by a simple nomenclature. For example, D66 loading denotes 66 mH coils spaced 4,500 ft apart. H88 loading denotes 88 mH coils spaced 6,000 ft apart. These two are the most common loading schemes for subscriber loops.*

The load coils are constructed using bifilar windings on a toroidal core made from highly compressed permalloy. The load coil is placed in series with each conductor of the cable pair as shown pictorially in Fig. 5-10.

The first load coil from the central office is located a half-section out (called *end section*, which is 2,250 ft for "D" loading and 3,000 ft for "H" loading). This allows loaded loops to be joined in the central office and cascaded if necessary. The precision with which loaded loops must be designed is covered in Chapter 6.

It is good practice during design and construction of subscriber loop plant to include terminals (or at least make the cable readily accessible) at properly spaced intervals for future load coil installation, even though they may not be initially required.

---

* Other loading schemes are described in [3].

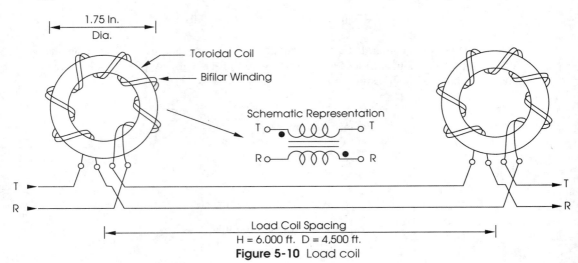

Figure 5-10 Load coil

5.11 Loaded Loop Secondary Parameters

The secondary transmission parameters of D66 and H88 loaded, air and filled core PIC are shown in Figs. 5-11 and 5-12.* The scales on these graphs are the same as Figs. 5-2 and 5-3 to allow direct comparison with nonloaded cables.† The values shown in Figs. 5-11 and 5-12 were calculated in terms of load section length and then adjusted to a per mile basis. The attenuation and phase constants shown are only valid for multiples of the section length, but fractional values can be used in practical problems. Note the sharp rolloff of loaded cable at about 3,400 Hz for H88 loaded cables and 4,000 Hz for D66 loaded cables. These are the approximate "cutoff" frequencies for the respective loading schemes. At lower frequencies there is essentially no difference between D66 and H88 loading.

Sometimes it is helpful to have a table of just the impedance and attenuation at 1,000 Hz for loaded and nonloaded cables. These values are given in Table 5-2 and can be used for design purposes without trying to scale the graphs previously presented. As can be seen from this table, the difference between air core and filled cables at voice frequencies is negligible.

5.12 Loaded Loops and High-Speed Data

While loaded loops enhance voice transmission over long distances, they present problems to high-speed (above 9,600 bps) data circuits. This is because there is considerable delay distortion, attenuation distortion and impedance distortion with loaded cables, especially at the band edges. *Envelope delay distortion* (EDD) is especially troublesome to high-speed data circuits. Transmission impairments such as these are discussed in Chapter 7. Circuits dedicated to high-speed data transmission are always put on nonloaded facilities.

---

*   Appendix C shows how the secondary parameters are derived for loaded cable.

†   These graphs were produced by calculating the secondary parameters from the primary constants shown in Table 5-1.

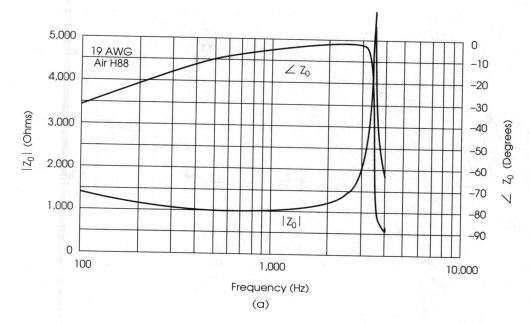

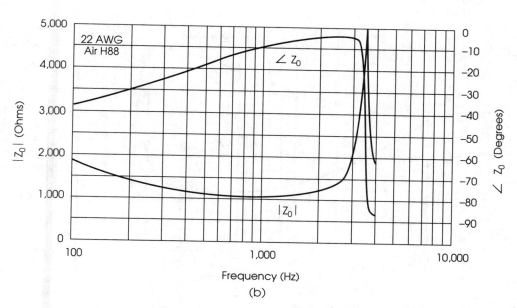

Figure 5-11 Loaded cable pair secondary parameters, characteristic impedance, PIC 55°F (continued on the following pages)

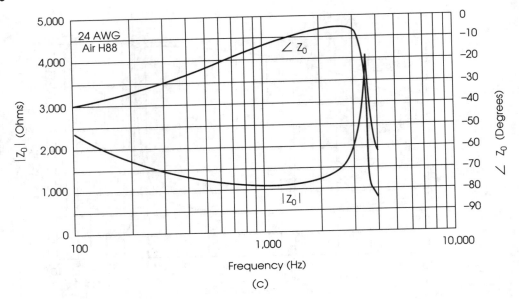

(c)

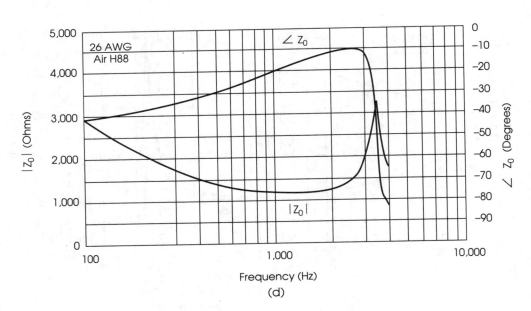

(d)

Figure 5-11 (continued)

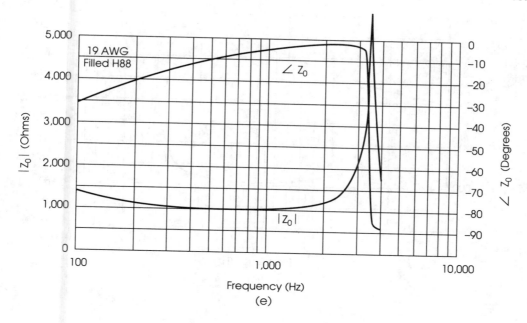

(e)

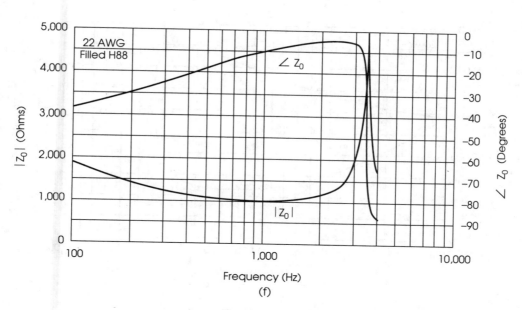

(f)

Figure 5-11 (continued)

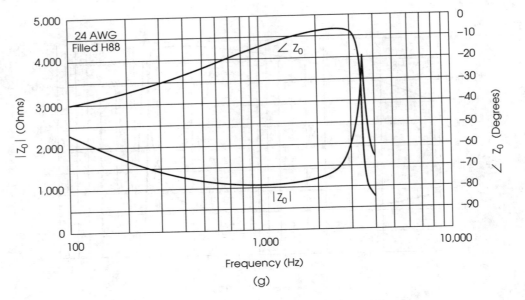

(g)

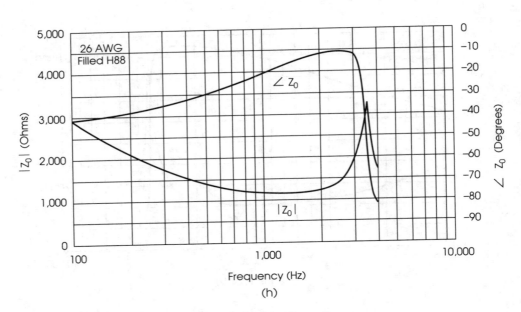

(h)

Figure 5-11 (continued)

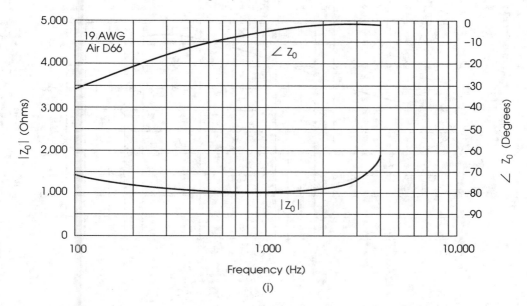

(i)

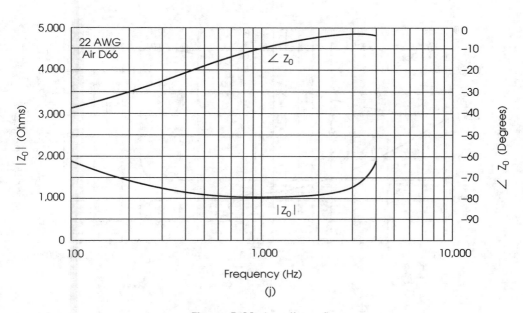

(j)

Figure 5-11 (continued)

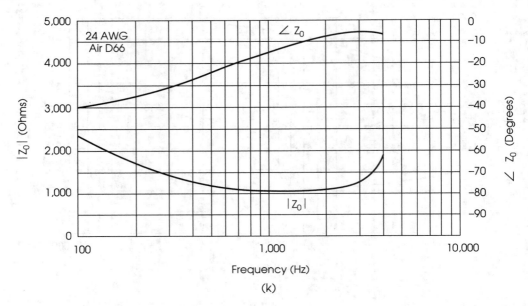

(k)

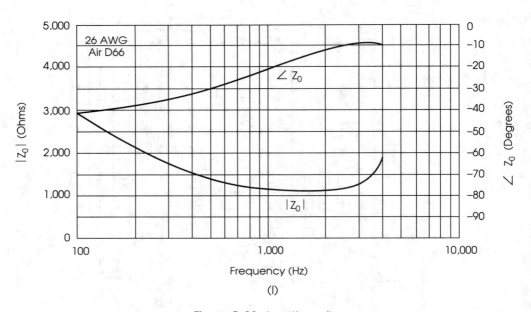

(l)

Figure 5-11 (continued)

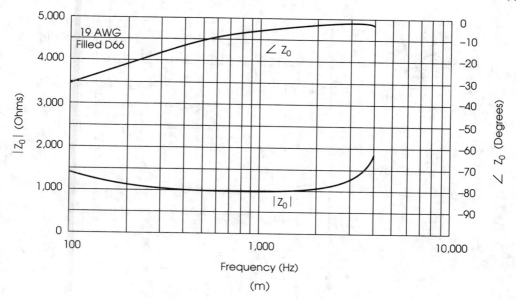

(m)

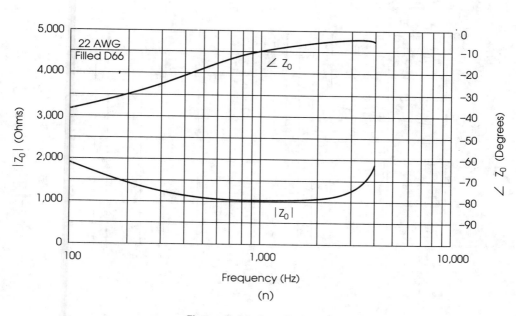

(n)

Figure 5-11 (continued)

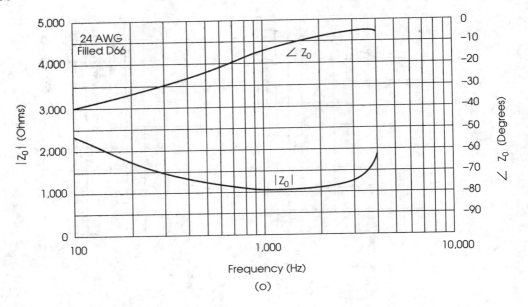

(o)

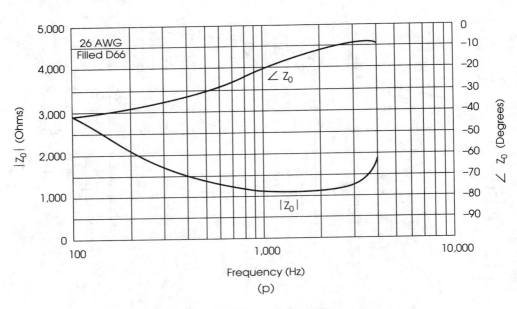

(p)

Figure 5-11 (continued)

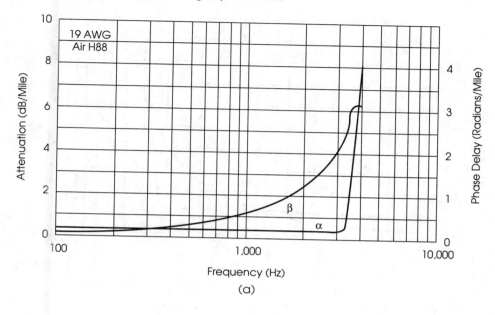

(a)

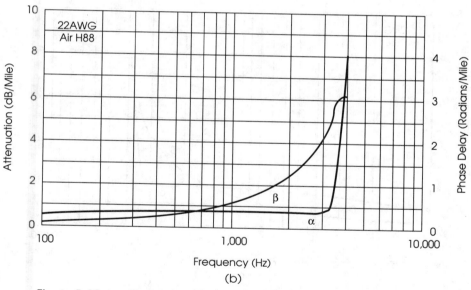

(b)

Figure 5-12 Loaded cable pair secondary parameters, attenuation and phase delay, PIC 55°F (continued on the following pages)

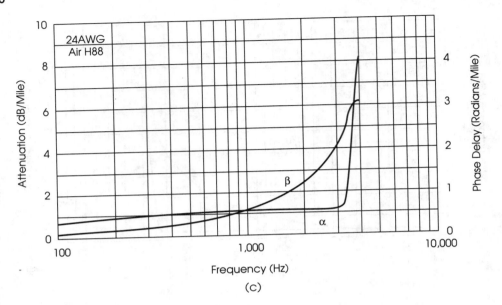

(c)

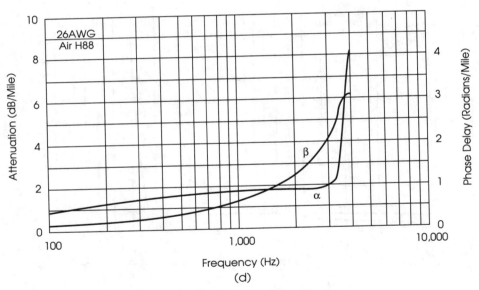

(d)

Figure 5-12 (continued)

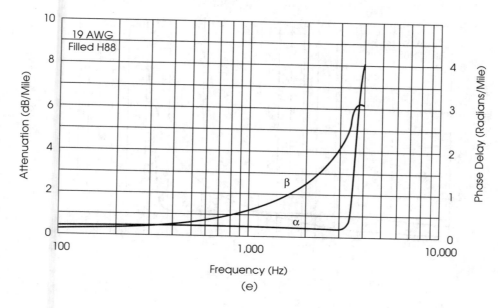

(e)

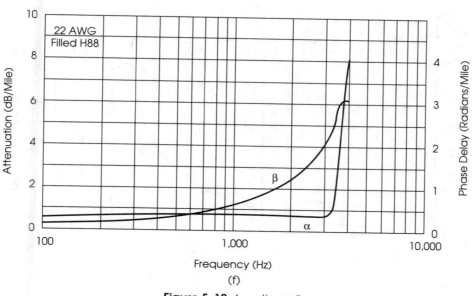

(f)

Figure 5-12 (continued)

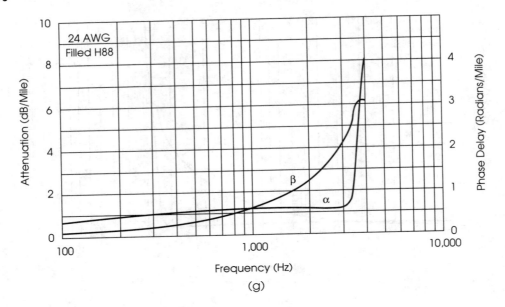

(g)

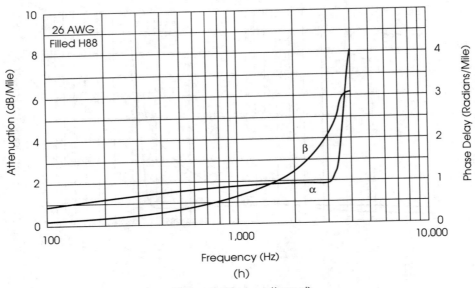

(h)

Figure 5-12 (continued)

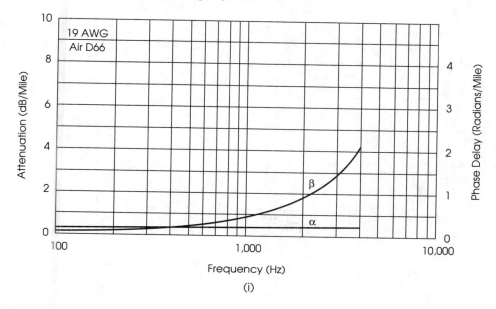

(i)

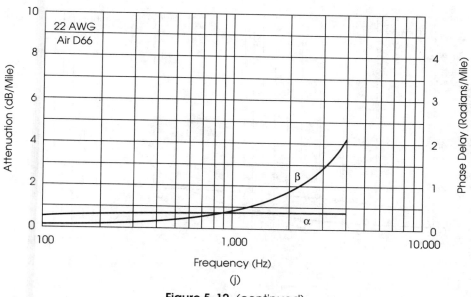

(j)

Figure 5-12 (continued)

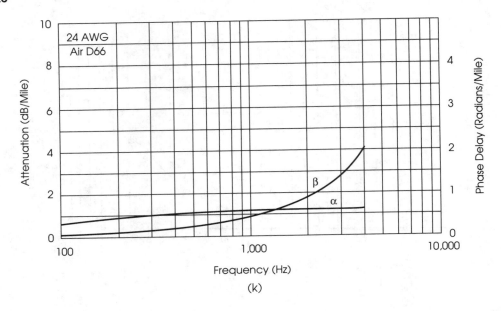

(k)

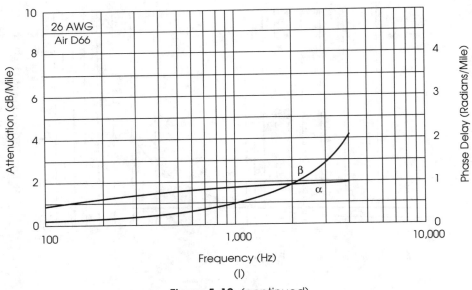

(l)

Figure 5-12 (continued)

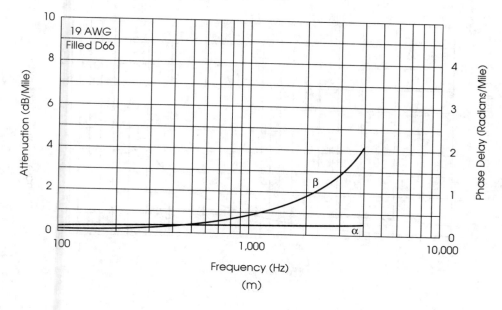

(m)

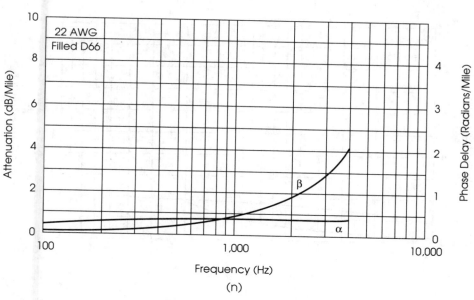

(n)

Figure 5-12 (continued)

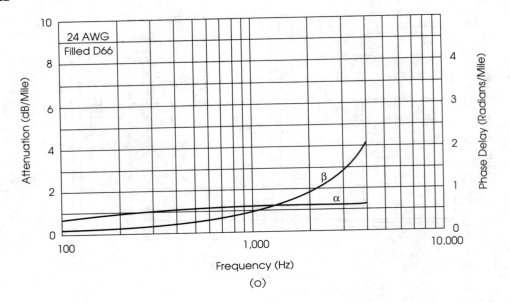

(o)

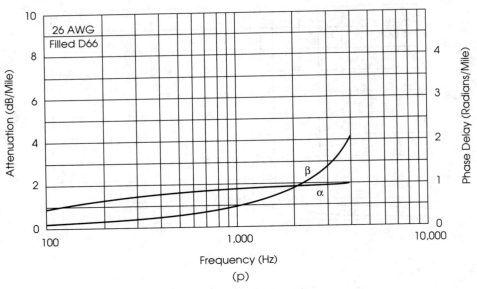

(p)

Figure 5-12 (continued)

5.13 Applying Loaded Loops to Subscriber Service

It is very important that loaded plant is applied to subscriber service according to a rigid set of rules. Severe transmission degradation will result if there are any deviations. One rule is:

A subscriber should never be connected between load coils

Otherwise, the attenuation, attenuation distortion and impedance distortion will be unacceptable. For example, if a subscriber is connected between load coils, the loss at 1,000 Hz may be, say, 10 dB, but at 1,500 Hz it may be 15 dB, and at 2,500 Hz it may be back to 10 dB. The original design loss may have been 5 dB at 1,000 Hz. The solution is to always cut the pair dead (open circuit) beyond the subscriber to avoid loaded bridged taps. (This simple solution actually applies to all plant, whether loaded or nonloaded.)

The general rules for applying loaded pairs are:

1. Do not connect a subscriber more than 12,000 ft (D66 loading) or 9,000 ft (H88 loading) past the last load coil (called subscriber end-section).
2. Do not connect subscribers between load coils under any circumstances.
3. Cut the pair dead past the subscriber's connection to the cable if possible. If this is not possible, be sure the pair (bridged tap) is not loaded beyond the subscriber's connection, per (2) above, and include the bridged tap length when determining if the end section falls within the limits of (1) above.

Additional information on loading can be found in [13,14].

5.14 Cost Basis for Loop Choice

As with all other practical problems, cost tradeoffs are to be expected in deciding the makeup (gauge and loading) of any given cable route. The generally accepted ranking of cable gauge and loading is shown in Table 5-3. Obviously, this table applies to new installations. On a given route with cable already installed, loading would almost always be the clear choice over installing a new, larger gauge cable for subscribers beyond 18,000 ft. except where digital loop carrier is more economical.

The ranking shown in Table 5-3 only considers H88 loading; however, when D66 loading is being considered, the ranking would not change. D66 loading has a slight economic disadvantage when compared to H88 because of its shorter section length.

In many companies, the choice between D66 and H88 loading is made by the ranking engineer's personal preference. This apparent lack of economic forethought may not be as bad as it sounds. Advocates of the two loading schemes can argue the advantages, economic and otherwise, of each, but neither will be the clear winner. The only possible exception might be the case of a large cable serving a large number of subscribers beyond the 18,000 ft nonloaded cable limit. However, in this case, it is more likely that digital loop carrier would be used rather than loaded cable, anyway.

Table 5-3 Loop Choice

Rank	AWG	Circuit Type
1	26	NL
2	24	NL
3	26	H88
4	24	H88
5	22	NL
6	22	H88
7	19	NL
8	19	H88

REFERENCES

[1] IEEE Std. 823-1989, *IEEE Standard Methodologies for Specifying Voicegrade Channel Transmission Parameters and Evaluating Connection Transmission Performance for Speech Telephony*. New York: Institute of Electrical and Electronics Engineers, 1989. Available from IEEE Service Center.

[2] IEEE Standard 820-1984, *IEEE Standard Telephone Loop Performance Characteristics*. New York: Institute of Electrical and Electronics Engineers. Available from IEEE Service Center.

[3] Hamsher, D.H. *Communication System Engineering Handbook*. New York: McGraw-Hill Book Company, 1967.

[4] *Understanding Transmission*, Vol. 7, Lee's ABC of the Telephone, 1976. Available from ABC Teletraining, Inc.

[5] *Understanding Transmission*, Vol. 8, Lee's ABC of the Telephone, 1976.

[6] *Transmission Systems for Communications*. Bell Telephone Laboratories, Inc., 1982. Available from AT&T Customer Information Center.

[7] REA TE&CM Section 406, *Transmission Facility Data*, August 1977. Available from Rural Electrification Administration.

[8] *Transmission Considerations for Outside Plant*. Automatic Electric Company, General System Practice 946-101-040, 1968. Available from GTE Practices Manager.

[9] Van Valkenberg, M. E. *Network Analysis*. Englewood Cliffs, NJ: Prentice-Hall, Inc., 1964.

[10] *CCITT Blue Book, Volume V, Telephone Transmission Quality*, Series P Recommendations, 1989, p. 334. Available from NTIS.

[11] "Physical and Transmission Characteristics of Customer Loop Plant." *Bell System Technical Journal*, Vol. 48, No. 10, December 1969, p. 3,344.

[12] Moore, T. L. "Digital COE Return Loss." A "writeup" by the author, REA Transmission Branch Chief, September 11, 1987. Available from Rural Electrification Administration.

[13] *Loading Systems for Voice-Frequency Telephone Cables*, Technical Bulletin 852-533, Automatic Electric Company, General System Practice 852-050-050, 1965. Available from GTE Practices Manager.

[14] REA TE&CM Section 424, *Design Guideline for Telecommunications Subscriber Loop Plant*. Available from Rural Electrification Administration.

6

Loop Design

The large majority of loops are two-wire (one-pair) and used in regular switched service at voiceband frequencies. This chapter emphasizes the design of loops for this application, but information is provided on special services and four-wire loops used for private line services.

6.1 Planning

The intent of loop design is to provide satisfactory transmission and signaling while taking into account the economics of the situation. The adequacy of any loop design method is directly attributable to the planning associated with the services to be provided on the loop. The planning process is specifically oriented toward the outside plant facility and identifies the features shown in Fig. 6-1.

A wire center (see Chapter 1) serves some overall area. This area is broken into sections that meet network requirements and application strategies and allows convenient administration. These areas may overlap and change over time according to the application strategy. Wire center areas include the following sections, which are illustrated in Fig. 6-2.

- Distribution area, which defines the developed or soon to be developed geographical area served by the wire center

- Rural area, which defines the thinly developed areas within the wire center boundaries

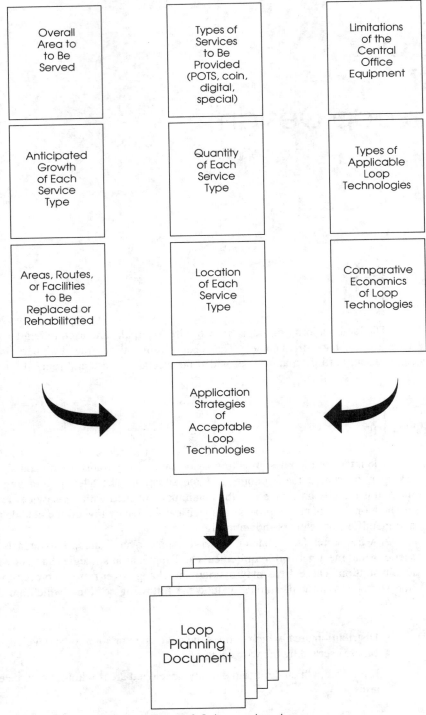

Figure 6-1 Loop planning

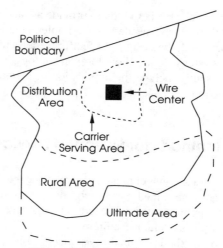

Figure 6-2 Wire center area

- Carrier serving area, which defines the areas to be served by pair gain systems and digital loop carrier
- Ultimate serving area, which defines the ultimate area to be served by the wire center

Sizing of loop facilities for areas not already served can be quite difficult because:

- Growth and demand over long periods are difficult to predict, and the loop facility to be used is highly dependent on these factors.
- Loop technologies are changing, and more options are becoming available (all of which reduce the cabling requirement).
- A highly detailed knowledge is required of land use, demographics, and area economy and this information is not readily available.
- The regulatory environment can change.

Despite these difficulties, general sizing rules for loop facilities can be used for planning purposes when more detailed information is not available. These are:

- Allot the equivalent of two cable pairs to each living unit in a developed or soon to be developed area.
- Allot the equivalent of two cable pairs to each 100 ft² of building space not used for living purposes.

The above rules require "equivalent" cable pairs. This means the chosen loop technology should provide these pairs at the subscriber's premises and at the wire center. The actual facility between the wire center and the user may not use metallic cable pairs at all (for example, it could be a radio system or optical fibers). The number of living units and building space will have to be estimated from community plans and, perhaps, historical development in the area.

The loop facilities plan is written to provide as much detail as is desired, but progressively more detail is always needed as the implementation time is approached. After the plan has been prepared, the design of specific feeder and distribution routes can proceed. The application strategy defines how loop technology is applied or deployed in the field. All strategies presently include the application of metallic loops, which are described in the following sections.

6.2 Loop Design Methods for Switched Services

How the various conductor gauges are designed into the loop, and the resulting characteristics, are determined by the loop design method. The various methods use the transmission requirements for switched services and the signaling limitations of the serving central office as default requirements.

One common method is called *resistance design*. Another, used by many telephone companies and advocated by the Rural Electrification Administration (REA) and referred to here as *loss design*, is based on a maximum loss value measured at 1,000 Hz. The end result of these two methods, in terms of transmission and signaling, is essentially the same. Other design methods are also used. For example, the Bell Operating Companies may use resistance design, *unigauge design*, *long route design*, among others, depending on the application or the time of implementation. All methods try to provide adequate transmission while minimizing the plant investment.

The following rules apply to switched loops; they do not necessarily apply to loops used for point-to-point (dedicated) service. This is because loops used for point-to-point applications usually are designed on a case or application basis. These dedicated loops usually include transmission conditioning equipment that tailors the overall circuit characteristics according to some specific requirement, as discussed later.

The basic rules for the resistance design and loss design methods are presented here. Where maximum conductor lengths are specified, they include the length of bridged taps.

The general rules for resistance design shown below, which have been used for a number of years, are illustrated in Fig. 6-3. Since the loop resistance varies with temperature, the chart in Fig. 6-3(a) should be used for 100° F (38°C) design temperature (buried applications), and Fig. 6-3(b) should be used for 140° F (60°C) design temperature (aerial applications) [1]:

1. Limit conductor loop resistance to 1,300 Ω maximum using mixed gauges.
2. Limit length of nonloaded loops to 18,000 ft maximum (15,000 ft for 26 gauge).
3. Load all loops over 18,000 ft but less than 24,000 ft.
4. Use digital loop carrier on loops over 24,000 ft.

The Bell System revised the above rules slightly in 1983 for their own purposes, although the principles are applicable anywhere.* The revised rules are essentially identical to those previously described, but the conductor resistance for loops between 18,000 and 24,000 ft is limited to 1,500 Ω (rather than 1,300 Ω) and H88 loading is used for loops over 18,000 ft (15,000 ft for 26 gauge). ·

---

* References to the Bell System generally refer to it in the pre-divestiture sense. Even so, the technical aspects still apply for the most part to the individual companies. See .[2]

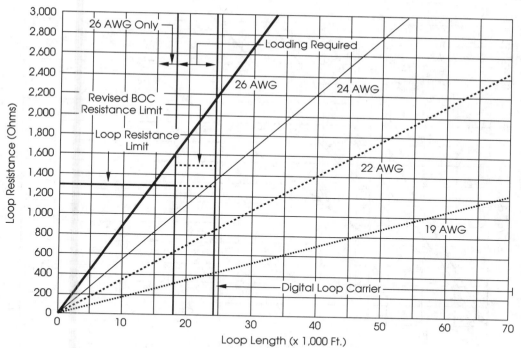

Figure 6-3(a) Resistance loop design, 100°F (38°C) (buried plant)

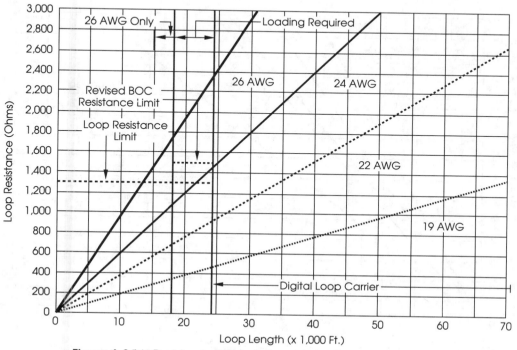

Figure 6-3(b) Resistance loop design, 140°F (60°C) (aerial plant)

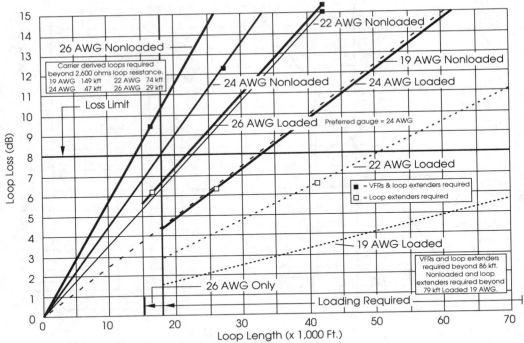

Figure 6-4(a) Loss loop design, 100°F (38°C) (buried plant)

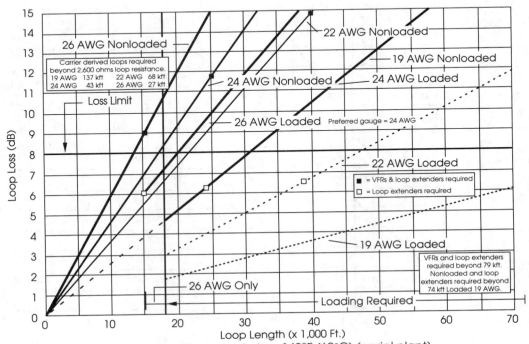

Figure 6-4(b) Loss loop design, 140°F (60°C) (aerial plant)

The general rules used in the loss design method by REA, and described in their loop design guideline, are shown below and illustrated in Fig. 6-4. As with the resistance design method, two charts are given: Fig. 6-4(a) is used for 100° F (38°C) design temperature, and Fig. 6-4(b) is used for 140° F (60°C) design temperature [3–5]:

1. Limit loop loss to 8 dB maximum at 1,000 Hz.
2. Limit length of nonloaded loops to 18,000 ft maximum (15,000 ft for 26 gauge).
3. Load all loops over 18,000 ft (REA advocates D66 loading).
4. Use loop extenders and VFRs on loops with over 1,500 Ω conductor resistance.
5. Use carrier derived loops on loops with over 2,600 Ω conductor resistance.
6. Use 24 gauge conductors where possible within the above guidelines, but mixed gauges are permissible. Avoid 26 gauge conductors in loaded loops.

Implicit in each design method is the flexibility to use single or mixed cable gauges depending on the situation. An objective is to use a single gauge in each distribution area identified in the planning process, and this is quite easy to do when a particular distribution area is compact (equivalent radius approximately 3 mi).

With any design method, the use of mixed gauges (for example, 26 and 24 gauge or 24 and 22 gauge or any other combinations) is handled in a straightforward manner. If the design is based on resistance, then the resistances of each gauge are tabulated and added together to determine if the total resistance to a particular distribution point meets the resistance criterion. Similarly, if the design is based on loss, the losses for each gauge on a route are added to determine if the total loss meets the loss criterion. In mixed gauge applications, the smaller gauges are placed closer to the CO with progressively heavier gauges away from the CO.

6.3 Special Services

Loops used for other than regular switched service may require different design methods and special considerations. Such loops are considered to be used in special (also called *private line* or *dedicated line*) services. For most short-haul, dedicated line applications, the previously given design charts can be used by modifying the constraints. For purposes here, "short haul" means less than 30 mi long, although it can also mean having a round-trip delay of less than 6 ms. The delay criteria is important in loops with two-wire to four-wire conversion.

Some special services are listed below for short-haul applications. All losses are referred to the central office interface and do not account for losses in the switching system itself. Modern digital switching systems introduce approximately 0.0 to 0.5 dB additional loss, while analog switching systems introduce 0.5 to 1.0 dB additional loss.

- Foreign Exchange — objective loss is 0 to 5.0 dB from the central office line circuit providing dial tone to the terminal equipment; maximum loss is 8.0 dB.

- Private Branch Exchange (PBX) — objective loss on loops connected as central office trunks for a PBX is 0 to 3.0 dB (3.0 dB maximum with tie trunks; 5.0 dB without tie trunks). None of the PBX stations should have a loss exceeding 8.0 dB to the serving central office line circuit.

- Off-Premises Extensions — objective loss is 0 to 5.0 dB from the central office line circuit (providing the primary access line) to the off-premises station terminal equipment; maximum loss is 8.0 dB.

- Secretarial Answering Service — same as off-premises extensions.

- Centrex — the maximum loss for a Centrex station line served from the central office line circuit is 5.0 dB; maximum loss for the attendant console is 2.0 dB. This applies to analog Centrex lines only.

6.4 Via Net Loss Method

Another design method, called *via net loss* (VNL), is used for private line type long-haul circuits (greater than 30 mi long or greater than 6 ms round-trip delay). Loops used in local switched service generally fall outside this category. Nevertheless, VNL is worth exploring for completeness because loops are used as the "tail-circuit" or end-link of almost all long-haul circuits. Also, the loop may constitute a portion of a circuit comprising private as well as telephone company facilities, and the VNL method may need to be applied. The VNL method is not needed when the circuit is four-wire *and* does not have any two-wire to four-wire conversion.

The 6 ms delay referred to above comes into play because it is at that point that delayed echo can become annoying. The longer the circuit, the longer the delay, and the more loss is required in a circuit to reduce the echo to an acceptable level.

The minimum loss on any private line circuit is 4.0 dB to ensure stability from singing; an additional 0.5 dB is added to account for normal variations in line-up and drift. This gives an overall minimum loss of 4.5 dB.

The VNL method specifies the minimum *additional* loss a long-haul circuit must have so that echo problems are avoided. Since each type of circuit also has a maximum allowable loss, the actual design loss for that circuit will fall between two values such that:

$$4.5 \text{ dB} + \text{VNL} \leq \text{Design Loss} \leq \text{Maximum Allowable Loss}$$

The *maximum allowable loss* for any given circuit is determined by its application. A typical maximum value for a nonswitched circuit that does not interconnect with the PSTN is 16.0 dB, although 10.0 dB is considered an objective maximum. These values compromise received level with noise performance and echo control.

The required via net loss (or minimum additional loss) of a circuit is calculated from the following formula:

$$\text{VNL} = (\text{VNLF} \times \text{Length} + 0.4 + \text{D}) \text{ dB}$$

In this equation, VNLF is the *via net loss factor* (also called *echo path loss factor*) for the particular type of facility in dB per mile, Length is the one-way facility length in miles, and D is additional loss that must be added to compensate for additional delays added by equalization devices. The 0.4 dB factor takes into account variations among connection losses caused by misalignment and temperature.

VNLF is based on the propagation velocity of the particular facility type. Compromise values are used because it almost would be impossible to account for each type of facility in a long-haul circuit. The following VNLF values are given in [6]:

> All four-wire Carrier Facilities, VNLF = 0.0015 dB per mile
>
> Two-wire Exchange Cable Facilities, VNLF = 0.04 dB per mile
>
> Four-wire Exchange Cable Facilities, VNLF = 0.017 dB per mile

D is determined as follows [6]:

> If no equalization is provided, D = 0
>
> If equalization is provided, D = 0.1 (d1+d2+d3+ ... +dn) dB

In the above, d1, d2, ..., dn are the 1,000 Hz absolute round-trip delays in ms for all equalization devices in the circuit.

If a long-haul circuit is made up of more than one type of facility (for example, cable and carrier), the individual echo path loss factors (VNLF × Length) are added for each facility type. The 0.4 dB factor is added only once.

The analysis of the VNL method can be simplified somewhat by using fixed values for ranges of circuit lengths as shown in Table 6-1 [6].

Table 6-1 Overall Loss vs. Circuit Length

Length (Miles)	Loss (dB)
0 to 700	6
701 to 1,300	7
1,301 to 2,000	8
Over 2,000[a]	4

[a]Note: Echo suppressors or echo cancellers required.

There are many other special service circuits and design aspects that require consideration. See the appropriate references for descriptions of transmission objectives associated with these circuits [1,6,7].

6.5 Variation of Design Parameters with Temperature

When loops are designed according to the foregoing methods, it is helpful to have detailed cable pair data at various temperatures. Figure 6-5 shows the variation of dc resistance and 1,000 Hz loss with temperature in the form of factors. For practical problems, loss variation with temperature at voiceband frequencies is considered to be due to dc resistance variation. A rule of thumb is to increase the resistance by 4 percent

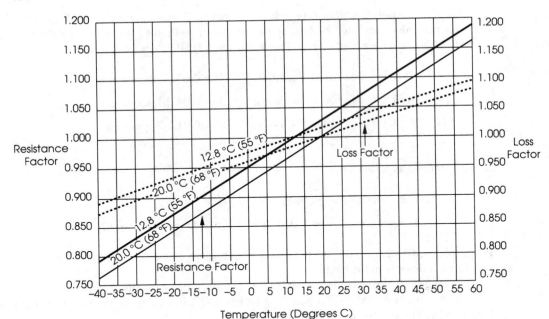

Figure 6-5 Resistance factor and loss factor vs. temperature

and loss by 2 percent for every 18°F (10°C) increase in temperature.* A more exact analysis would take into account skin effect, which for purposes here is considered negligible at 1,000 Hz.

Table 6-2 shows the dc resistance and loss for various nonloaded cable gauges at 100°F (38°C) and 140°F (60°C). A similar chart can be made for loaded loops that would take into account the load coil resistance. The resistance and loss at 100°F and 140°F are emphasized because these are the worse-case temperatures at which predominantly buried and predominantly aerial loops are presently designed. In other words, if the maximum desired loop loss under all reasonable temperature conditions is 8 dB, the loop length giving this loss would be calculated at 100°F for predominantly buried plant, and so on. Additional tables and formulas for temperature correcting transmission parameters are available from the cable manufacturers or applicable references [8,9].

Obviously, loops will be built where the temperature of the earth (and consequently of the copper conductors) at common burial depths never reaches (say) more than 50°F (10°C) and the ambient air temperature never reaches more than 70°F (21°C). In these cases, it would seem that designing for 100°F (38°C) and 140°F (60°C) temperatures would be overdesign. Good design practice, however, requires some amount of conservatism, and there is essentially no economic penalty in designing for the higher temperatures. Also, the possibility exists of having both buried and aerial facilities along a given route. In this case, the dominating facility type (buried or aerial) will determine the design temperature to be used.

---

* The equation for resistance variation is $R_T = R_{T0} [1 + \rho_{T0} (T - T0)]$, where R_T is the resistance at temperature T, R_{T0} is the resistance at temperature T0, and ρ_{T0} is the temperature coefficient of resistivity per degree Celsius at temperature T0. For copper, $\rho_{T0} = 0.00401/°C$ at 15°C and 0.00393/°C at 20°C. Loss variation is approximately equal to the square root of resistance variation.

Table 6-2 Dc Resistance and 1,000 Hz Loss at Design Temperatures, Nonloaded PIC

	Design Temp.	19 AWG	22 AWG	24 AWG	26 AWG
Resistance (Ohms/Mile)	@ 55°F	83.7	167.3	265.5	428.0
	@ 100°F	92.1	184.0	292.1	470.8
	@ 140°F	99.6	199.1	316.0	509.3
Loss (dB/Mile)	@ 55°F	1.24	1.78	2.26	2.88
	@ 100°F	1.30	1.87	2.37	3.02
	@ 140°F	1.35	1.95	2.47	3.15

6.6 Loading

The resistance and loss design methods discussed in the preceding sections specify loading on loops at some point. Since inserting a load coil in a distributed parameter transmission line can introduce impedance discontinuities (and reflection), the spacing requirements for load coils must be very precise to minimize this effect (maximize return loss). The most common subscriber loop loading schemes are "H88" and "D66" as explained in Chapter 5.

General Telephone and Electric Co. (GTE) affiliated companies generally use H88 loading and require [10]:

1. The average spacing should not deviate from the desired spacing by more than ± 2 percent.

2. On a specific project, no loading section should deviate from the average spacing on the route by ± 2 percent.

3. The average difference from the average spacing (disregarding sign) should not exceed 0.5 percent of the average loading section length.

Companies funded by the REA use the following specification for D66 loading [3]:

1. The average spacing should not deviate from the desired spacing by more than ± 3 percent.

2. Deviation of the length of longest individual sections from the average spacing should be within ± 3 percent.

3. The average difference of the individual section spacings from the average spacing (disregarding sign) should not exceed 2 percent.

The specifications used by other companies may vary slightly from those shown here. Regardless of the actual specification, special care during construction is always needed to give the required precision. If this is done, the transmission performance of the loop will be predictable, and its return loss will be reasonably high.

The dc resistance of the load coil must be considered in loaded loop design. Load coils add between 5.5 and 8.5 Ω loop resistance at each load point, depending on whether the coils are standard or mini types (mini coils have higher resistance). Therefore, if a subscriber is located just beyond the fifth load point, the total loop resistance would include that of the cable plus 28 to 43 Ω for the load coils. The resistance of load coils varies with temperature in the same manner as cable pairs. Since the contribution of load coil resistance to the typical loaded loop is relatively small, this variation is usually ignored.

6.7 Voice Frequency Repeaters and Loop Extenders

Voice frequency repeaters (VFRs) and *loop extenders* are an integral part of loop design. Voice frequency repeaters used on two-wire switched loops generally provide up to 15 dB gain and are applied on loops with loss greater than 10 dB. If the loop is non-loaded, high-frequency gain equalization is provided to compensate for the loop's inherent high-frequency rolloff characteristic. Equalization is not needed on loaded loops. Also included in the VFR is a line build-out network to provide impedance matching for various cable gauges and loading schemes.

Most VFRs used in subscriber loop applications determine the direction of the loudest talker at any particular instant and add gain to that signal while attenuating the signal from the other direction by the same amount. All modern VFRs include data detection circuitry to disable the device during data transmissions; this is required because of the VFRs directional characteristics. VFRs are made to be transparent to dc signaling and supervision and ringing.

The procedure associated with using a VFR entails determining the net gain required. This is found by calculating or measuring the loop loss at 1,000 Hz and then finding the *net gain* from:

$$\text{Net Gain} = \text{Loop Loss} - \text{Desired Net Loss}$$

where

$$2 \text{ dB or } 3 \text{ dB} \leq \text{Desired Net Loss} \leq 8 \text{ dB to } 10 \text{ dB} \leq \text{Loop Loss}$$

From the above equations, the *desired net loss* is not less than 2 or 3 dB and never more than 8 to 10 dB, but this will vary with the engineering policy of the company using these devices. In any case, some loss is required to improve the overall circuit return loss, which will help prevent singing (oscillation) due to impedance mismatches and subsequent reflections.* The block diagram of Fig. 6-6 shows a typical VFR, in this case a negative-impedance repeater. Some VFRs convert the two-wire loop to a four-wire circuit internally, amplify both directions of transmission independently and then convert back to two-wire.

Loop extenders are used wherever the loop has too much resistance for proper signaling. For example, a loop extender is required if a subscriber with a 1,700 Ω loop is

---

* There is also some device dependency in this requirement. Some early VFRs must be operated with a desired net loss of 4 dB to minimize stability problems.

connected to a central office with a 1,200 Ω loop signaling limit. Similarly, a loop extender would be required on a 2,400 Ω loop used with a line circuit with a signaling limit of 1,900 Ω.

Loop extenders extend the signaling range by boosting the voltage applied to the loop. The boost is generally 36 or 48 V. Since the central office power supply is nominally 48 V, a total voltage of 84 or 96 V would be available for signaling. The actual voltage applied to the loop is a nonlinear function of loop current and loop resistance. The extra voltage is applied in a balanced manner so as to not upset the overall balance of the circuit. Many loop extenders have provisions for boosting the ringing voltage, too. Figure 6-7 is a block diagram for a typical loop extender.

Most modern switching systems have special line circuits for long loops. These incorporate the equivalent of a VFR and loop extender into the central office line circuit. Alternately, external loop extenders and VFRs, combined onto a common circuit card if needed, are available from several manufacturers. A variation of the loop extender, called a *dial long line* or *long line adapter,* is used with PBX and some key systems to extend the signaling range and remove dial-pulse distortion caused by long loops. These devices are usually located at the subscriber's premises, while VFRs and loop extenders are located in the central office.

6.8 Signaling and Transmission Limits

There are some signaling limitations associated with loops used to provide regular switched services. Older switching systems may have a 1,200 or 900 Ω loop limit depending on the type of system being used. This means the loop resistance, including the terminal equipment, must not exceed these values. All modern switching systems will function properly with a 1,900 Ω loop (including the terminal equipment). However, transmission may be compromised on these longer loops without line treatment, as explained earlier.

It is important to notice the difference between the 1,300 Ω loop limit specified in the resistance design method (discussed previously) and the 1,900 Ω line circuit limit. The loop limit is based on transmission requirements and only includes the loop conductor resistance. The 1,900 Ω line circuit limit is based on signaling requirements and includes the outside plant conductor resistance, premises wiring loop resistance, as well as the terminal equipment resistance. The combination of the premises wiring and terminal equipment is usually considered to have 430 Ω resistance (30 Ω premises wiring and 400 Ω terminal equipment).

In rural areas or where the subscriber is located a long distance from the central office or DLC remote terminal, loops may exceed the line circuit transmission and signaling limits. In these cases, VFRs and loop extenders are used as discussed in the previous section.

6.9 Loop Current

A 1,900 Ω loop (including premises wiring and telephone instrument) plus a 400 Ω central office battery feed resistance (in the central office line circuit) will allow about 20 mA of loop current to flow when the central office battery is at 46 V. This is the

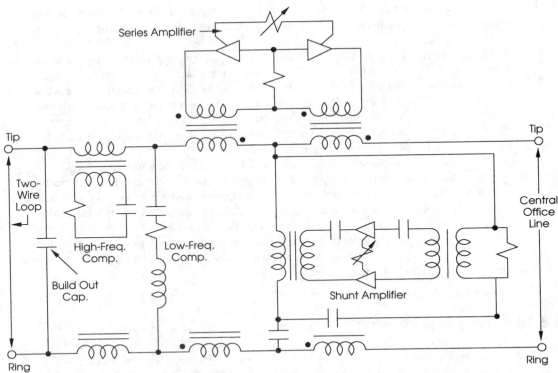

Figure 6-6 Negative impedance repeater for two-wire loop applications

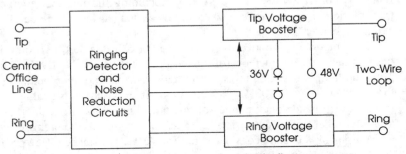

Figure 6-7 Loop extender block diagram

minimum voltage at which most central offices reliably operate, although some will operate as low as 44 V, which represents the discharged state of the battery. The system voltage is actually a nominal 52.1 V, which is based on a 24-cell lead-acid battery commonly used in telecommunication systems. Some people refer to a nominal system voltage of 48 V, which is the open circuit voltage of a fully charged 24-cell lead-acid battery. The battery is float charged at the slightly higher system voltage (52.1 V) to maintain a full charge.

The Electronic Industries Association (EIA) requires a minimum loop current of 20 mA for electronic telephone instruments designed and marketed under EIA Standard

EIA-470. Similar standards are used for regular electromechanical instruments, such as the original 500 set, but these instruments will generally work, although less efficiently, under low loop current conditions (less than 20 mA). The original 500 set required 23 mA loop current to fully meet its transmission specifications, but it would "talk" with considerably lower loop current.

6.10 Four-Wire Loops

Four-wire loops are used in many telecommunication services as discussed previously. In fact, practically every application other than regular switched subscriber service and dc control loops will use a four-wire loop. A typical four-wire circuit is shown in Fig. 6-8. Its most important feature is a separate cable pair for the transmit and receive directions. In some applications, the four-wire loop is converted to two-wire (using a hybrid) at each end to accommodate the two-wire terminal and central office equipment as discussed in Chapter 5.

The design rules for four-wire circuits depend on the application and include the desired loss, equalization and other attributes (such as conditioning) peculiar to it. Frequently, the VNL method is used, which was previously discussed. The loss values for some special service voice circuits also were previously given; a portion of the transmission circuits for these special services could be (and, many times, are) provided on four-wire transmission facilities.

With four-wire circuits, some design considerations are:

- The hybrid losses must be considered in designing loops if two-wire to four-wire conversion takes place

- Conditioning specifications must be considered if data services are involved (see Chapter 8)

- The overall loss of four-wire circuits is determined using any of the previously discussed methods while taking into account the circuit length and application

6.11 Loop Lengths

Loop lengths, and consequently their transmission characteristics, are unquestionably the biggest variables in the design of telecommunication transmission systems. Over the years, the Bell system and REA have performed loop surveys to determine what lengths characterize the telephone systems in the United States [5,11]. The results are interesting.

Systems financed by REA are predominantly rural systems, while Bell operated systems are both urban and rural. The average loop surveyed by REA has a length of about 19,300 ft (3.7 mi), and in the Bell system the average length is almost 10,800 ft (2.0 mi). For systems surveyed by REA, 90 percent of all loops were shorter than 45,000 ft (8.5 mi), and in the Bell system 90 percent of all loops were shorter than approximately 19,000 ft (3.6 mi). There is some question as to what the longest loop in history is, but loop lengths greater than 114,000 ft (21.6 mi) are in use.

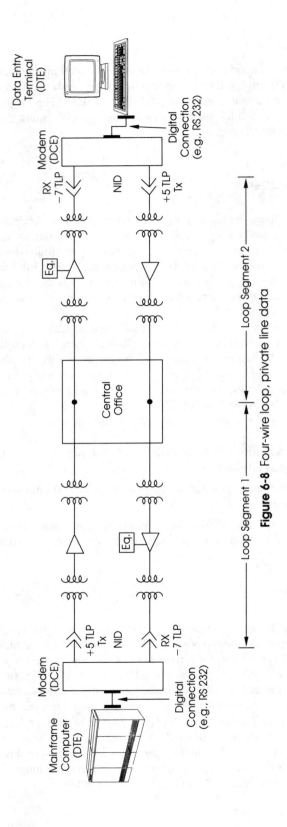

Figure 6-8 Four-wire loop, private line data

6.12 Digital Loop Carrier and Analog Pair Gain Devices

The use of digital loop carrier is required in the resistance design method discussed above. Analog carrier systems are implicit to the loss design method (as are digital loop carrier systems). These systems use completely different transmission techniques to provide service to many subscribers over only one or several cable pairs. The requirements for their use are acknowledged here, but more complete discussions are delayed until Chapter 9.

REFERENCES

[1] *Notes on Transmission Engineering*, United States Independent Telephone Association, 1971.

[2] *Engineering and Operations in the Bell System*. Murray Hill, NJ: AT&T Bell Laboratories, 1983. Available from AT&T Customer Information Center.

[3] REA TE&CM Section 424, *Design Guidelines for Telecommunications Subscriber Loop Plant*. July 1988. Available from Rural Electrification Administration.

[4] REA TE&CM Section 426, *Subscriber Loop Computation Design-by-Loss Method*. Available from REA.

[5] 1986 REA Loop Survey, *1987 REA Engineering Seminar Record*. Available from REA.

[6] *Voice Grade Entrance Facilities for Extending Customer-Provided Communication Channels*, Bell System Transmission Engineering Technical Reference, PUB 43101, May 1969. Available from BELLCORE Customer Service.

[7] *Transmission Design Considerations and Objectives, Switched Special Services and Private Branch Exchange Services*, Compatibility Bulletin No. 102. Available from AT&T Customer Information Center.

[8] *Understanding Transmission*, Vol. 8, Lee's ABC of the Telephone, 1976. Available from ABC Teletraining, Inc.

[9] REA TE&CM Section 406, *Transmission Facility Data*, August 1977. Available from REA.

[10] *Loading Systems for Voice-Frequency Telephone Cables*, Technical Bulletin 852-533, Automatic Electric Company, General System Practice 852-050-050, 1965. Available from GTE Practices Manager.

[11] "The Last Bell System Subscriber Loop Survey," *Telephony*, October 5, 1987. Available from Telephony Publishing Corp.

7

Transmission Impairments

A variety of transmission impairments must be considered when designing and using loops. The impairments that can be encountered during transmission on a loop are:

- Loss
- Circuit noise
- Impulse noise
- Distortion
- Interference

This is not an exhaustive list of transmission impairments that may be encountered on any given telecommunication channel. Rather, it is a list of those impairments that may be attributed to the loop itself. The effects of each are illustrated in Fig. 7-1. The transmission loss on loops has already been discussed in Chapter 5. Perhaps the next most important transmission impairment is *noise*.

7.1 Noise

Noise is any interfering signal on the telecommunication channel. There must be a noise source, a coupling mechanism and a receptor. The relationship among the three is illustrated in Fig. 7-2. Noise sources are either man-made or natural. Practically any piece of electrical or electronic equipment can be a man-made noise source, and power lines are perhaps the most pervasive of all these. Natural noise comes from lightning and other

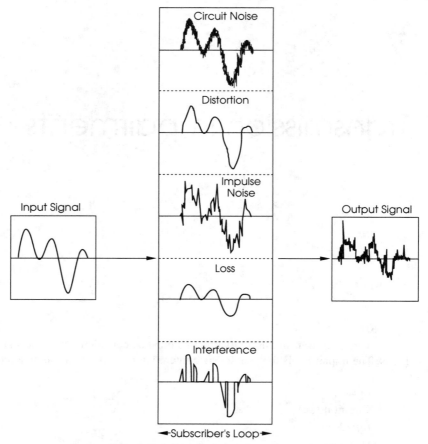

Figure 7-1 Transmission impairments

atmospherics, random thermal motion of electrons and galactic sources, as well as electrostatic discharges.*

Noise is coupled by radiation, induction and conduction. The predominant coupling mode in subscriber loops is by induction from nearby power lines. The other coupling modes exist to some extent, too, depending on the situation. For example, noise can be conducted into the loop through insulation faults or poor or faulty grounding methods.

The loop itself can be a noise receptor and, as will be discussed later, there are limits on the amounts of noise allowable on it. The terminal equipment connected to a loop and the network are also noise receptors. The coupling mechanisms can be very complex. Indeed, the termination equipment at each end of the loop is subject to conducted noise from the loop itself. The reverse is also true. Therefore, it is important to specify maximum acceptable noise levels and define how noise affects telecommunication

---

* Perhaps the most intriguing natural noise is the "whistler," which is thought to be caused by the interaction of lightning currents and the earth's magnetic field; resonances cause frequency selection, and these are induced into long distance transmission systems. The whistler is not usually heard on short-haul circuits.

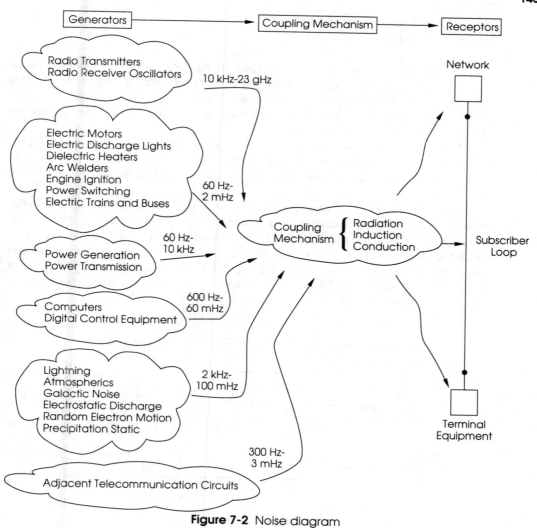

Figure 7-2 Noise diagram

systems*. On subscriber loops, noise can be categorized into four types: *crosstalk, circuit noise, power influence* and *impulse noise*, each of which is discussed in the following sections.

7.2 Crosstalk

Crosstalk was briefly discussed in Chapter 4. It is any extraneous signal on a circuit caused by signals on adjacent circuits. Crosstalk falls into two categories:

---

* The general subject of noise, its effect on systems, and its reduction falls under the subject of electromagnetic compatibility. This is covered quite well in [1].

1. Unintelligible crosstalk ("babble")

2. Intelligible crosstalk

The latter is most disturbing to listeners because it removes any impression of privacy. It can be caused by a single disturbing channel with enough coupling to spill into adjacent circuits. Unintelligible crosstalk is usually caused by a large number of disturbing channels, none of which is of sufficient magnitude to be understood, or extraneous modulation products in carrier systems.

Crosstalk can be further categorized as near-end and far-end. As these names imply, near-end crosstalk is caused by crosstalk interference at the near end of a circuit with respect to the listener; far-end crosstalk is crosstalk interference at the far end as shown in Fig. 7-3.

Crosstalk of any kind is caused by insufficient shielding, excessively large disparity between signal levels in adjacent circuits, unbalanced lines or overloaded carrier systems. Crosstalk is a statistical quantity because the number of sources and coupling paths is usually too large to quantify. Crosstalk caused by the loop at voice frequencies is rare except in extreme cases of poor maintenance or facility damage which manifests itself in the form of line unbalance. If it exists at all, crosstalk is inseparable from other noise, so it will not be considered further as a separate problem.

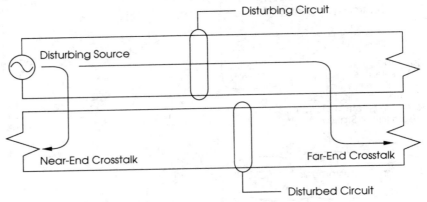

Figure 7-3 Crosstalk

7.3 Circuit Noise and Power Influence

The noise that appears across the two conductors (tip and ring) of a loop, and is heard by the subscriber, is called *circuit noise* (also called *message circuit noise, noise metallic* or *differential noise*). The noise can be due to random thermal motion of electrons (known as *white noise* or *Gaussian noise*) or static from lightning storms, but on subscriber loops its most likely source is interference from power line induction. For the purposes of this section, then, "circuit noise" and "interference" are assumed to be the same. Noise from wet cable and faulty mechanical splices in cable pairs is discussed later.

The total noise power on a loop is related to the noise bandwidth. Since particular frequencies affect the various services (for example, voice, data and radio studio material) differently, weighting curves have been designed to restrict the frequency response of the noise measuring sets with which objective tests are made. This frequency response restriction is called *weighting*.

Noise, in voice applications, is described in terms of decibels (dB) above a noise reference when measured with a noise meter containing a special weighting filter. There are four common filters that are used to provide the necessary weighting:

- C-message
- 3 kHz flat
- Program
- 15 kHz flat

The most common filter is called a C-message filter and measurements are based on dBrnC (decibels with respect to reference noise, C-message weighted). The noise reference is 1 picowatt (pW)(–90 dBm); therefore, a properly calibrated meter will read 0 dBrnC when measuring a 1,000 Hz tone having a power of –90 dBm.

C-message weighting is primarily used to measure noise that affects voice transmission when common telephone instruments are used, but it also is used to evaluate the effects of noise on data circuits. It weights the various frequencies according to their perceived annoyance such that frequencies below 600 or 700 Hz and above 3,000 Hz have less importance.

The "3 kHz flat" weighting curve is used on voice circuits, too, but all frequencies within the 3,000 Hz bandwidth carry equal importance. This filter rolls off above 3,000 Hz and approximates the response of common modems. It generally is used to investigate problems caused by power induction at the lower power harmonic frequencies or by higher interfering frequencies. Frequencies in these ranges can affect data transmission as well as voice frequency signaling equipment.

The "Program" weighting curve is used with voice circuits that require bandwidth in the order of 8 kHz or more (such as in the distribution of radio or television program audio material). This curve emphasizes frequencies between 1 and 8 kHz. The "15 kHz flat" weighting curve is also used on these types of circuits, but it actually carries little weighting (it is essentially "flat" from 20 Hz to 15 kHz).

A comparison of the various weighting curves is shown in Fig. 7-4.* Noise measurements on any particular loop with the 3 kHz, program or 15 kHz filters will generally be higher than with the C-message filter (because of the higher bandwidth and less overall weighting). For example, if 3 kHz white noise with a total power of 0 dBm is applied to a circuit and then measured with an instrument containing a C-message filter, the meter will read 88.0 dBrnC (–2.0 dBm). With a 3 kHz filter, the meter will read 88.8 dBrn (–1.2 dBm), and with a 15 kHz filter, the meter will read 90.0 dBrn (0.0 dBm). All meters will read 90.0 dBrn with a 1,000 Hz, 0 dBm tone.

The maximum acceptable circuit noise on subscriber loops is 20 dBrnC, or 20 dB above the reference noise level. At a –6 TLP (for example, at the receiving end of a loop with 6 dB loss), this noise level would be measured as 26 dBrnC0. As discussed in Chapter 5, the average signal level on voice circuits is around –27 dBm0. Therefore, the signal-to-noise ratio (SNR) would be 37 dB for the average call in this case.† If a different weighting curve was used, say 3kHz flat, the measured noise level could be higher,

---

* These curves were developed from various sources, one of which was [3]. The exact specifications for the C-message filter can be found in [2].

† This is found as follows: Convert the noise level to dBm by subtracting 90 dB and then subtract the new value from the signal level, or –27 dBm0 – (26 dBrnC0 – 90 dB) = 37 dB.

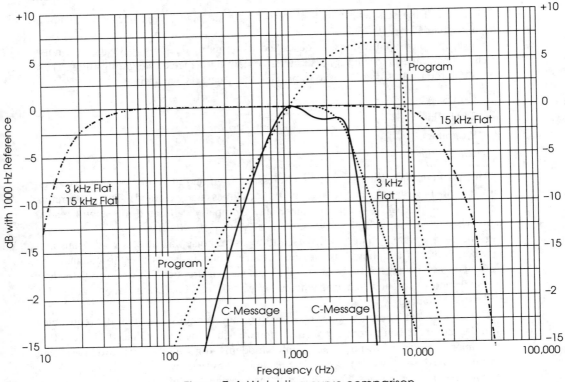

Figure 7-4 Weighting curve comparison

which would give a lower SNR. Therefore, if SNR measurements are used for evaluating a loop, they must be referred to a particular noise bandwidth. A 30 dB SNR is entirely acceptable on voice circuits from a subscriber standpoint.

On long rural loops, an additional 6 dB of noise is generally allowed, due to practical reasons, giving a new maximum of 26 dBrnC in this case. If this is measured at a –6 TLP, the noise level would be 32 dBrnC0. If the average signal level was –35 dBm0 on a particular call, the SNR would be 23 dB, which may not be acceptable on a voice call.

In practice, the average loop will measure around 10 or 11 dBrnC. The lower the circuit noise, in dBrnC, the better. The requirements for noise measurements using 3 kHz flat weighting have been established at less than 40 dBrn 3 kHz flat. The requirements for wideband (program and 15 kHz flat) voice circuits are not as well established. Measurements on any given loop with a 3 kHz or wideband filter will give higher readings than with a C-message filter because of the wider noise bandwidth.

It should be noted that the foregoing noise limits on subscriber loops apply only to the loop when measured by itself. Circuit noise on long-haul circuits that include one or more loops as well as other transmission equipment will be somewhat higher. This is entirely acceptable out of practical necessity. The allowable noise levels are related to circuit length; the longer the circuit, the higher the allowable noise level.*

In addition to circuit noise, noise from tip and ring to ground, called *power influence* (PI), is an important parameter. Power influence is similar to *noise-to-ground* (Ng), which is also called *longitudinal* or *common-mode noise*, and related by the following expression:

* For examples, see [4,5].

Power Influence, $PI = Ng + 40$ dB

It is important to know if PI or Ng is being measured by the transmission or noise test set during troubleshooting. All modern sets built for the telecommunication industry are calibrated to read PI directly, but a number of older sets are not calibrated this way. Power influence is almost always caused by inductive interference from power lines.

Normally, the longitudinal currents, which are induced into the loop by nearby power lines, cannot be heard by the subscriber because these currents are of equal magnitude and flowing in the same direction on both conductors. This gives a zero differential noise voltage (the shield and earth act as return conductors). If the loop becomes unbalanced, however, these longitudinal currents become unbalanced, which causes a differential noise current and, consequently, a differential noise voltage to develop. The differential noise voltage, or circuit noise, is heard as hum or other interfering signal.

Figure 7-5 illustrates the difference between longitudinal and differential currents on the loop. The maximum acceptable power influence level is 80 dBrnC. The lower the power influence, in dBrnC, the better. When C-message power influence readings exceed 80 dBrnC, additional measurements should be made with the 3 kHz flat filter to determine if the measurement point is safe.

A measured value exceeding 126 dBrn 3 kHz flat usually means the lower power line harmonic frequencies exceed 50 V, which is considered unsafe. Measurements made with the 3 kHz flat filter will always exceed C-message readings, by as much as 44 dB, due to the higher response of the 3 kHz flat filter at the lower end and the distribution of power frequency harmonics at that end of the spectrum [6].

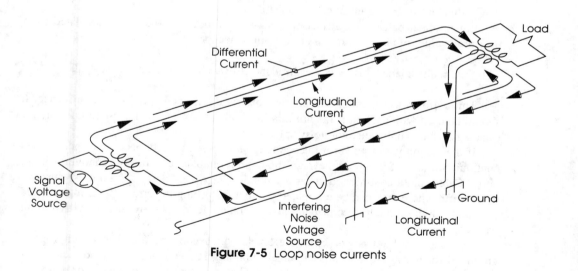

Figure 7-5 Loop noise currents

7.4 Balance

Sufficient line balance must be maintained for two reasons:

- To limit the magnitude of power line harmonics or other longitudinal currents that are converted to circuit noise in terminal equipment

- To limit unbalanced longitudinal currents in cable pairs that may cause crosstalk in adjacent circuits

The first reason is especially important to regular telephone instruments, which are designed to have low response at the fundamental power line frequency, 60 Hz, but will respond quite well at power frequency harmonics, especially those above 300 Hz. The second reason is important from an overall quality of service standpoint in that a single noisy circuit could upset a large number of adjacent circuits.*

The balance of the loop itself (also called *longitudinal-to-metallic balance* or just *longitudinal balance*) is specified as 60 dB minimum. The higher the balance, in dB, the better. Minimum terminal equipment balance (in this case called *metallic-to-longitudinal balance*) is specified in FCC Part 68 as shown in Fig. 7-6 [7]. Metallic-to-longitudinal balance measures the conversion of metallic currents in the terminal equipment to longitudinal currents that could be injected into the loop and disturb adjacent circuits.

Also shown in this figure are the longitudinal-to-metallic balance requirements specified by the EIA for various types of terminal equipment [8–10]. In this case, the concern is for the ever-present longitudinal currents on the loop being injected into the terminal equipment and converted into metallic noise. The requirements for the typical central office line circuits are slightly different, as shown in Fig. 7-7.

The relationship among power influence, circuit noise and circuit balance is important for loop testing. Longitudinal currents (and longitudinal noise) always exists on all loops, to some extent. And there is always some degree of line unbalance, either from the cable manufacturing process or unbalanced devices connected to the loop, such as is the case with divided ringing. Almost all circuit noise is caused by the conversion of longitudinal noise as a result of circuit unbalance.

Longitudinal balance usually is not measured directly. Rather, it is calculated from measured values of circuit noise and power influence, or

Circuit Balance (dB) = Power Influence (dBrnC) – Circuit Noise (dBrnC)

This formula assumes that all circuit noise is due to converted power influence. It should be used with caution if the noise is from other sources, such as radio interference (that is not due to unbalance) or noisy splices.

If the magnitude of power influence is great enough, usually because of poor shield continuity or lack of grounding, even a small circuit unbalance will give annoying circuit noise. Cable shield continuity and earth grounding provide a path to drain noise currents to the earth where they can be dissipated without disturbing the circuit. Therefore, shield continuity and grounding contribute just as much to proper transmission as circuit balance.

A cable with high power influence levels will usually be found to be improperly grounded (or not at all) and missing shield bonding straps. Once that is corrected, any residual circuit noise is almost always due to unbalance (a poor splice on one or both conductors of the pair, a resistance short from tip or ring to ground, or unbalanced equipment connected to the loop).

---

* This discussion has no relationship to hybrid balance described in Chapter 5.

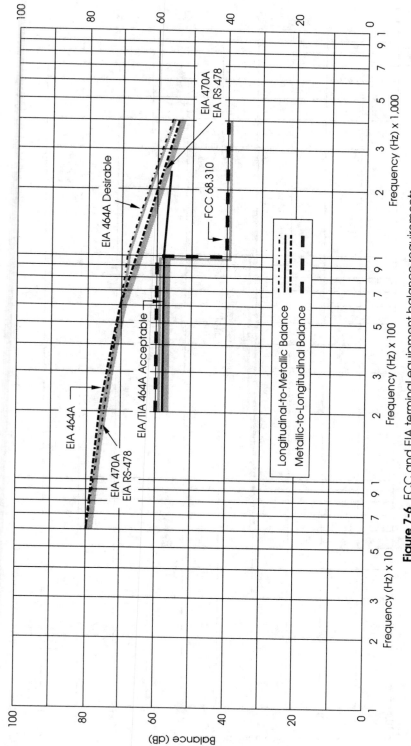

Figure 7-6 FCC and EIA terminal equipment balance requirements

151

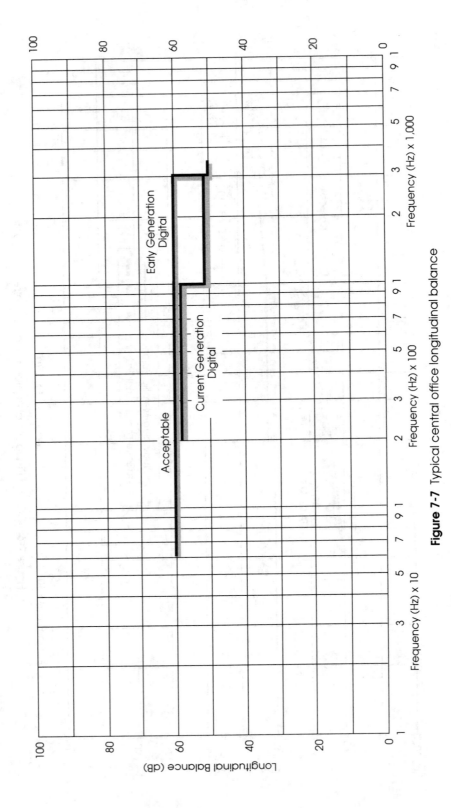

Figure 7-7 Typical central office longitudinal balance

7.5 Summary of Loop Transmission Objectives

Table 7-1 summarizes the loop transmission objectives used throughout the telephone industry as they relate to the previous discussions.

Table 7-1 Loop Transmission Objectives

Transmission Quality	Circuit Noise dBrnC	Circuit Noise dBrn3 kHz	Power Influence dBrnC	Circuit Balance dB	Circuit Loss dB
Acceptable	≤20	≤40	≤80	≥60	≤8
Marginal	20-30	40-60	80-90	50-60	8-10
Unacceptable	>30	>60	>90	<50	>10

Referring to Table 7-1, measurements in the "acceptable" range mean the loop requires no additional attention after the measurements are made. "Marginal" means the loop requires some attention within a reasonable time period according to the administrative policies of the company that owns the facility. "Unacceptable" means the loop requires immediate attention.

These objectives may be approached from a statistical standpoint as discussed in Chapter 5. For example, a company may decide that at least 98 percent of all loops have characteristics considered acceptable, no more than 2 percent considered marginal and 0 percent considered unacceptable at any given time. The plant is designed, built and maintained accordingly.

See the references for standards related to measuring transmission characteristics and loop performance criteria [2,11,12].

7.6 Impulse Noise

Data circuits are particularly sensitive to impulse noise. Impulse noise, heard as clicks, is usually defined as a voltage increase of 12 dB or more above the background (rms) noise lasting 10 ms or less. Its main source is from switching transients in electromechanical switching systems, maintenance activity on an adjacent circuit or electrical system switching transients. It is less of a problem with properly grounded electronic switching systems.

Impulse noise objectives vary with the type and makeup of the circuit. Usually, a threshold is established and counts are made of any impulse noise that exceeds that threshold in a given time period. When impulse noise tests are made on a single circuit, the usual specification is 15 counts in 15 min. When a group of circuits is being tested, shorter time intervals are used.

On subscriber loops, the background noise threshold is 59 dBrnC when measured at the central office [4]. On long-haul circuits, the threshold can vary from 54 to 71 dBrnC0. The latter figure (71 dBrnC0) implies a 6 dB signal-to-impulse noise ratio with a −13 dBm0 signal.

The impulse noise objectives for subscriber-to-subscriber switched connections are no more than 15 impulse noise counts in 15 min on 80 percent of all connections at a threshold 5 dB below the received signal level [13]. The received signal level is established by sending a 1,004 Hz tone through the connection. This will give the transmission level point to which the noise measurements are referenced.

7.7 Impedance Distortion and Return Loss

In addition to noise and circuit loss on loops, other impairments, such as impedance distortion, attenuation distortion and envelope delay distortion, warrant consideration, too. *Impedance distortion* is the variation of loop impedance with frequency. Ideally, impedance should be constant throughout the voiceband. As previously seen in Chapter 5, however, impedance varies with frequency, cable pair gauge and type of loading, if any.

From a power transfer standpoint, it is important that terminal equipment match the loop impedance with a complex conjugate impedance. This ensures maximum power transfer across the loop but, as discussed in Chapter 5, this is not always possible. A compromise match is used, which trades off power transfer, return loss and practicability. For an analysis of the maximum power transfer (conjugate match) and image match situations as they relate to return loss, see [14].

Return, echo and *signal reflection* are synonymous in the immediate context. Any echo in a circuit becomes objectionable if the echo is sufficiently delayed and of sufficient magnitude. Echo at some frequencies is perceived to be more annoying than others. To the talker, echo can cause complete loss of concentration and can make conversation very difficult. Listener echo is distracting and also can completely disrupt a conversation. Listener and talker echo are discussed later.

On circuits with considerable delay, as is the case on satellite circuits or most long-haul circuits, the complete elimination of echo gives the impression of less delay than really exists. Echo cancelers and echo suppressors are used in long haul voice applications. Additional information on echo cancelers and echo suppressors can be found in [6,15].

It should be noted that echo is seldom a problem when loops are considered by themselves because they are relatively short and have very small delays. Nevertheless, it is important that the loop does not contribute to echo problems and, therefore, a discussion of return loss is in order.

Return loss is a measure of the signal reflected back to the source at any impedance mismatch. Stated another way, it is the magnitude of the circuit reflection coefficient expressed in decibels. The higher the return loss, the better the impedance match and the lower the reflected signal. Mathematically, reflection coefficient is

$$\text{Reflection Coefficient, } R = \frac{(Z_L - Z_S)}{(Z_L + Z_S)}$$

where

$$Z_L = \text{load impedance}$$

$$Z_S = \text{source impedance}$$

From this, return loss is defined as

$$\text{Return Loss, } RL = -20 \log |R| \text{ dB}$$

where

$$R = \text{as defined above}$$

The source and load can be defined at any point in the circuit, but in loop transmission problems, it is only necessary to consider points where serious mismatches can occur. These are at junctions of loop segments that use different loading schemes and at loop termination points*. Of these, the most serious is at termination points with two-wire to four-wire conversion.

The most prevalent four-wire to two-wire conversion point is at digital central office line circuits or, in two-wire analog central offices, at four-wire trunk interfaces. At the input to a loop, the central office can be considered as the source (with source impedance Z_S) driving the loop plus the terminal equipment (the terminal equipment having load impedance Z_T) as shown in Fig. 7-8.

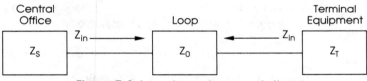

Figure 7-8 Loop impedance notation

The impedance of a loop not terminated in its characteristic impedance was given in Chapter 5 as

$$Z_{in} = Z_0 \frac{Z_T + Z_0 \tanh (\rho l)}{Z_0 + Z_T \tanh (\rho l)}$$

where

$Z_{in}=$ input impedance of the loop terminated in impedance Z_T

$Z_0=$ loop characteristic impedance

$\rho=$ loop propagation constant per unit length

$l =$ loop length

The above impedance is looking toward the terminal equipment from the central office. If the impedance looking into the loop from the terminal equipment end (toward the central office) is needed, it can be found from

---

* Points in a loop where the cable gauge changes (say from 26 gauge to 24 gauge) also cause reflections, but these are considered negligible.

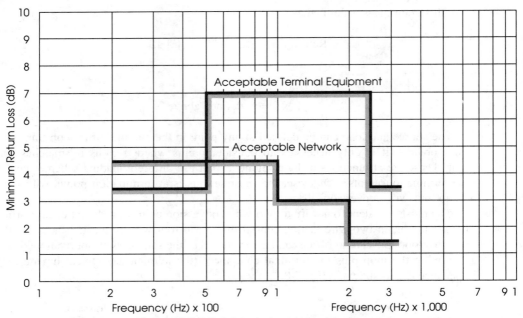

Figure 7-9 Minimum return loss objectives

$$Z_{in} = Z_0 \frac{Z_S + Z_0 \tanh(\rho l)}{Z_0 + Z_S \tanh(\rho l)}$$

where

Z_{in} = input impedance of the loop terminated in the central office impedance Z_S

Z_0, ρ, and l = as defined above

The return loss for any loop with any termination impedance can be obtained by substituting the input impedance from these equations for Z_L in the reflection coefficient equation.

Return loss is frequently measured or calculated with respect to some standard impedance. Two situations exist for this calculation. One considers the return loss at the central office line circuit looking toward the loop. In this case, the terminating impedance at the end of the loop, Z_T, is that of the terminal equipment. The other considers the return loss at the terminal equipment, again looking toward the loop. Here, the terminating impedance, Z_S, is that of the central office line circuit.

The minimum objective return loss for the terminal equipment itself, relative to the standard compromise impedance of 600 Ω, is shown in Fig. 7-9. Also shown in this figure is the objective return loss, relative to the same impedance, for the loop when looking back toward the central office from the terminal equipment end of the loop [16]. Again, the former objective is for terminal equipment, while the latter requirement applies to the loop terminated in a central office line circuit.

As previously noted, a circuit with high return loss causes little reflection of a signal. The impedance discontinuities (reflection points) on such a circuit are small. Signals, such as voice signals, reflected back and forth on a circuit, if not attenuated (that is, subjected to a high return loss), can cause annoying echo to both the talker and listener, as previously noted.

Echo back to the talker on circuits with little round trip delay is not distinguishable from sidetone and is not annoying unless it is excessive. High-level echo on circuits with considerable delay, however, such as on long terrestrial circuits or any satellite circuit, makes conversation difficult for both parties.

Echo can be classified as *talker echo, listener echo* or *singing,* as illustrated in Fig. 7-10. Singing, or oscillation, only occurs when the overall gain of the round-trip circuit is greater than one at the singing frequency, which is generally between 800 and 2,400 Hz. Proper design of four-wire circuits with two-wire conversion (or any two-way circuit with gain) requires that this condition be carefully avoided.

Referring to Fig. 7-11, the loss from a two-wire port at one end to a two-wire port at the other end is the sum of the splitting and insertion losses in the hybrid at each end less the circuit gain in the transmit or receive circuit (it does not matter which because they both are the same in almost all cases), or

$$\text{Two-Wire Loss} = 3.5 - \text{Circuit Gain} + 3.5 \text{ dB}$$

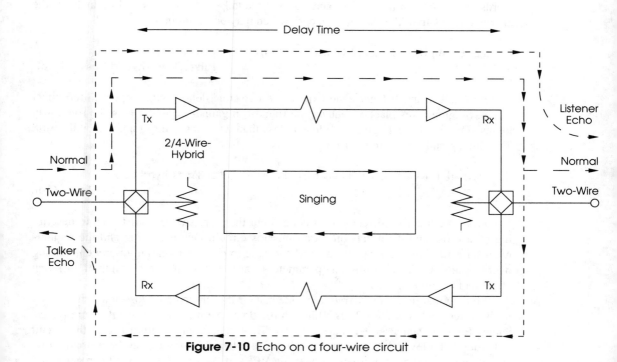

Figure 7-10 Echo on a four-wire circuit

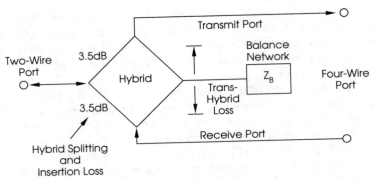

Figure 7-11 Echo Losses

Talker echo is the signal reflected from the mismatch at the listener's hybrid and heard by the talker. Talker echo loss takes into account the trans-hybrid loss at the far end (which may be different from the near end) and the gains of the circuit in each direction, which are the same, or

$$\text{Talker Echo Loss} = 3.5 - 2 \times \text{Circuit Gain} + \text{Trans-hybrid Loss} + 3.5 \text{ dB}$$

Listener echo takes place when the signal traverses the hybrid at each end (in other words, is reflected at the listener and again at the talker). Listener echo loss includes the effects of trans-hybrid losses at each end, which may be different, or

$$\text{Listener Echo Loss} = \text{Listener Trans-hybrid Loss} - 2 \times \text{Circuit Gain}$$
$$+ \text{Talker Trans-hybrid Loss} + 3.5 \text{ dB}$$

Both talker and listener echo experience two time delays with respect to the direct signal. Singing takes place whenever the round-trip gains are greater than the round-trip losses. That is, if the singing path loss is less than zero, instability (singing) will result. The singing path loss is found from

$$\text{Singing Path Loss} = \text{Listener Trans-hybrid Loss} + \text{Talker Trans-hybrid Loss}$$
$$- 2 \times \text{Circuit Gain}$$

From the previous discussion, it is apparent there are several terms used in describing return loss and its effects on a transmission circuit. One is *singing* and the requirement for a *singing margin*. That is, it is desirable to provide a margin to prevent singing over circuits as the transmission parameters vary seasonally, as a result of different alignment methods, or drift.

Singing margin is considered to be adequate if the singing path loss at any frequency in the voiceband is at least 2 dB, although the objective minimum is 4 dB. More typical values found in actual systems are 8 to 10 dB. When singing margin is low the circuit will sound "hollow" or "like you are talking in a barrel." Singing can be a problem on any circuit, including subscriber loops using VFRs, if the sum of the round-trip gains and losses provides a net gain.

Singing return loss (SRL) is a measure frequently encountered in transmission systems. It is a frequency-weighted power measurement usually specified at lower (260 to 500 Hz, called SRL LO) and upper (2,200 to 3,400 Hz, called SRL HI) frequency bands and is not considered except in circuits with a two-wire to four-wire conversion.

Another measurement of interest is *echo return loss* (ERL). This is a frequency-weighted power measurement of the reflected or echo signal in the 560 to 1,965 Hz band [17]. The weighting takes into account the relative annoyance to the user of the various echo frequencies, specifically, the band of frequencies between 600 and 2,000 Hz.

Usually, 6 to 8 dB of echo return loss is required at any potential reflection point. Well designed terminal equipment provides 12 to 14 dB or more under most conditions. In tests of a large number of calls in several central offices, the echo return loss at the central office line circuit was found to be around 11 dB with a 2.5 to 4.5 dB standard deviation [18]. As with singing return loss, ERL is not considered except in circuits with two-wire to four-wire conversion.

The loop designer, builder and user will have a certain amount of control over the contribution the loop has to inadequate return loss. By following accepted loop design rules and using established construction practices, the loop can be made to have a known characteristic impedance and relatively small impedance discontinuities. Specifications can then be written for terminal equipment to provide return loss within acceptable limits. In turn, the terminal equipment can be designed to provide a standard impedance match, which was discussed in Chapter 5. If two-wire to four-wire conversion is needed, the balance impedance in the hybrid can be adjusted to match the loop.

7.8 Attenuation Distortion

Attenuation distortion is the change in circuit loss with frequency. It is also known as *frequency response*. Ideally, attenuation should be constant throughout the frequency band of interest. Unfortunately, it is not as seen from the frequency response curves in Chapter 5 for various nonloaded loop types. Unless it is excessive, attenuation distortion is not noticeable to the human ear. Attenuation distortion manifests itself on voice calls by changing the sound of the talker's voice as it is heard by the listener. The change may be dramatic enough to render the voice unrecognizable. On a data circuit, attenuation distortion can manifest itself in the form of errors through loss of signal energy at critical frequencies.

The inherent attenuation distortion in subscriber loops used in regular switched service is not objectionable except in extreme cases. On voice transmissions, excessive low-frequency slope degrades voice quality, while excessive high-frequency slope degrades intelligibility. On data transmissions using *phase shift keying* (PSK) methods, both low- and high-frequency slope affects performance, while only high-frequency slope affects *frequency shift keying* (FSK) [17]. Some slope is considered necessary for stability.

Attenuation distortion is frequently specified in terms of the "Three Tone Slope" as discussed in Chapter 5. The slope objectives for loops used in special switched services (for example, PBX trunks and foreign exchange lines) are similar to regular switched loop objectives. It is not an extremely critical parameter on subscriber loops. Typically, the losses at 400 and 2,800 Hz, with respect to 1,000 Hz, should be as listed in Table 7-2.

Line conditioning (explained later) is used to compensate for the loop's inherent attenuation distortion.

Table 7-2 Attenuation Distortion Limits^a

Frequency	Limit
400 Hz 2,800 Hz	−1 dB < 1,000 Hz Loss < 3.0 to 5.0 dB −1 dB < 1,000 Hz Loss < 4.5 to 7.5 dB

^a This information is from (5). Slightly different limits are used in (14). There is little practical difference.

7.9 Envelope Delay Distortion

Envelope delay distortion (EDD, also called group delay distortion) is distortion in the rate of change of phase shift with frequency of a signal. Ideally, the rate of change should be constant with frequency, and it is approximately so in the voiceband with non-loaded cables. With loaded cables this is not the case, especially near the cutoff frequency.

Envelope delay distortion is defined as the difference, in time units such as microseconds, between the maximum and minimum envelope delay within the frequency band of interest. If the difference is zero then, by this definition, there is no EDD, but this is hardly ever the case in practical systems.

Voiceband signals (not just voice signals but all signals in the voiceband, including data signals) are made up of many frequencies. Each particular frequency propagates at a different velocity (called *phase velocity*) due to the facility's inherent transmission characteristics. This causes phase delay. If the relationship between the resulting phase shift and frequency is nonlinear, the facility will cause delay distortion.

This can be visualized by considering the signal output from a typical data modem as shown in Fig. 7-12(a). In this figure, the variable in each sampling interval is represented by a bipolar or zero voltage. The actual variable could be phase or voltage or both. The spectrum of this signal contains many frequency components, the amplitude and frequency/phase relationships of which actually carry the information being transmitted.

If the transmitted signals of Fig. 7-12(a) were observed on an oscilloscope with the time base adjusted to show two intervals, then each successive interval of the signal stream would be superimposed on each other. This is called an *eye pattern*, which is shown in Fig. 7-12(b). The clean transitions of the transmitted signal give a wide eye pattern, as would be expected for an undistorted signal.

Due to the delay characteristics of the cable (or any transmission medium for that matter), the individual components of the signal become dispersed. If the dispersion is excessive, the result will be *intersymbol interference* where the signal energy in a given keying interval is overlapped by signal energy from other keying intervals, thereby degrading it. This is illustrated in Fig. 7-12(c). The recovered data will show jitter in the transitions. If the jitter is too great, the far-end modem will not be able to properly demodulate the signal, which will result in errors. The eye pattern for the degraded received signal is shown in Fig. 7-12(d). The eye is significantly closed, which indicates distortion (although, in this case, probably acceptable).

Envelope delay distortion is the principal cause of intersymbol interference (and consequently errors) on high-speed data circuits. The human ear is not sensitive to it unless it is quite pronounced, in which case the conversation may be unintelligible. Excessive

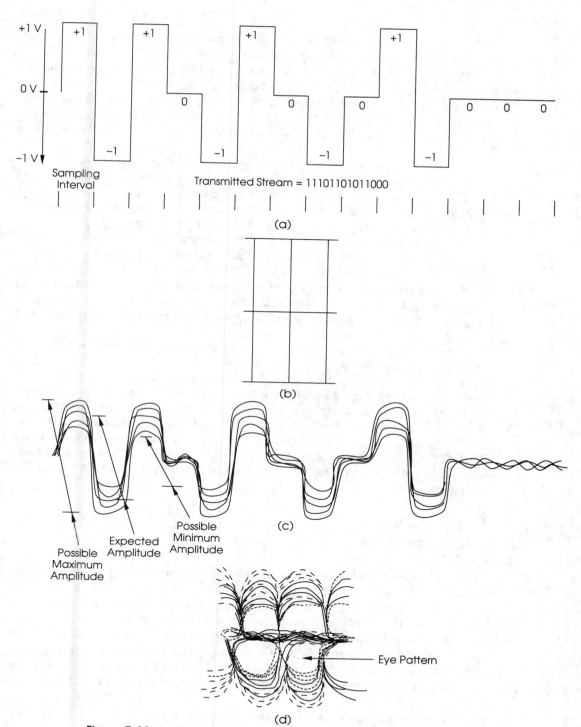

Figure 7-12 (a) transmitted waveform; (b) transmitted waveform as viewed on an oscilloscope with time base set to 2 sampling intervals; (c) received waveform; (d) received waveform as viewed on an oscilloscope with time base set to two sampling intervals

EDD at the upper edge of the voiceband can cause "ringing" in the conversation. Excessive EDD at the lower edge can cause "speech blurring" [17].

Not all EDD results from the loop; in fact, very little does. EDD results from any part of the circuit where a nonlinear relationship exists between phase shift and frequency. Usually this occurs at the terminal and intermediate equipment. Some data transmission modulation techniques are more susceptible to intersymbol interference than others, which can explain why some modems of a given speed give better performance than others.*

Propagation velocity is the reciprocal of *phase delay*. In nonloaded cables, the propagation velocity of the signal components increases approximately monotonically with frequency, which gives a relatively constant phase change as discussed above. In loaded cables, the velocity is relatively constant except as the cutoff frequency is approached, where it drops quite rapidly; it then increases beyond the cutoff frequency.

Here are some examples: With 24 gauge, nonloaded cable at 1,000 Hz, the phase velocity is about 22,000 miles per second (mi/s), increasing approximately linearly to 40,200 mi/s at 3,400 Hz, and 44,000 mi/s at 4,000 Hz. With 24 gauge, H88 loaded cable at 1,000 Hz, the velocity is about 10,300 mi/s, dropping to 7,100 mi/s at 3,400 Hz, and then increasing to 8,100 mi/s at 4,000 Hz.† Since phase shift (delay) and velocity are related, it is easy to see that phase shift in the region around cutoff is far from linear (that is, distorted) for the loaded cable.

Figure 7-13 shows the envelope delay (per mile) for nonloaded loops, and Fig. 7-14 shows the envelope delay for loaded loops.

For most analog applications, and within reasonable limits, the absolute delay of a signal is not considered a transmission problem. Therefore, in many envelope delay distortion specifications, the delay is referenced (normalized) to some midband frequency, usually 1,700 or 1,800 Hz. For a 24 gauge nonloaded loop, the maximum EDD is 8.9 µs/mi for the 1,000 to 3,400 Hz frequency band. For a 24 gauge, H88 loaded loop, the EDD is 220 µs/mi in the same band. If the frequency band of interest is narrowed to cover just 1,000 to 2,600 Hz with 1,700 Hz reference, the EDD for the two loops is 2.8 and 32.5 µs/mi, respectively.

7.10 Data Transmission

Using a conventional modem (binary modulation scheme such that 1 baud = 1 bit per second (bps) without software-controlled error correction and no special coding), the highest expected speed on a short, unconditioned, unswitched local loop is about 9,600 bps. The modem in this case will require and use more bandwidth than 3,100 Hz.

If the modem circuit is switched in the local area, it may be possible to achieve 2,400 or 4,800 bps without software-controlled error correction or special coding, although reliable operation at the higher speed is unlikely. The limitation is generally in the switching equipment, and a multilevel modulation scheme will normally be necessary (where 1

---

* There are many factors that differentiate modems from each other. Sensitivity to intersymbol interference is only one of them.

† These figures apply to a cable with the particular primary constants described in Chapter 5. There can be significant variations between the phase velocities of similar cables. This does not cause problems to the loop designer or user, however, because phase velocity usually is not a parameter that directly enters the loop design process.

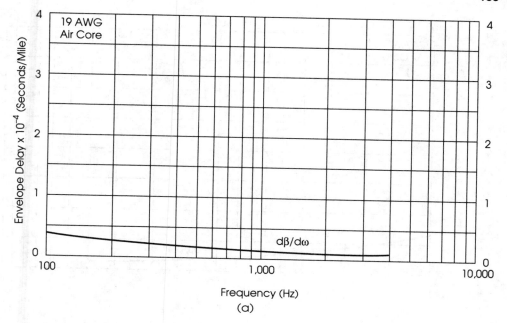

(a)

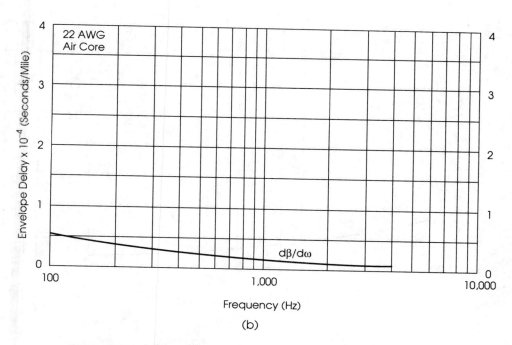

(b)

Figure 7-13 Nonloaded cable pair envelope delay: (a) PIC, 55°F, 19 AWG air; (b) PIC, 55°F, 22 AWG air; (c) PIC, 55°F, 24 AWG air; (d) PIC, 55°F, 26 AWG air; (e) PIC, 55°F, 19 AWG filled; (f) 55°F, 22 AWG filled; (g) PIC, 55°F, 24 AWG filled; (h) PIC, 55°F, 26 AWG filled.

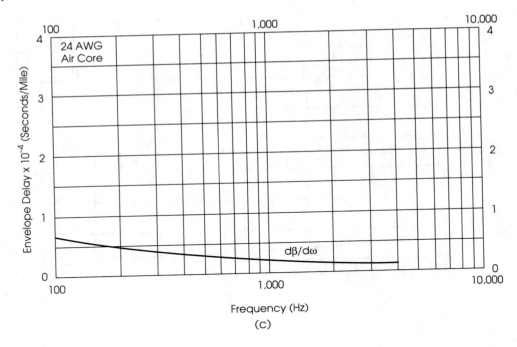

(c)

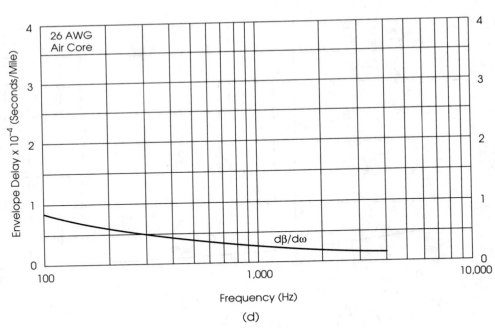

(d)

Figure 7-13 (continued)

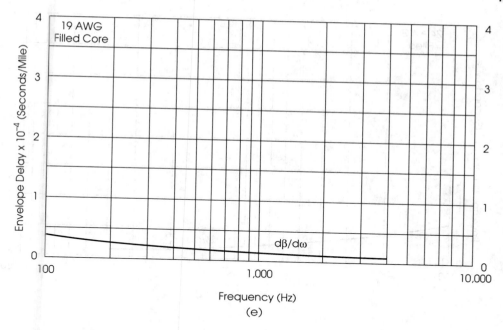

Frequency (Hz)

(e)

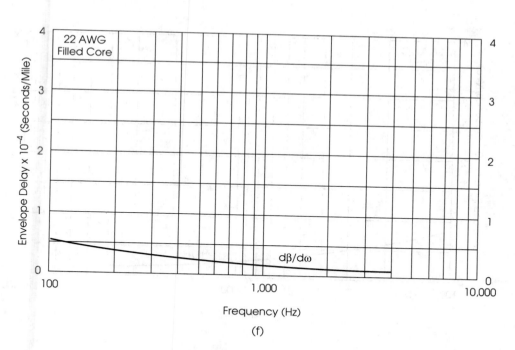

Frequency (Hz)

(f)

Figure 7-13 (continued)

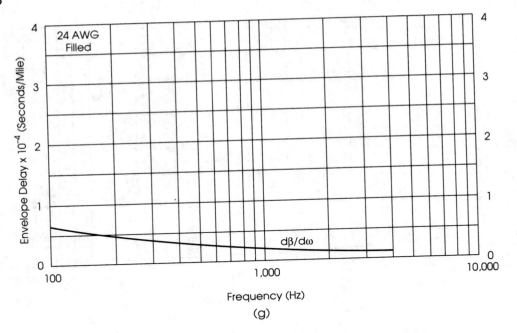

(g)

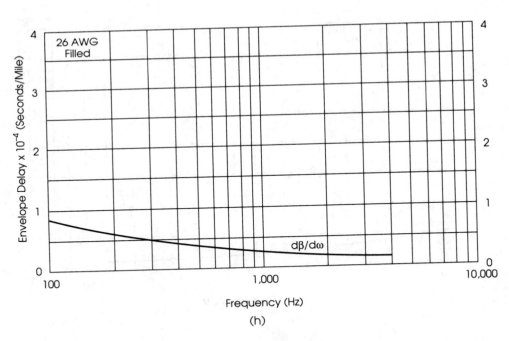

(h)

Figure 7-13 (continued)

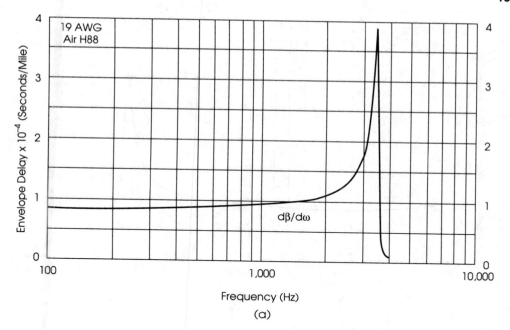

(a)

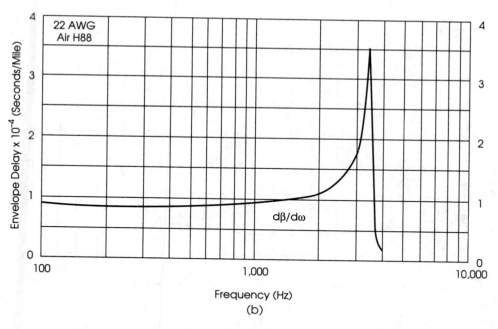

(b)

Figure 7-14 H88 loaded cable pair envelope delay: (a) PIC, 55°F, 19 AWG air; (b) PIC, 55°F, 22 AWG air; (c) PIC, 55°F, 24 AWG air; (d) PIC, 55°F, 26 AWG air; (e) PIC, 55°F, 19 AWG filled; (f) PIC, 55°F, 22 AWG filled; (g) PIC, 55°F, 24 AWG filled; (h) PIC, 55°F, 26 AWG filled.

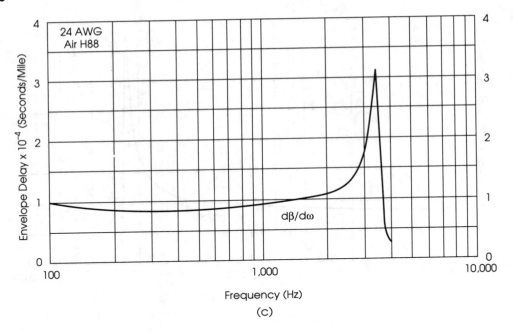

(c)

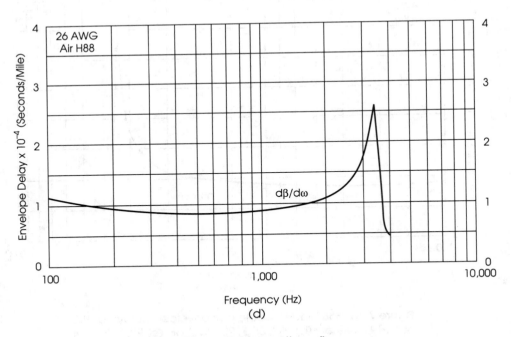

(d)

Figure 7-14 (continued)

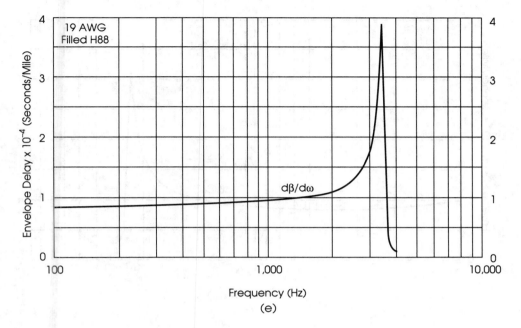

(e)

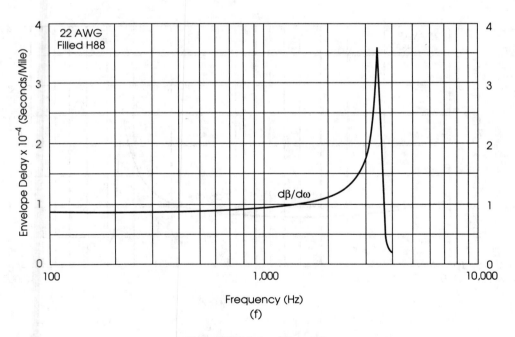

(f)

Figure 7-14 (continued)

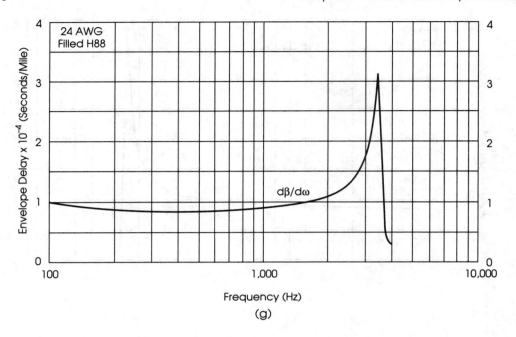

(g)

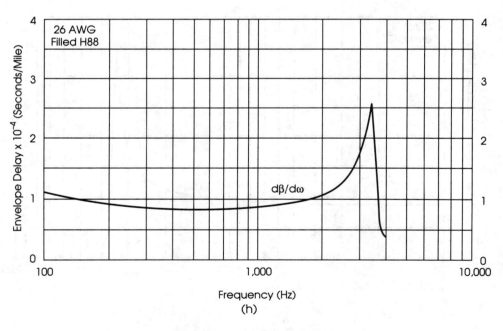

(h)

Figure 7-14 (continued)

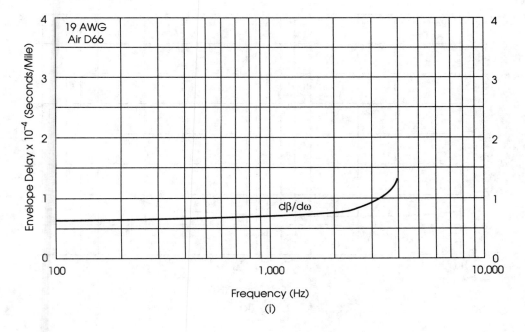

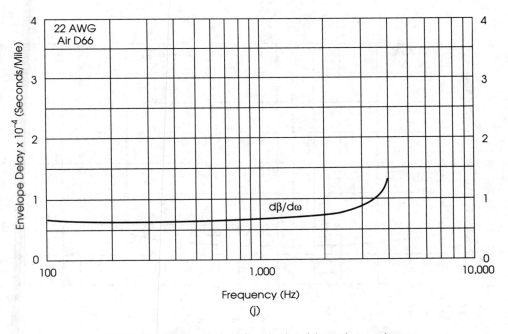

Figure 7-14 (continued): D66 loaded cable pair envelope
delay: (i) PIC, 55°F, 19 AWG air; (j) PIC, 55°F, 22 AWG air; (k)
PIC, 55°F, 24 AWG air; (l) PIC, 55°F, 26 AWG air; (m) PIC, 55°F, 19
AWG filled; (n) PIC, 55°F, 22 AWG filled; (o) PIC, 55°F, 24 AWG
filled; (p) PIC, 55°F, 26 AWG filled.

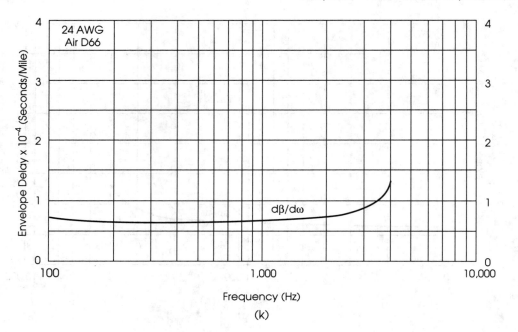

(k)

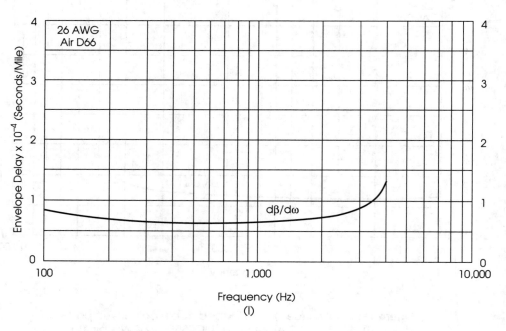

(l)

Figure 7-14 (continued)

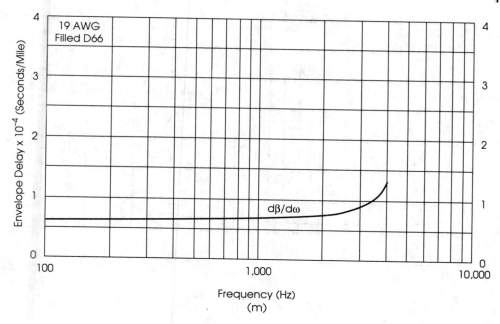

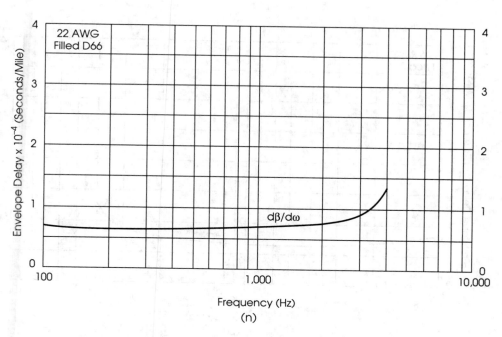

Figure 7-14 (continued)

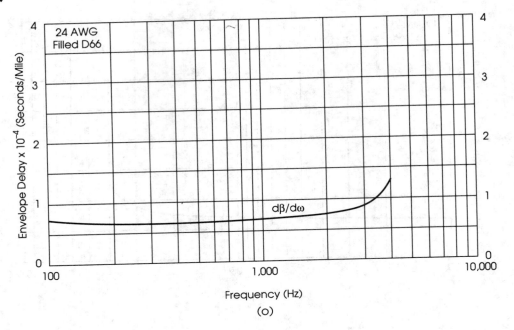

(o)

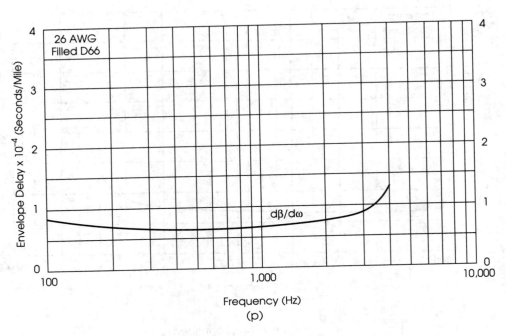

(p)

Figure 7-14 (continued)

baud = 2 bps or 4 bps) for reliable operation at higher speeds. If the switched call is carried by satellite, or the loop consists of a satellite transmission circuit, the best is 300 bps (binary modulation without software-controlled error correction); long distance, switched terrestrial circuits do somewhat better.

Dial-up (switched) modem circuits operate under much more severe conditions than dedicated circuits. This is due to the introduction of additional impairments by switching systems and widely varying and unpredictable loop characteristics. For example, the switching system line circuit at best offers a compromise impedance match to the loop, which may be loaded or nonloaded cable, long or short. Also, the line circuit sharply filters signals outside the voiceband (causing severe envelope delay distortion at the band edges).

The line circuit must work with loop lengths and characteristics of great variation, as previously noted. It would be uneconomical to individually adjust each line circuit to match its associated loop (the difficulty can be appreciated by considering a 50,000-line central office). Long-term administration of these loops would be virtually impossible.

Impairments introduced by the line circuit can be limited, but variations within practical limits still present a particularly hard job for high-speed modems. Of course, 9,600 bps dial-up modems and error correcting software are commonplace now, but the actual throughput can be considerably less than 9,600 bps because of the error correcting and coding schemes required and used. Also, most modern 9,600 bps dial-up modems actually modulate the line signal using multilevel schemes. For example, a typical 9,600 bps modem may operate at 2,400 baud using a quadrature amplitude modulation scheme where 1 baud = 4 bps. The required bandwidth in this case will be at least 2,400 Hz, which is achievable in most switched and private line loops. Data compression techniques are used to boost throughput.

7.11 Transmission Impairments of Cascaded Loop Sections

Transmission impairments of cascaded loop sections add up as follows to give the values for the overall circuit: *

1. Loss, in dB, is added algebraically for each frequency.
2. Envelope delay distortion, in time units, is added algebraically for each frequency band.
3. Circuit noise, in dBrnC, is added on a power basis (that is, converted to absolute power levels, added algebraically, and then reconverted back to dBrnC).
4. Impulse noise, in counts, is added algebraically for each noise level measured.

For example, consider the following circuit consisting of two cascaded sections with the characteristics shown in Table 7-3.

The loss of each segment is added algebraically (8.0 + 3.4 = 11.4) as are EDD (27 + 12 = 39) and impulse noise (10 + 25 = 35) for each segment. Circuit noise is converted to power levels in milliwatts, added, and converted back to decibels ($1.26 \times 10^{-7} + 7.94 \times 10^{-8} = 2.05 \times 10^{-7}$ mW = –67 dBm = 23 dBrnC).

* More rigorous methods of combining parameters can be found in [19].

Table 7-3 Cascaded Circuit Example

Impairment	Segment 1	Segment 2	Total
Loss	8.0 dB	3.4 dB	11.4 dB
EDD,			
1 kHz-2.5 kHz	27 μs	12 μs	39 μs
Circuit Noise	21 dBrnC	19 dBrnC	23 dBrnC
Impulse Noise,			
59 dBrnC Threshold	10 Counts	25 Counts	35 Counts

7.12 Loop Testing

All of the impairments previously discussed are easily measured with the appropriate test equipment. Such tests are performed whenever a new circuit is placed into service. In addition, the telephone company may perform routine or otherwise periodic tests on subscriber loops. Such tests may consist of foreign voltage, leakage resistance and capacitance unbalance tests as well as noise and circuit balance. Loops with abnormal foreign voltage, leakage or capacitance will be noisy or have excessive loss.

The routine tests on switched loops are usually performed automatically during early morning hours when the loop is least used. Many loops may be tested during any given session. Simple leakage tests can require only a few seconds, with more extensive tests requiring as much as 1 min. Manual tests may be made at any time after a trouble call is made.

Depending on the results of a given test, a determination may be made if a fault exists in cable plant or terminal equipment. Many times the tests are sensitive enough to detect a problem before it is noticed by the subscriber.

When automatic loop testing equipment is first installed or adjusted to test a new group of loops, it is usually set to find gross faults first. These include hazardous voltages (over 50 Vac or 135 Vdc) and insulation faults (less than 250,000 Ω tip or ring to battery or ground and tip to ring). If noise measurements are made, the initial settings are to find those loops with noise in the unacceptable ranges, as previously discussed. As these troubles are cleared (repaired), the sensitivity of the test equipment is increased to find the next most serious types of faults. This process continues until all troubles and potential troubles are found and cleared.

REFERENCES

[1] Violette, et al. *Electromagnetic Compatibility Handbook.* New York: Van Nostrand Reinhold Co., 1987.

[2] IEEE Std. 743-1984, IEEE *Standard Methods and Equipment for Measuring the Transmission Characteristics of Analog Voice Frequency Circuits.* New York: Institute of Electrical and Electronics Engineers. Available from IEEE Service Center.

[3] *Operating and Service Manual*, Model 3551A Transmission Test Set, Figs. 3-1 and 3-2. Hewlett-Packard, 1974.

[4] *Notes on the BOC Intra-LATA Networks—1986*, Technical Reference TR-NPL-000275. Available from BELLCORE Customer Service.

[5] *Transmission Design Objectives, Switched Special Services and Private Branch Exchange Services*, Compatibility Bulletin 102, AT&T, February 21, 1975. Available from BELLCORE Customer Service.

[6] Freeman, R. L. *Telecommunication System Engineering*. New York: John Wiley & Sons, 1989, p. 21.

[7] *Federal Communication Commission Rules and Regulations*, Part 68, Par. 68.310. Available from the Superintendent of Documents.

[8] EIA/TIA-464-A-1989, *Private Branch Exchange (PBX) Switching Equipment for Voiceband Applications*. Available from Electronic Industries Association.

[9] ANSI/EIA-470-A-1987, *Telephone Instruments with Loop Signaling*. Available from EIA.

[10] EIA-RS-478, *Multi-Line Key Telephone Systems (KTS) for Voiceband Applications*. Available from EIA.

[11] REA TE&CM Section 452, *Specialized Telephone Noise Measurements and Investigation*. Available from REA.

[12] IEEE Std. 820-1984, *IEEE Standard Telephone Loop Performance Characteristics*. Available from IEEE Service Center.

[13] *Transmission Systems for Communications*. Bell Telephone Laboratories, Inc., 1982. Available from AT&T Customer Information Center.

[14] Fennick, J. *Quality Measures and the Design of Telecommunications Systems*. Dedham, MA: Artech House, 1988.

[15] Lindberg, B. C. *Troubleshooting Communications Facilities*. New York: John Wiley & Sons, 1990.

[16] *Compatibility Information for Telephone Exchange Service*, Technical Advisory TA-NPL-000912, BELLCORE, February 1989. Available from BELLCORE Document Registrar.

[17] CCITT Blue Book, Volume V, *Telephone Transmission Quality, Series P Recommendations*, 1989. Available from NTIS.

[18] Waugh, J. P. "The Trick Is to Not Intrude." *Telephone Engineer and Management*, October 15, 1989.

[19] IEEE Std. 823-1989, *IEEE Standard Methodologies for Specifying Voicegrade Channel Transmission Parameters and Evaluating Connection Transmission Performance for Speech Telephony*. New York: Institute of Electrical and Electronics Engineers. Available from IEEE Service Center.

8

Transmission Improvement

A number of methods and devices are used to improve transmission under circumstances encountered in the loop environment. This chapter is devoted to the practical application of these devices and methods. *Lumped loading*, which improves transmission on long loops, was discussed in Chapter 5, so it will not be covered here.

8.1 Cable Shields

In many cases, transmission improvement is nothing more than noise reduction. Grounding of cable shields is one of the most fundamental methods of noise control in loops. This was discussed in Chapter 7. To be effective, cable shields must be grounded in all enclosures, such as pedestals and aerial terminals, or anywhere the cable shield is exposed. The latter requirement is for safety, and noise control is a by-product.

In spite of the previous statements, there may be situations where it is undesirable to ground the shield at a particular location. This may be because of unusual ground potential rise at that site or for other reasons. These cases are rare, however, and thorough study and tests are required to ensure that not grounding an exposed shield will yield the expected results and not compromise safety.

In joint-use plant, where telephone and power facilities share a common supporting structure, the *multi-grounded neutral* (MGN) of the power system, if available, must be grounded and the telecommunication cable shield bonded to it wherever the shield is exposed. This not only enhances cable noise performance but also enhances personnel safety because the shields are maintained at a potential equal to the enclosure and adjacent equipment. At least four grounds per mile of line are required.

It is commonly thought that burying telecommunication cables in the same trench with power cables leads to noise problems on the telecommunication cables and that separation by some small distance will solve the problem. In reality, if noise is a problem, separating the cables by, say, even the width of a road probably will not help. A more important reason for separating the cables is safety and reducing the chance of damage to the telecommunication cable by an arcing fault in the power cable insulation.

8.2 Inductive Coordination

There may be situations where shielding, bonding and grounding are properly installed and the circuit is reasonably balanced, but the circuit noise level due to power line induction is still too high. This calls for a process called *inductive coordination* with the power utility serving the area [1]. This is a coordination process between telecommunication and electric utilities to ensure a full understanding of telecommunications noise problems and their solutions. These solutions are frequently a cooperative effort.

If noise at particular harmonics suddenly appears on telecommunication facilities, it is possible that the electric utility recently installed power factor correction capacitors on a nearby line. On three-phase power systems with power factor correction, the odd-triple harmonics (180, 540, 900 Hz) are the worse. Single-phase systems put out harmonics at 300, 420, 660 Hz. Systems with large nonlinear loads may cause strong interference at any harmonic. The only way to tell what frequencies are causing the problem is to measure them individually with a spectrum analyzer or frequency selective level meter.

8.3 Noise Mitigation Methods

If inductive coordination fails to provide the desired results and other methods (such as assuring shields are bonded and grounded properly) are ineffective, noise mitigation devices can be installed on the loop. Such devices can be quite effective for solving any of the problems shown in Fig. 8-1. Typical noise mitigation devices are induction neutralizing transformers, drain coils and noise chokes. These are seldom designed into subscriber loop plant from the beginning because normal construction and maintenance methods will usually preclude noise problems except in the most severe cases.

The neutralizing transformer is designed to block longitudinal currents at powerline harmonic frequencies. The application of such devices is shown in Figs. 8-2(a) and 8-2(b). The transformer most often contains multiple windings, each of which is wired in series with a loop, but single-line neutralizing transformers are available. The added dc loop resistance is in the order of 50 ohms and insertion loss is typically 0.5 dB at 1,000 Hz. These transformers are usually located at the subscriber premises, but CO locations are also used.

The neutralizing transformer depends on a certain amount of longitudinal ac excitation current for its operation. One of two ways can be used to provide the excitation current. At locations served by multiple loops, a spare pair can be connected to one of the windings in the neutralizing transformer as shown in Fig. 8-2(a). This method is economical only if a spare pair exists all the way from the central office to the subscriber premises. If no spare pair is available or if the premises are served by only one loop, an external excitation network can be connected as shown in Fig. 8-2(b). This excitation net-

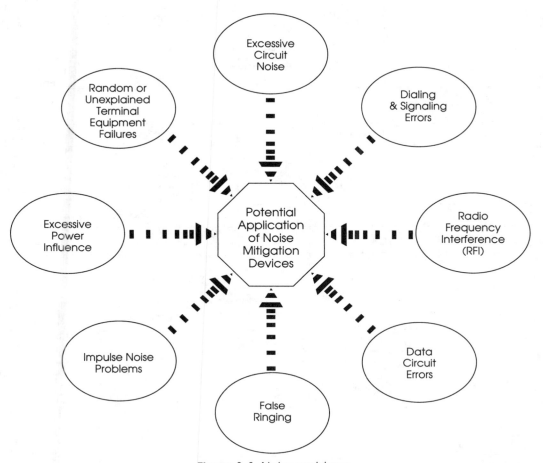

Figure 8-1 Noise problems

work is a drainage reactor tuned to 60 Hz. In some situations, the neutralizing transformer will work satisfactorily without the excitation network or the spare pair.

Drain coils (also called harmonic drainage reactor) are used to drain longitudinal currents to ground. Drain coils can be optimized for various frequencies and usually are used with either neutralizing transformers, as shown in Fig. 8-2(b), or noise chokes. The drain coil can be located at the end of the loop opposite to the transformer or choke, or at the same end. Some experimentation may be necessary to find the optimum combination and type of noise mitigation devices. In particularly severe noise environments, two drain coils connected in parallel will be necessary, one optimized for 60 Hz and another for powerline harmonics.

Noise chokes are similar to neutralizing transformers and can be located at the subscriber's premises or the CO, or both. They are placed in series with the loop and add about 50 to 100 ohms dc resistance to it. Insertion loss is typically 0.5 dB at 1,000 Hz. Noise chokes are used to block longitudinal currents that cause equipment upset or signaling problems. Typical applications are shown in Figs. 8-2(c) and 8-2(d). Noise chokes are available in 35 V and 70 V units, which indicates the maximum longitudinal voltage rating. The 70 V unit is used if the measured ac voltage from the loop tip and ring to ground

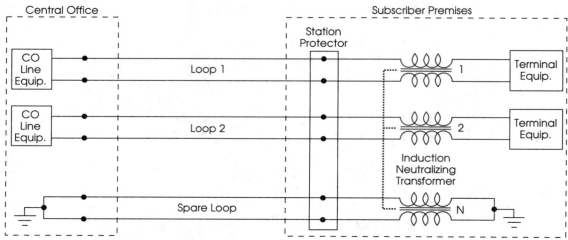

(a) multiple winding induction neutralizing transformer with excitation pair

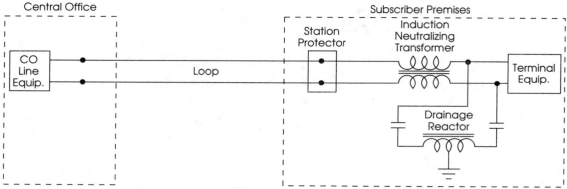

(b) single winding induction neutralizing transformer with external excitation network

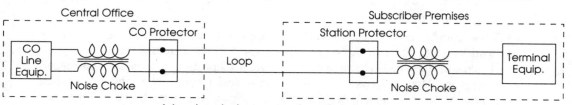

(c) noise choke on regular subscriber loop

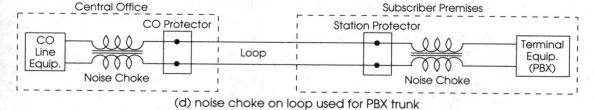

(d) noise choke on loop used for PBX trunk

Figure 8-2 Application of noise mitigation devices

without the transformer installed is between 35 and 70 V. The 35 V unit is used for longitudinal voltages less than 35 V.

The voltage is found by shorting the tip and ring together and measuring the voltage to ground with a high impedance voltmeter. The loop should be disconnected from any load during this measurement. Also, several measurements may be necessary over a period of time because the longitudinal voltage can vary with time of day and the season. If the voltage measures above 70 V or if it is anticipated to rise above this value, other mitigation methods will be necessary. Operation of a noise choke above its rated voltage will cause it to saturate and the noise will increase.

Some noise mitigation devices may not be compatible with various transmission or signaling systems connected to the loop. This is particularly true of carrier systems. Special neutralizing transformers are available for such applications.

Many times noise from RFI, such as a local radio station, is caused by demodulation of the radiated, induced or conducted radio signal in the telephone set itself. A more generalized term is EMI, which describes the source as any electromagnetic signal rather than a signal at just radio frequencies.

Ferrite beads, tuned coil/capacitor combinations or capacitors alone can eliminate or reduce this type of noise. RFI is most annoying to voice conversations and seems to have little effect on modems unless it is excessively high. Situations will exist where RFI is not heard but still causes signaling problems in terminal equipment.

Generally, properly designed and constructed loops do not contribute to RFI problems. Also, properly designed terminal equipment is not overly sensitive to RFI because of internal filtering, but there are practical limits on the level of filtering possible in consumer-type sets. A full discussion of RFI and its reduction at terminal equipment is beyond the scope of this book, but a few practical solutions using RF filters are worth mentioning.

To be most effective, RF filters must be installed in or at the telephone instrument because that is where the demodulation usually takes place. Also, RFI is usually a localized problem at only certain types of terminal equipment. For example, a local radio station may be heard at interfering levels on one telephone set, but not on another in the same household. Typical solutions to RFI are discussed in readily available literature [2–5]. Some successful and easy to implement solutions are shown in Fig. 8-3 and discussed below:

1. Insert the tip and ring conductors through ferrite beads, close to or inside of the telephone set, to reduce the longitudinal (common-mode) noise [Fig. 8-3(a)].
2. Insert the tip and ring conductors individually through ferrite beads, close to or inside of the telephone set, to reduce metallic-mode (differential-mode) noise. The same number of beads should be installed on each conductor to provide a balanced circuit [Fig. 8-3(b)].
3. Wrap the telephone set cord around a split toroid or rectangular core. This provides the same results as (1) [Fig. 8-3(c)].
4. Connect capacitors (typically 0.01 or 0.001 μF) tip-ground, ring-ground, and tip-ring, close to or inside of the telephone set, to reduce the common-mode and differential noise. The capacitors should always be high-quality/high-frequency types, rated at least 600 V and wired to provide a balanced connection [Fig. 8-3(d)].

5. Connect capacitors (0.01 to 0.001 μF as above) across the telephone set transmitter. This filters the demodulated RFI caused by the transmitter nonlinear elements [Fig. 8-3(e)].

6. If the terminal equipment is ac powered, use power line filters or wrap the power cord around a split toroid or rectangular core close to the terminal equipment. This reduces noise conducted into the equipment from the power line [Fig. 8-3(f)].

7. Use any combination of the above.

The ferrite beads or toroidal cores used to reduce RFI problems should be lossy at the interfering signal frequency and efficient at voice frequencies. Typically, RFI is from AM broadcast band transmitters in the range of 500 kHz to 1,600 kHz, so materials lossy at these frequencies should be used. A number of companies provide suitable beads and core materials for this and other frequency ranges [6–8].

Other noise sources are wet cable and noisy splices. Either of these gives a crackling or frying noise. Noise due to a wet cable, which can be a problem with air-core cables but not with modern filled cables, can be eliminated by drying or replacing the cable. Drying requires finding and repairing all leaks and then flooding the cable under pressure with an inert gas such as nitrogen to purge the moisture, and then keeping it pressurized with dry air. The only way to repair a noisy splice, except as discussed in the next section, is to replace it. A short-term solution is to swap the circuit to another pair that is not noisy, but this is considered poor administrative practice as a long-term solution for obvious reasons. A thorough treatment of noise and noise mitigation can be found in many reference sources [9–17].

8.4 Sealing Current

Many times a cable pair suitable for use as a regular switched line will initially work just as well as a dedicated (nonswitched) data line. This can occur where a switched loop is disconnected and then reconnected as a data line. After some period of time, however, the data line will become noisy or show excessive loss. The reason for this is that during use as a switched line, at least 20 mA of loop current was flowing when the line was in use (off-hook). This current flow tended to keep the mechanical splices clean of oxides or high-resistance films. With private lines carrying voice or data signals, however, the only currents that flow on the loop are the very low-level signals themselves (this is called a "dry" loop). These low-level currents are not large enough to keep the splices clean, and they will "noise up" or appear as a high-impedance circuit to the signal. A simple solution is to use "sealing current" on loops that do not carry at least 20 mA dc during use.

Sealing current generators apply a balanced 20 mA dc (some are adjustable 10, 20 or 30 mA) onto the loop (this is called a "wet" loop). They can be applied to two-wire or four-wire circuits with equal success. Most sealing current generators have a "flash" feature that initially pulses the loop with a high value current to clear splice oxidation. After a few seconds the current is automatically reduced to the steady-state value. The sealing current generators can be mounted in a relay rack reserved for VF treatment equipment or mounted on the main distributing frame in the central office.

Two sealing current applications are shown in Fig. 8-4. A two-wire loop [(Fig. 8-4(a)] has repeat coils at each end. Repeat coils are impedance matching transformers

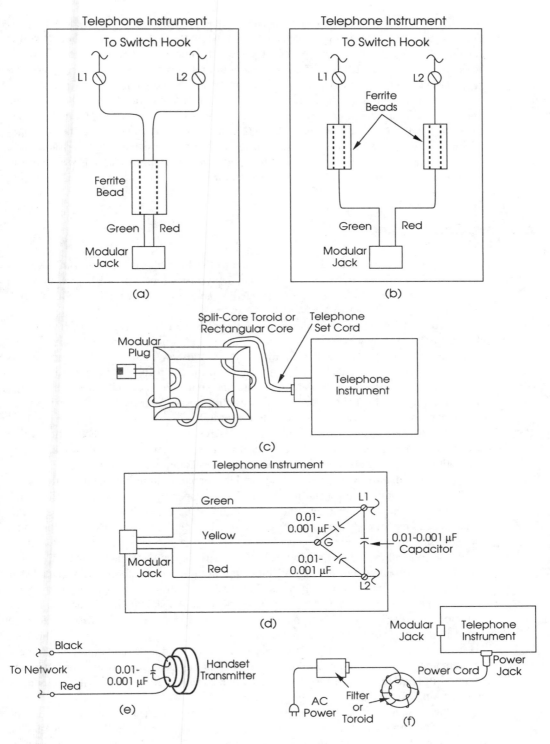

Figure 8-3 RF filters

specially designed to maintain their electrical characteristics with dc on the windings. The sealing current generator is connected as shown to the A-B leads of the repeat coil at one end. The A-B leads of the repeat coil at the other end are shorted together to provide dc continuity. A capacitor is used at the generator end to provide continuity at voice frequencies. The four-wire loop has a similar arrangement as shown in Fig. 8-4(b).

Most sealing current generators have maximum loop resistance limits. The limit for a four-wire loop will be twice that for a two-wire loop due to the different simplex resistance. In a two-wire loop, the sealing current flows through each conductor but in opposite directions. Therefore, the loop resistance and simplex resistance are the same. In a four-wire loop, the conductors in each direction are connected in parallel, which halves the resistance seen by the sealing current generator.

8.5 Line Conditioning

When high speed data signals are applied to the loop, the various transmission parameters, especially attenuation and envelope delay distortion, must be held within well defined limits. These parameters are controlled by amplifiers and equalizers which usually are installed at the ends of the cable facility.

If required, equalization is almost always applied to the receive side of a four-wire circuit. Sometimes, however, predistortion equalization is provided on the transmit side. (Note that present high-speed data circuits are almost always point-to-point arrangements made up from a four-wire circuit with separate transmit and receive paths.)

The inherent loss of a loop used in private line applications can be reduced by adding gain with amplifiers. This has to be done carefully to prevent the loop from singing if two-wire conversion is used at any point in the circuit.

Equalizers are used to offset a loop's high-frequency rolloff characteristic, which affects both attenuation and envelope delay distortion. The application of equalizers and other devices to control transmission characteristics is called *line conditioning*.

On switched, two-wire loops, as discussed in Chapter 6, loop treatment is straightforward and does not require special techniques if the proper equipment is used. With four-wire dedicated circuits, however, line conditioning is used to tailor a loop to particular transmission characteristics. Modern transmission equipment allows this to be done on a "cookbook" or prescription basis.

Most companies (telephone companies and circuit vendors) have standardized the various types of line conditioning for four-wire circuits. Three tables are provided that describe the basic transmission characteristics of leased lines available from many companies. In each of these tables, the attenuation distortion is shown with respect to the attenuation at 1,004 Hz. The envelope delay distortion is given in terms of the difference between the maximum and minimum envelope delay (in microseconds) within the frequency band shown. All values are for circuits from vendor demarcation point to vendor demarcation point. The overall characteristics of cascaded links from more than one vendor will have to be determined from the characteristics of each using the techniques described in Chapter 7.

Table 8-1 compares the characteristics of lines with various types of "C" conditioning [18]. The nomenclature used (C1, C2, etc.) originated with the Bell System (AT&T). It was adopted by many non-Bell operating companies as well. This list is not exhaustive. Additional types of conditioning may be available under this nomenclature from a

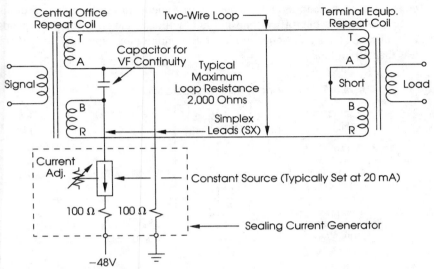

Figure 8-4(a) Two-wire application of sealing current generator

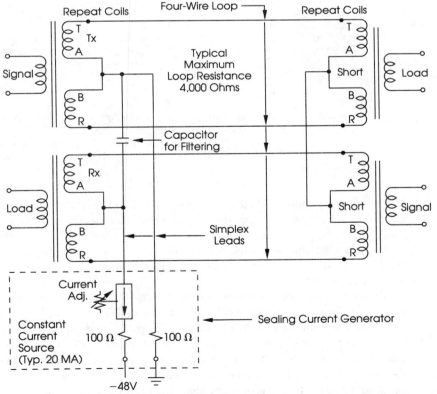

Figure 8-4(b) Four-wire application of sealing current generator

particular telephone company. The conditioning specifications listed in Table 8-1 are considered to be end-to-end, so they will include the characteristics of the end-links (loops) as well as interoffice transmission facilities. The circuit noise depends on the circuit mileage. The circuit noise limit for all conditioning types is 31 dBrnC0 for a circuit less than 50 mi long.

Table 8-1 "C" Conditioning Specifications

Freq. Band (Hz)	Atten. Dist.[a] (dB)	Freq. Band (Hz)	EDD (μs)
Basic (no conditioning) 500–2500 300–3000	−2 to +8 −3 to +12	800–2600	1750
C1 Conditioning 1000–2400 300–2700 2700–3000	−1 to +3 −2 to +6 −3 to +12	1000–2400 800–2600	1000 1750
C2 Conditioning 500–2800 300–3200	−1 to +3 −2 to +6	1000–2600 600–2600 500–2800	500 1500 3000
C4 Conditioning 500–3000 300–3200	−2 to +3 −2 to +6	1000–2600 800–2800 600–3000 500–3000	300 500 1500 3000
C5 Conditioning 500–2800 300–3000	−0.5 to +1.5 −3 to +3	1000–2600 600–2600 500–2800	100 300 600

[a] With respect to 1,004 Hz.

Most modern high-speed modems (up to around 20 kbps) will function properly over a single-link C2 conditioned line. Higher grade lines (such as C4 and C5) are specified to provide improved performance, higher speeds, or to ensure that the overall circuit composed of cascaded links meets the performance criteria of C2 conditioning. Other conditioning specifications exist, such as "D" conditioning, which controls signal-to-noise ratio and nonlinear distortion.

Although some companies still use the "C" conditioning nomenclature, it is becoming obsolete. With the divestiture of AT&T, the specification of end-to-end transmission facilities has become more difficult because the public network now has multi-vendor and multi-dimensional characteristics. A given link vendor will provide lines with predetermined characteristics according to the facilities owned and operated by them and them only. As a result, BELLCORE has developed standardized "Voice Grade" (VG) circuit types with the characteristics shown in Table 8-2 [21].

Table 8-2 BELLCORE Voice Grade Types Acceptance Limits

Freq. Band (Hz)	Atten. Dist.[a] (dB)	Freq. Band (Hz)	EDD (µs)
Voice Grade 1 504–2504 404–2804 304–3004	−1.5 to +7.5 −1.5 to +9.5 −2.5 to +11.5		None specified
Voice Grade 2 404–2804 304–3004	−0.5 to +3.5 −0.5 to +4.5		None specified
Voice Grade 3 404–2804 304–3004	−0.5 to +2.5 −0.5 to +4.5		None specified
Voice Grade 4 304–504 504–2504 2504–2804 2804–3004	−0.5 to +3.0 −0.5 to +1.5 −0.5 to +2.5 −0.5 to +3.5		None specified
Voice Grade 5 404–2804	−0.5 to +4.5		None specified
Voice Grade 6 504–2504 404–2804 2804–3004	−0.5 to +2.5 −0.5 to +3.5 −0.5 to +4.5	804–2604	650
Voice Grade 7 404–2804 304–3004	−0.5 to +1.5 −0.5 to +4.5	804–2604	650
Voice Grade 8 404–2804 304–3004	−0.5 to +1.5 −0.5 to +4.5	804–2604	650
Voice Grade 9 404–2804 304–3004	−0.5 to +1.5 −0.5 to +4.5	804–2604	650
Voice Grade 10 504–2504 404–2804 304–3004	−1.5 to +7.5 −1.5 to +9.5 −2.5 to +11.5	804–2604	1700
Voice Grade 11 304–3004 1204–2604	−0.5 to +4.5 −0.5 to +0.5	804–2604	650
Voice Grade 12 504–2804 304–3004	−0.5 to +0.5 −0.5 to +2.0	804–2604	650

[a] With respect to 1,004 Hz.

As with "C" conditioning, all VG types have a circuit noise limit that depends on the circuit mileage. For circuits from 0 to 50 mi long, the maximum circuit noise is 30 dBrnC0. Many VG types include specifications for impulse noise, and some include phase jitter and distortion limits. Also, most companies can provide optional transmission characteristics not listed in the table. Voice grade types are used by Bell Operating Companies and have been or are being adopted as well by non-Bell companies. In most situations, the VG types are for end-links only and do not cover interoffice transmission facilities.

Interoffice transmission links are required to complete the make-up of long distance lines. Interoffice transmission characteristics are covered by "Service Type" specifications that originated with AT&T upon divestiture. Some non-AT&T interoffice facility vendors have adopted these specifications, but variations can and do exist. Therefore, it is necessary to study the specifications in detail to determine their application with a particular circuit arrangement.

Table 8-3 shows some of the characteristics of the most commonly used AT&T Service Types [22]. Not all characteristics are shown in this table; as with VG types, many service types also will include specifications for impulse noise, and some include phase jitter and distortion limits. For most service types, the circuit noise is measured in absolute terms (dBrnC0) or as a signal-to-noise ratio with a holding tone, or both. Virtually all interoffice facility links provided by AT&T use some type of compandored carrier rather than voice grade metallic loops, so signal-to-noise ratio is an appropriate parameter for this situation. Other specifications exist such as those used by the U.S. military.*

8.6 Bridged Tap Isolators

Many times, excessive loss on an otherwise properly designed loop is caused by bridged taps. A bridged tap, illustrated in Fig. 8-5, is any portion of a loop that is not in the path between the central office and the subscriber's terminal equipment. It may be an unused cable pair connected at an intermediate point or an extension of the circuit beyond the subscriber's location.

The cable pair associated with the bridged tap is open circuited and appears as added capacitance, so it adds a frequency-dependent bridging loss (also called reflection loss) to the loop. The exact loss value depends on the length and gauge of the bridged tap.† For practical problems, however, a bridged tap is considered to add about 0.2 to 0.5 dB loss to the loop per 1,000 ft of tap length at 1,000 Hz.

Bridged tap isolators (BTIs, also known as *saturable inductors* or *bridge lifters*) are used when bridged taps are long and unavoidable such as in multiparty service or with off-premises extensions. These devices use a saturable core inductor with bifilar windings. Their physical construction is very similar to load coils, but a toroidal core of compressed ferrite material or permalloy tape is used to give the saturable characteristic.

In the case of an off-premises extension, the primary access line and extension line are each connected to the central office line circuit through a BTI as shown in Fig. 8-6.

---

 * For example, telecommunication circuits used by the U.S. military are specified by various Defense Communications Agency (DCA) documents, the most important of which is DCA Circular 300–175–9 "DCS Operating — Maintenance Electrical Performance Standards."

 † An analysis of the reflection loss caused by a bridged tap of any length connected at any point in a loop is provided in Appendix E.

Table 8-3 AT&T Service Types Acceptance Limits

Freq. Band (Hz)	Atten. Dist.[a] (dB)	Freq. Band (Hz)	EDD (μs)
Service Type 1 304–404 404–2804 2804–3004	−3 to +12 −2 to +9 −3 to +12		None specified
Service Type 2 304–404 404–2804 2804–3004	−3 to +12 −2 to +6 −3 to +12		None specified
Service Type 3 304–504 504–2504 2504–2804 2804–3004	−2 to +9 −2 to +6 −2 to +8 −2 to +11		None specified
Service Type 4 404–2804	−4 to +12		None specified
Service Type 5 304–404 404–504 504–2504 2504–2804 2804–3004	−3 to +12 −2 to +10 −2 to +8 −2 to +10 −3 to +12	804–2604	1750
Service Type 6 304–404 404–2804 2804–3004	−3 to +12 −2 to +6 −3 to +12	804–2604	1250
Service Type 7 304–404 404–2804 2804–3004	−3 to +12 −2 to +5 −3 to +12	804–2604	550
Service Type 8 304–404 404–2804 2804–3004	−3 to +12 −1 to +4 −3 to +12	804–2604	400
Service Type 9 304–1204 1204–2604 2604–3004	−3 to +12 −3 to +3 −3 to +12	804–2604	600
Service Type 10 304–504 504–2804 2804–3004	−2 to +6 −1 to +3 −2 to +6	804–2604	2000

[a] With respect to 1,004 Hz.

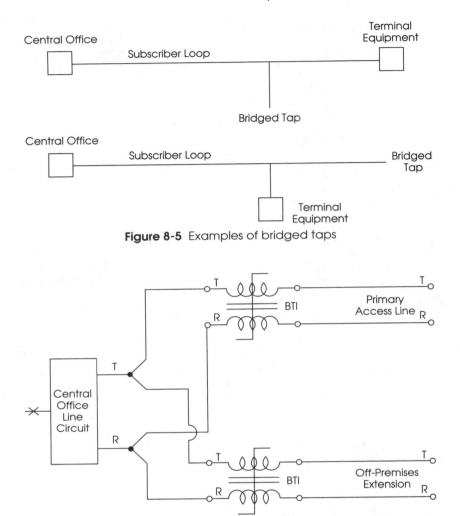

Figure 8-5 Examples of bridged taps

Figure 8-6 Using bridged tap isolators with off-premises extension

Referring to this figure, when no current is flowing in the loop (idle or on-hook condition), the BTI inductance is high (around 20 H); therefore, it presents a high ac impedance (125,000 Ω at 1,000 Hz) and little bridging loss. When one of the lines is seized, current flows in the BTI associated with the busy loop, saturating the inductor and causing the inductance to rapidly decrease by a factor of 1/2,000 to about 10 mH. The lower inductance presents a lower impedance (60 Ω at 1,000 Hz) and allows normal transmission on the busy loop. Meanwhile, the bridged tap from the other line is isolated by the other BTI, which has no current flowing through it. If necessary, both the primary and extension line can be used at the same time as long as care is taken to ensure that the loop current through each BTI is above 20 mA (which is necessary to ensure the saturated condition).

Bridged tap isolators are normally installed in the central office, but they sometimes appear in the field. Generally, they should be installed as close to the bridged tap as possible. A BTI adds 20 to 45 Ω dc resistance and about 0.3 to 0.5 dB of insertion loss at

1,000 Hz to the busy loop. Also, BTIs should not be used on long loops (with low loop current) with electronic telephone instruments. A BTI will compound the difficulties these instruments already experience on loops with low loop current.

Finally, although not shown in Fig. 8-6, BTIs are optionally available with a 5,600 Ω shunting resistor across each winding. In most cases, the BTIs should be equipped with the resistors, especially if the BTI is located in the field. The resistors lower the Q of the BTI and eliminate flutter caused by 60 Hz induced current. More information on bridged tap isolators can be found in available literature [18,19].

8.7 Junction Impedance Compensators

Where loaded loops that have different loading schemes are combined (for example, D66 to H88), a junction impedance compensator is used to match the impedance of the two. This reduces signal reflection at the junction. Junction impedance compensators include a series inductor (similar to a load coil but with around 44 mH inductance) and two capacitors for matching the two lines.

8.8 Line Build-Out

Sometimes it is impossible to place a load coil within the required spacing tolerance, or a section of line is rerouted, which changes the distance between load points. In these cases, build-out lattice networks or build-out capacitors are used to simulate the missing length of line. They add capacitance and resistance or just capacitance in the required amounts.

The build-out lattice network is preferred because it most accurately simulates the missing section of line and, therefore, reduces signal reflection (increases return loss) at the build-out point. Figure 8-7 shows the schematic for a build-out lattice.

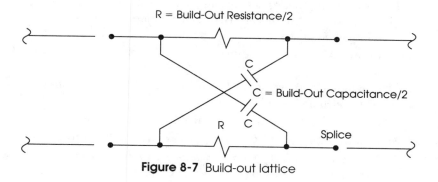

Figure 8-7 Build-out lattice

Even with lattice networks there will be some reflection since the lattice, using lumped capacitors and resistors, cannot exactly simulate the distributed characteristics of the missing length of cable. The reflections can be minimized, however, by locating the lattice as close to the center of the short section as possible. A more detailed discussion of using lattice networks can be found in [20].

Other schemes have been devised to simulate missing lengths by using pieces of exchange cable connected in series or shunt or both. The series building out cable is usually a smaller gauge (higher resistance) than the main cable. One pair of the build-out cable is installed in series with the main cable pair, and two or three pairs (with their far ends open circuited) are installed in parallel. When properly designed, this will add the proper amount of resistance and capacitance, but the actual length will be less than if only a single pair is installed in series. A similar installation results with the shunt (parallel) only build-out or other combinations of shunt and series build-out. These types of installations are rarely used because field administration of the cables at the splice point is difficult.

REFERENCES

[1] IEEE Standard 776-1987, *IEEE Guide for Inductive Coordination of Electric Supply and Communication Lines*. New York: Institute of Electrical and Electronics Engineers. Available from IEEE Service Center.

[2] Violette, J. L. N. et al. *Electromagnetic Compatibility Handbook*. New York: Van Nostrand Reinhold Company, 1987.

[3] *Interference Handbook*. Federal Communication Commission, 1986. Available from Superintendent of Documents.

[4] Nelson, W. R. *Interference Handbook*. Radio Publications, Inc., 1981. Available from the publisher.

[5] Ott, H. W. *Noise Reduction Techniques in Electronic Systems*. New York: John Wiley & Sons, 2nd Ed., 1988.

[6] Texpro Sales Canada Inc., 4087 Harvester Road, #10, Burlington, Ontario, Canada L7L 5M3 (416) 333-1344.

[7] Palomar Engineers, P.O. Box 455, Escondido, California (619) 747-3343.

[8] Amidon Associates, 12033 Otsego Street, North Hollywood, California, 91607.

[9] *A Diagnostic Guide for Reducing Inductive Interference, Electrical Protection and Interference Department*. Bell Laboratories. Available from AT&T Customer Information Center.

[10] Brewer, M. L. *Noise Investigation Flow Charts*. Available from ABC Teletraining Inc.

[11] Gundrum, R. *Power Line Interference Problems and Solutions*. Available from ABC Teletraining Inc.

[12] Durst, C. E. *Noise Reduction*. Available from ABC Teletraining Inc.

[13] Haskell, Jr., N. H. *Shield Continuity Testing*. Available from ABC Teletraining Inc.

[14] Tokarz, R. F. *Solving Noise and Transmission Problems in Telephone Loop Plant*. Available from Telephony Publishing Corp.

[15] REA TE&CM Section 451, *Telephone Noise Measurement and Mitigation*. Available from REA.

[16] REA TE&CM Section 452, *Specialized Telephone Noise Measurements and Investigation*. Available from REA.

[17] SNC Manufacturing Company, Inc., 101 Waukau Avenue, Oshkosh, WI 54901 (414) 231-7370.

[18] *Telecommunications Transmission Engineering*, Vols. 1, 2 and 3. Winston-Salem, NC: Western Electric Company, Inc. Technical Publications, 1975. Available from AT&T Customer Information Center.

[19] REA TE&CM Section 428, *Application and Use of Bridged Tap Isolators (BTI) for Subscriber Loops*. Available from Rural Electrification Administration.

[20] GTE Practice 852-050-070, *Cable Building-Out Procedures, Engineering Applications*. Available from GTE Practices Manager.

[21] *Voice Grade Special Access Service Transmission Parameter Limits and Interface Combinations*, Technical Advisory TA-TSY-000335, BELLCORE, Dec. 1989. Available from BELLCORE Document Registrar.

[22] *Maintenance of Two-point Private Lines*, FAA Order 6000.22. Aug. 9, 1976, Dept. of Transportation, Federal Aviation Administration.

9

Pair Gain Devices

Both the *loop resistance* and *loop loss* design methods discussed in Chapter 6 require carrier systems beyond certain loops lengths. The resistance design method requires *digital loop carrier* (DLC), while the loss design just specifies "carrier," which implies either digital or analog. Both are discussed in this chapter.

The bandwidth required by any carrier system is considerably greater than that required by a single subscriber on a regular analog loop using baseband transmission. Since it is the intent of this book to restrict detailed discussion of transmission and signaling to narrowband applications (around 4 kHz), the protocols used by carrier systems for transmission will only receive superficial treatment here. A more complete discussion will be given in another volume.

9.1 Subscriber Loop Carrier

Pair gain devices encompass a class of equipment referred to as *subscriber loop* carrier. "Subscriber loop carrier" is a generic term given to an equipment group used to provide service to a number of subscribers without the usual need for one or two cable pairs for each subscriber. These carrier systems can use either digital or analog transmission methods. When the method is digital, DLC is a more specific term used. If analog transmission methods are used, then the systems are called *analog subscriber carrier*.

9.2 Digital Loop Carrier

As the name implies, digital loop carrier replaces the analog loop by using a digital carrier facility. Most systems employ T1 carrier, which operates at the DS-1 rate (1.544

Mbps) using *time division multiplexing* (TDM) and *pulse code modulation* (PCM). The technical specifications for digital loop carrier are described in [1] and [2]. With DLC, two cable pairs can provide service to at least 24 four-wire or two-wire circuits as shown in Fig. 9-1. Although only two pairs are required for one T1 digital span line, redundancy is almost always provided. Therefore, two digital lines are usually used, which require four cable pairs. Additional pairs are sometimes used for fault location activities and maintenance communications (order wire); these can be shared with other digital lines on the same route.

Digital loop carrier is especially economical on longer loops, but it provides a very economical solution to providing regular switched and special services in many applications on shorter loops, too. Because digital loop carrier requires only a relatively few cable pairs to serve a large number of subscribers, it can be easily and quickly applied in situations where limited cable facilities may be available. Some of these are shown in Fig. 9-2.

Although most of the applications shown in this figure imply fairly high subscriber density, this is not a prerequisite for economical DLC use. Digital loop carrier also is used to replace aging central office switching systems or to supplement them in such a way that all new subscribers or existing subscribers requiring advanced services are placed onto the DLC. This removes the requirement for:

- Additional investment in expensive electromechanical switching equipment with limited service capability, and
- Additional investment in complete stand-alone central office systems that would be required to provide the advanced services.

When growth in an existing central office switching system is frozen and DLC is used to supplement it, the process is called "capping" or overlay.

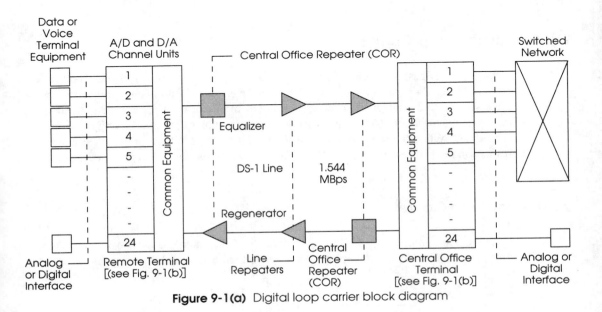

Figure 9-1(a) Digital loop carrier block diagram

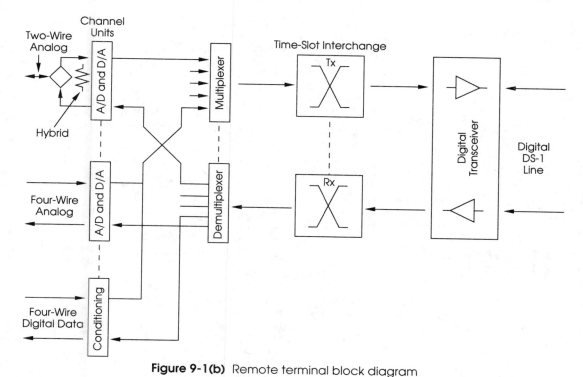

Figure 9-1(b) Remote terminal block diagram

The DLC is made up of a central office terminal, a remote terminal and span lines. These, in turn, are made up of a few basic units:

1. *Channel unit.* This provides the appropriate interface for the circuit being served (for example, regular two-wire service (POTS), four-wire transmission only, digital data, foreign exchange, etc.). The channel unit provides analog-to-digital (A/D) and digital-to-analog (D/A) conversion and other BORSCHT (or mirror BORSCHT) functions.*

2. *Multiplexer/demultiplexer.* This combines (splits out) the digital streams on the digital side of each channel unit into (from) a single higher speed stream.

3. *Time slot interchange* (TSI). This allows a circuit appearing on one channel at the remote terminal to appear on a different channel at the central office terminal.

4. *Digital line interface.* This conditions the high-speed digital signal for transmission over twisted cable pairs. This interface is also called a "digroup."

The remote and central office terminals provide mirror image functions. For example, the DLC interface detects ringing and interfaces to the central office line circuit by providing on-hook and off-hook signaling and impedance matching. At the remote end, the DLC interface provides ringing, loop current and emulates the central office line circuit including test access.

Most manufacturers of digital switching systems integrate the DLC central office terminal functions such that A/D and D/A conversions are not needed at the central office

---

* See Chapter 1 for a description of BORSCHT.

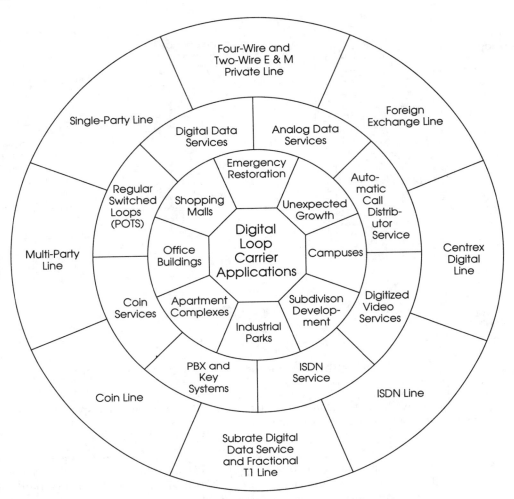

Figure 9-2 Digital loop carrier applications

end. This is called a "direct digital interface." These interfaces are mostly proprietary, which prevents the remote equipment of one manufacturer from being used with the switching system of another manufacturer. However, the industry is working toward standardization, which will eliminate these interface restrictions [1,3].

Digital loop carrier basically extends the central office line circuit or other interface out to some remote location, generally beyond the economical signaling or transmission limits of regular cable pairs operated in the analog environment. Depending on the particular system, the distance can be over 200 mi. The actual distance is determined by the amount of transmission delay and jitter the DLC can tolerate and still stay in synchronization with the remote terminal.

Timing and clocking is a crucial function of any digital system. The remote terminal receives its clocking information from the central office terminal via the incoming high-speed digital bit stream. Typically, the remote terminal then loops this timing information back to the central office on the outgoing bit stream. The central office terminal is able to tolerate only so much difference between its transmit clock and receive clock. The actual amount depends on the buffering designed into the system.

A significant advantage of DLC is in data transmission where low *bit error rate* (BER) and a high percentage of *error free seconds* (EFS) are required. DLC systems offer BER on the order of 10^{-7} or better, which would be nearly impossible to obtain over long distances with terrestrial analog cable facilities and modems now available.*

Analog loop facilities used for data transmission are sensitive to the "bursty" nature of impulse noise. The EFS over any given time period are greater for analog facilities than for digital facilities because digital facilities are less sensitive to this impairment.

In most cases, regular loop design rules, as described in Chapter 6, would apply from the DLC remote terminal location to the subscriber. This means the service can be provided well beyond the DLC remote terminal. For voice-grade (analog) services, the distance is usually equivalent to 1,900 Ω loop resistance. A wide variety of voice-grade channel units is available (Fig. 9-2).

Digital data services provided from the DLC have distance limitations according to the data speed, but the distance is typically 12,000 ft. Channel units can be provided for data services up to 64,000 bps per channel. Some systems are capable of providing channel units with speeds equal to multiples of 64,000 bps. For example, the so-called fractional T1 services can be provided with N × 64 kbps where N is an integer between 1 and 24. It should be noted that these services are not restricted to DLC; they can be provided from the central office, too.

Digital loop carrier systems can be arranged in several different operational modes, depending on the application as shown in Fig. 9-3. Where the service being provided to regular switched subscribers have relatively low traffic (< 20 CCS per access line), a concentration mode can be used as shown in Fig. 9-3(a).

Concentration means a number of subscribers, N, have access to a smaller number of channels, C, between the remote and central office terminals such that C < N. The ratio of subscribers to channels, N/C, is called the concentration ratio and is typically 2 to 10. In the concentrated mode, a subscriber's use of a particular channel lasts only for the duration of the call.

Figure 9-3(b) shows a mode where the DLC provides access to N subscribers with N channels. In this case N = C and N/C = 1, or no concentration. Generally, with this mode, subscriber N1 is preassigned to channel C1, N2 to C2, and so on. These are called *dedicated connections* because the subscribers have a permanent connection to the central office (and not just for the duration of the call, as in the concentrated mode).

Another mode, shown in Fig. 9-3(c), combines the concentrated and nonconcentrated modes. In this case, the special services subscribers requiring permanent connections from the remote terminal are assigned a dedicated channel. The remaining subscribers are served on a demand basis with some predetermined measure of concentration. The amount of concentration or, more accurately, the number of subscribers that can be served by a limited number of channels is determined by the traffic load offered by those subscribers.

Digital loop carrier systems are highly complex with a heavy dependence on firmware-controlled microcomputers for their operation. System architecture, through redundancy and many internal self-test functions, reflects the need for high reliability in subscriber plant. To support this architecture, a typical DLC includes a number of electronic buses, shown in Fig. 9-4, such as:

*   When DLC is used with fiber optic transmission media, BER performance is usually several orders of magnitude better.

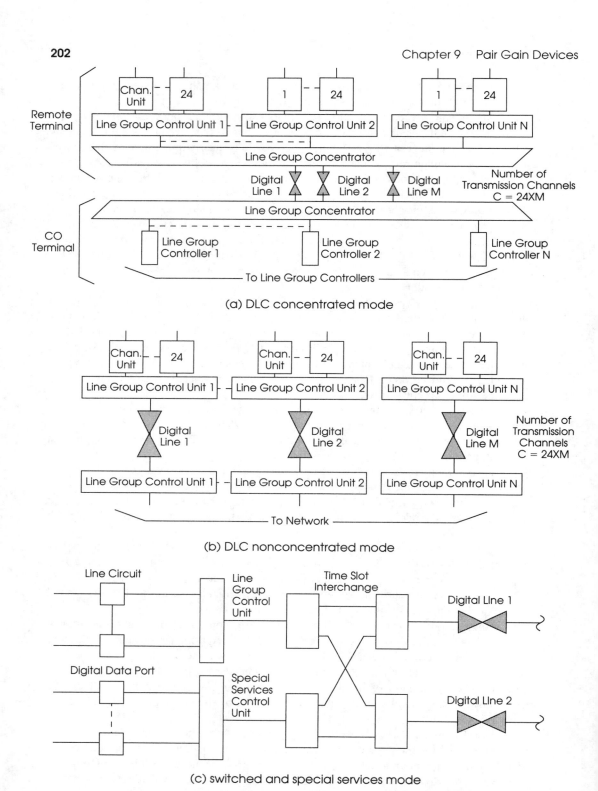

Figure 9-3 (a) DLC concentrated mode; (b) DLC nonconcentrated mode; (c) switched and special services mode

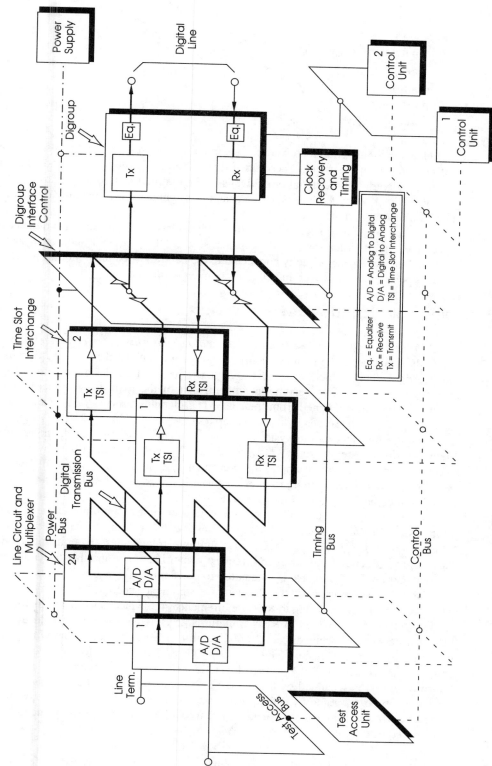

Figure 9-4 Typical digital loop carrier architecture

Power Supply

Digital Line

Digroup

Digroup Interface Control

Eq.

Eq.

Tx

Rx

Clock Recovery and Timing

Control Unit 2

Control Unit 1

Eq. = Equalizer I A/D = Analog to Digital
Rx = Receive I D/A = Digital to Analog
Tx = Transmit I TSI = Time Slot Interchange

Time Slot Interchange

2

1

Tx TSI

Tx TSI

Rx TSI

Rx TSI

Line Circuit and Multiplexer

Power Bus

Digital Transmission Bus

24

1

A/D D/A

A/D D/A

Timing Bus

Control Bus

Line Term.

Test Access Bus

Test Access Unit

203

- Digital transmission bus
- Timing bus
- Control bus
- Power bus
- Test access bus

Other functions required for proper operation are alarms, and alarm display, and a configuration control system. These are usually handled through a common interface such as a video display terminal or equivalent. The terminal is used to monitor the DLC operation as well as perform tests, make channel assignments, set operational modes and other administrative functions.

In switched applications, the DLC effectively isolates the subscriber from the central office line circuit. Therefore, call setup across the DLC requires additional steps as compared to a subscriber directly connected to the central office line circuit. From a subscriber's perspective, however, the DLC is completely transparent.

9.3 Analog Pair Gain Devices

Analog pair gain devices (also called *analog subscriber carrier systems*) are not explicitly specified in the common loop design methods. Nevertheless, they do fall into the "carrier" class, which is required, at least, in the loss design method. Analog subscriber carrier systems become an integral part of the loop design process through potential economies obtained from their use. The planning process (see Chapter 6) will identify the area to be served by these carrier systems.

Analog subscriber carrier systems depend on analog transmission methods (usually frequency division multiplex) to provide services to multiple subscribers over a single exchange cable pair. For example, a six-channel system provides a gain of five cable pairs; an eight-channel system provides a gain of seven pairs. A block diagram of a typical subscriber carrier system is shown in Fig. 9-5.

Frequency division multiplexing allows transmission of multiple carriers, each of which is *amplitude modulated* (AM). To conserve bandwidth, *single sideband* (SSB) transmission is frequently used.* Because multiple frequencies are transmitted over a fairly wide frequency band, level and frequency coordination with other telecommunication services on the same cable is mandatory to prevent interference.

Table 9-1 shows one of the frequency assignment schemes in present use. This particular scheme is according to REA requirements [4]. Typical specifications for analog carrier systems are provided in REA Bulletins [4,5]. Frequencies can extend up to 136 kHz if necessary (transmit direction only, central office reference). For AM operation, transmit levels range from about −7 dBm (±15 dB) at the lower frequencies to approximately 0 dBm (±5 dB) at the higher frequencies. Each receive carrier (and each transmit carrier) is separated by 8 kHz. If SSB operation is used, the carriers in a given direction can be separated by 4 kHz. Also, the signal levels are reduced by 10 dB with respect to AM operation. A six-channel system requires six transmit frequencies and six receive frequencies.

---

* The amplitude modulation process produces two sidebands plus the carrier. In single sideband transmission, one of the sidebands and the carrier are suppressed.

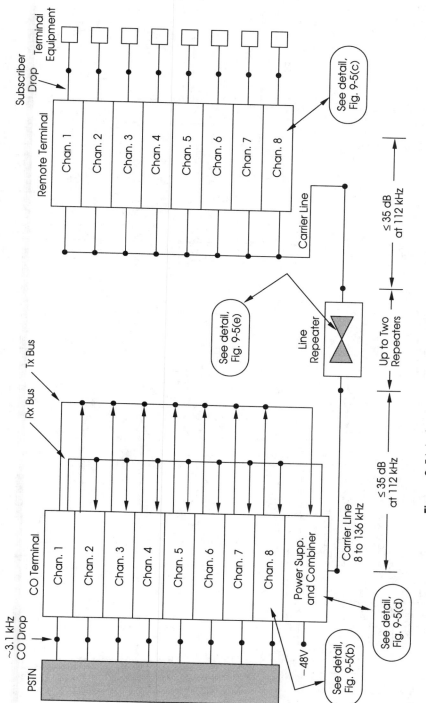

Figure 9-5(a) Analog subscriber carrier block diagram

205

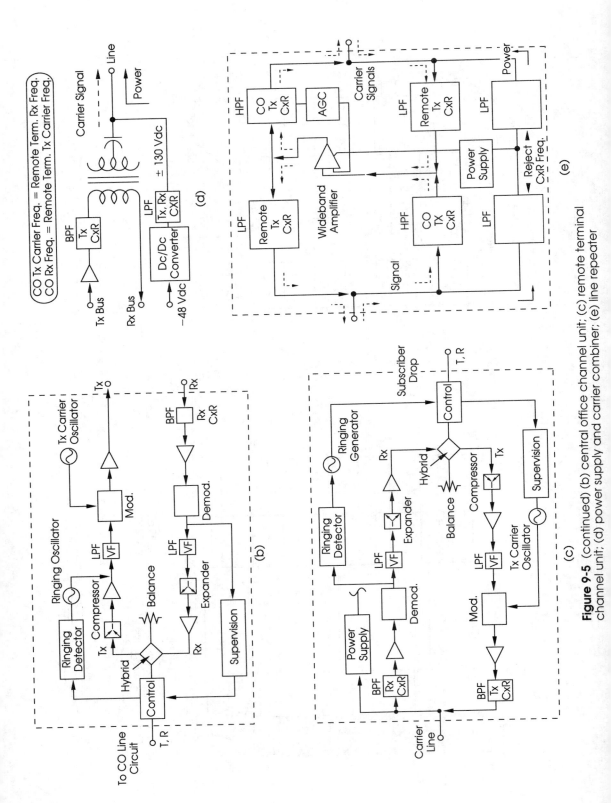

Figure 9-5 (continued) (b) central office channel unit; (c) remote terminal channel unit; (d) power supply and carrier combiner; (e) line repeater

Table 9-1 Analog Subscriber
Carrier Frequency
Assignments

Carrier Frequency (kHz)	
Receive	Transmit
8	64
12	68
16	72
20	76
24	80
28	84
32	88
36	92
40	96
44	100
48	104
52	108
56	112

Note: Receive and transmit
directions are with respect
to signals at the central
office.

The loop associated with subscriber carrier is designed for 35 dB loss (at 112 kHz) between the central office and the first repeater or remote terminal, between repeaters and between the last repeater and the remote terminal. Up to three repeaters can be equipped in a system that is loop powered (up to 140 dB total system loss is allowed).

Analog carrier systems typically use one of three powering schemes. These are:

- Loop powering
- Express pair powering
- Remote powering

Loop powering of remote equipment, including repeaters, is accomplished by using the same cable pair for powering as is used for signaling. The dc powering voltage (typically 270 V across the pair) is superimposed on the pair with the modulated carrier frequencies. In the express powering mode, the dc powering voltage is placed on a separate cable pair from the carrier frequencies. The equipment in this case will use a simpler design since impedance matching and coupling transformers will not have to carry dc and power filtering also will be simpler. With remote powering, all equipment external to the central office is powered by a power source located at or near the remote equipment.

In most situations, analog subscriber carrier is loop powered. This naturally limits the voltage and current available at a remote terminal. A negative consequence of this situation is the limited range over which the remote terminal can adequately signal and supervise a remote subscriber on the drop side of the equipment.* Unlike DLC, which can signal and supervise over a 1,900 Ω loop (from the remote terminal), analog subscriber carrier can typically signal and supervise over a 400 to 1,000 Ω loop. If the subscriber terminal equipment has a resistance of 400 Ω, the reliable operational distance is essentially zero in this case [6].

The aforementioned limitation can be overcome by boosting the drop voltage with an external power supply as shown in Fig. 9-6. This power supply is located on the subscriber's premises and must have a floating output (isolated from ground). It is placed in series with the tip or ring lead, observing proper polarity. Each volt of boost increases the signaling range by almost 50 Ω. This is an inexpensive loop extender that can be used as a field solution to a typical field problem.

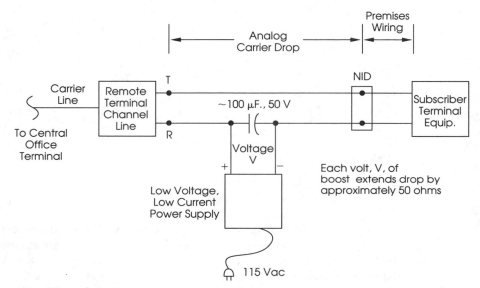

Figure 9-6 Analog subscriber carrier remote terminal loop extender

Another type of analog pair gain device provides service for two subscribers over a single pair. The block diagram for this device is shown in Fig. 9-7. One subscriber is served by conventional dc signaling and supervision. The other subscriber is served by a modulated carrier (a separate carrier frequency for each direction of transmission). Filters are required at the central office and subscriber premises to prevent the carrier frequencies from interfering with the central office line circuit and subscriber's terminal equipment. The single pair gain device is frequently used to provide service on short notice to a subscriber with a single pair drop.

Both types of systems described above provide regular switched services and are completely transparent to the subscriber. From a noise standpoint, carrier derived loops are usually superior to regular loops. Most manufacturers can provide channel units that are suitable for use with coin signaling as well as transmission-only (no signaling) circuits.

Systems with limited digital data and voice multiplexing capabilities are available from several manufacturers. These provide regular switched (exchange access) services

---

* The drop side of any telecommunication transmission equipment points toward the customer premises equipment. The line side points toward the transmission line.

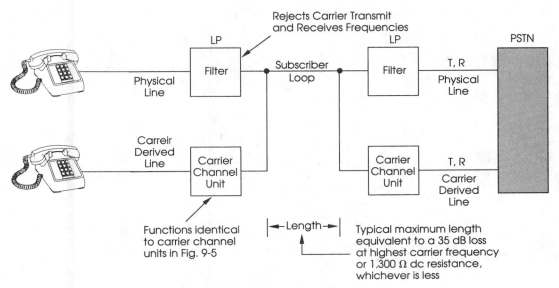

Figure 9-7 Single pair gain device

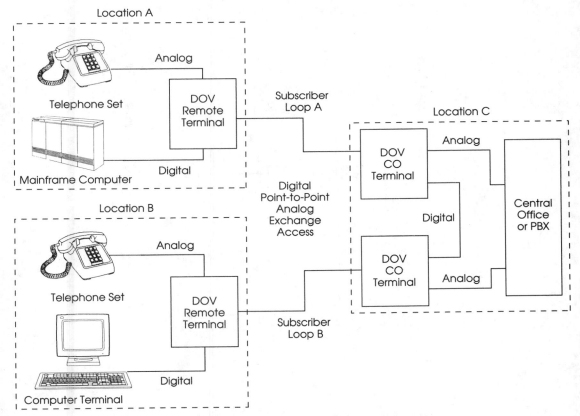

Figure 9-8 Typical data over voice (DOV) application

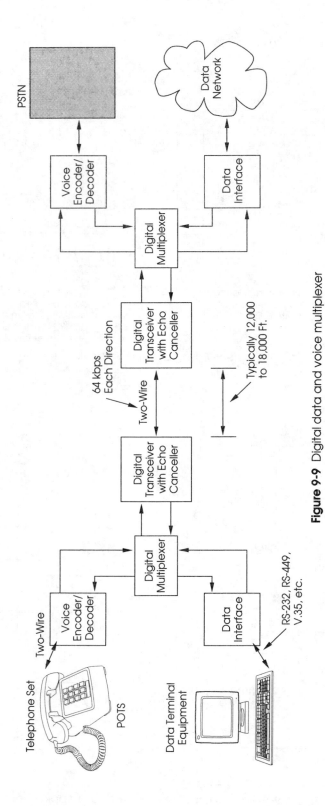

Figure 9-9 Digital data and voice multiplexer

as well as point-to-point data transmission. The transmission method can be analog or digital. The analog method uses a technique called data over voice or DOV. The data signal is transmitted using phase or frequency shift keying (PSK or FSK) with a carrier in the 100–200 kHz range. The voice portion is transmitted using regular voice frequency methods. The equipment is electrically similar to the single pair-gain device described previously. A typical application is shown in Fig 9-8.

The digital method, shown in Fig. 9-9, uses fully digital transmission. The voice signals are digitally encoded and multiplexed with the digital data signals into a 64 kbps stream. The digital method is a limited version of digital loop carrier.

REFERENCES

[1] *Integrated Digital Loop Carrier System Generic Requirements, Objectives and Interfaces*, Technical Reference TR-TSY-000303, Sept. 1986. Available from BELLCORE Customer Service.

[2] *Functional Criteria for Digital Loop Carrier Systems*, Technical Reference TR-TSY-000057, Nov. 1988. Available from BELLCORE Customer Service.

[3] *Digital Interface Between the SLC® 96 Digital Loop Carrier System and a Local Digital Switch*, Technical Reference TR-TSY-000008, Aug. 1987. Available from BELLCORE Customer Service.

[4] *Specification for Station Carrier Equipment*, REA Bulletin 345-56, Specification PE-62, March 1976. Available from REA.

[5] *Specification for Subscriber Carrier Equipment*, REA Bulletin 345-66, Specification PE-64, Oct. 1972. Available from REA.

[6] *EIA Standard 470-A-1987, Telephone Instruments with Loop Signaling*. Available from Electronic Industries Assoc.

10

Coin Line Services

Coin line (paystation) services use unique signaling schemes which have been devised to solve a specialized problem: that of providing public telephone services for a fee. The loop obviously is an important part of the overall coin line circuit. It must meet voice transmission requirements, which are identical to those for regular subscriber service, as well as accommodate the special signaling methods.

The transmission requirements have been discussed elsewhere in this book. This chapter emphasizes the signaling requirements of coin line services regulated by state public service commissions and the FCC.*

10.1 Paystation Installations

Any telecommunication device placed in a public area must meet a few basic requirements: it must be easy to use, reliable and able to withstand considerable physical abuse. It must also be designed to prevent fraudulent use. Modern paystations have a steel case and weigh over 50 lb. They include features to prevent fraudulent use by disabling the receiver, transmitter and dial during coin deposit or until the proper coins have been deposited. They have special slug detectors to minimize the successful use of counterfeit coins. Paystation instruments must be mounted within $1\frac{1}{2}°$ of vertical or else the coin mechanisms will reject even valid coins.

The simplest paystation installation costs well over $2,000. Because they are installed for public use, paystations are subject to vandalism. Paystations installed in high-use areas, such as airports, carry very high traffic, and they wear out quite fast. Coin

---

* Unregulated coin line services are beyond the scope of this book.

hoppers must be emptied regularly. These characteristics mean the paystations are very expensive to maintain, and the annual operational costs of a typical paystation can well exceed the original installation cost.

The intent of any paystation installation is to provide a public telephone service while at least covering the operation and maintenance costs plus capital recovery. Therefore, all components must be built for reliable and fault-free operation, or else the user may become angry and subject the instrument to "slam-downs" or worse. There always is revenue loss and higher maintenance in these cases.

10.2 Coin Detection

Mechanically, paystation instruments can be categorized as:

- Three-slot
- Single-slot
- Coinless

The three-slot instruments are older style units having a separate slot for each of the three coin denominations: nickel, dime and quarter. Each slot will perform various validity tests on the coins as they pass through. Rejected coins either will be returned without enabling a call or will jam in the chute. Valid coins will allow the call to proceed.

Single-slot instruments are more modern. One slot will accept the three coin denominations. The coins are then automatically directed into different testing chutes. Coinless paystations do not have any slots at all. They are used on operator assisted calls for third-party or calling card service billing only.*

On calls requiring additional deposits, such as toll calls, coins must be deposited as directed by the operator or *automated coin toll service* (ACTS) recorded announcement before the call will be extended.†

Two simple methods are used to signal coin deposits to the operator. In the first method, which is used in older instruments, as coins are deposited, they will follow one of three coin chutes as described above. After being tested on the way down the chute, valid coins will pass by either a cupped bronze gong (called "bell") or a helical flat wire gong (called "cathedral gong"). A nickel will strike the bell once and a dime will strike it twice (upper and lower edge). A quarter will strike the cathedral gong once.‡ The resulting sounds are picked up by the special coin signal transmitter in the paystation,

---

* Calling card service allows subscribers or paystation customers to dial billing information by using the DTMF keypad and without any operator assistance. Billing information can be sent anytime after the familiar "bong" tone.

† ACTS replaces the need for a human operator on many types of routine coin calls. By means of recorded announcements, the caller is directed to deposit the amount required for the call that was dialed. The ACTS equipment counts, collects or returns the coins as required.

‡ These bells and gongs go back at least 100 years, and the price for each sound has gone down since then. Consider the following item from "50 and 100 Years Ago" in the July 1990 issue of *Scientific American*: "July, 1890: A novel telephone station is being introduced in Connecticut. The instrument cannot be used unless a fee is paid. If five cents is dropped in the slot, it strikes a bell of a high note, once. A quarter strikes a bell of a lower note, once. A half dollar strikes that bell twice, while a silver dollar strikes a very low tone 'cathedral gong'."

which conveys the sounds to the operator via the loop. The actual frequencies of these sounds are around 1,100 Hz for the bell and 800 Hz for the gong. They are easy to distinguish by the operator because of their distinctly different sound (frequency, attack and decay time). Instruments using this type of coin signaling are not compatible with ACTS.

In the second method, used in modern instruments, the mechanical gongs are replaced by solid-state electronic circuitry. Coins are counted by an electronic totalizer (using trip switches), which generates a tone pulse (or burst) for each five cents deposited. Therefore, a nickel would generate one pulse, a dime two pulses and a quarter five pulses. The pulses are placed on the loop for transmission to the operator by simple transformer coupling.

On calls for which operator identification of the coins is needed (ACTS not available), a single 2,200 Hz tone burst can be used. Where ACTS is available, a dual tone of 1,700 and 2,200 Hz must be used. The level can be as high as 0 dBm at the instrument output, but this will depend on several factors such as loop length and off-hook voltage. The received level at the operator or ACTS must fall between 0 dBm and –28 dBm. For ACTS, the tone bursts representing the various coin denominations must follow the timing protocol shown in Fig. 10-1.*

The ACTS equipment will not recognize DTMF signals as coin deposits, but it is possible for the operator to mistake skillfully entered DTMF digits for coin denomination tones. This requires the DTMF pad to be disabled when coins could be deposited in all instruments except those served by ACTS. In some instruments, the receiver can operate as an inefficient transmitter over which fraudulent coin tones could be sent. Also, the transmitter itself could be used for this purpose, to say nothing of the potential problem caused by ambient noise. Therefore, the transmitter and receiver are disabled during the times when coins could be deposited.

The totalizer (also called rate register) in paystations has a "local mode" and "toll mode." In the local mode, the totalizer does not provide a readout or take action until the "initial rate" has been deposited. The initial rate is the deposit required to complete calls to other than free numbers. In the toll mode, immediate readout of the totalizer takes place. This is required on operator or ACTS-type calls where subsequent deposits are collected from the caller in order to complete the call.

Modern paystation instruments include some type of a rejector mechanism that will accept a very high percentage (80 percent or better) of genuine coins and reject the majority of slugs encountered in the field. It would be impossible to build a rejector mechanism that is 100 percent foolproof.

Rejector mechanisms operate as follows: The first step is to sort the coins by basic size (nickel, dime or quarter) and divert them to their respective channel or chute. Here they are individually checked for proper weight and diameter. If a coin passes these tests, it is tested for perforations (such as would be found on a washer) and released down an inclined rail. As it rolls down the rail, the coin is tested for proper thickness. Next, it passes by a permanent magnet, which will slow the coin if it is metallic. The speed at which the coin travels is determined by its material composition. Ferrous slugs will be slowed the most, plastic slugs will not be slowed at all. If it travels too fast or slow as it leaves the rail, a slug will strike certain deflectors and be diverted to the reject outlet. Some instruments test the coins for hardness and elasticity. Many times, counterfeit coins will jam in the chutes and require disassembly of the instrument to clear.

---

*   The data in this figure is from [1].

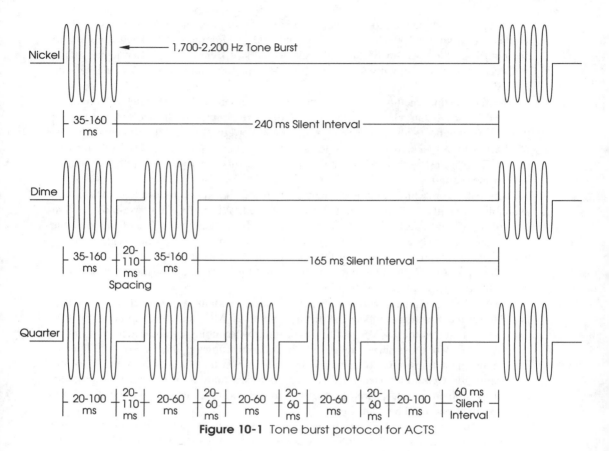

Figure 10-1 Tone burst protocol for ACTS

The rejector mechanism is a precision instrument which takes considerable experience to manufacture and considerable practice to adjust in the field. Only a few companies make good ones, and these are found in instruments made by many different manufacturers.

10.3 Postpay and Prepay

Traditional coin line services fall into two basic categories: *postpay* and *prepay*. There are many variations of each. These variations encompass functional differences in the way coins are collected, counted and returned and the voltages (and polarities) placed on the loop during signaling. Due to these differences, there must be a very close coordination between the central office line circuit and the paystation instrument. Each has a variety of options that must be set to ensure compatibility and successful operation.

The two most widely used types (semi-postpay and full prepay) will be discussed here. The basic difference between these two, as far as the user is concerned, is how coin deposits are treated.

The coins deposited into a semi-postpay (called "postpay" from here on) instrument are immediately collected and never returned or refunded (unless they are rejected) regardless of the call disposition. The coins deposited into a prepay instrument, on the other hand, may be returned or collected as determined by the call disposition. In addition, on calls requiring operator intervention, the operator has complete control over collecting and returning coins with prepay instruments. This is not the case with postpay. The basic operational differences are shown in Table 10-1.

Table 10-1 Semi-Postpay and Prepay

Type	Requirement	Coin Status
Semi-Postpay	No coin deposit required to dial	Always collected, no coin return
Coin First — Prepay	Must deposit coin to dial	Collect or return as required
Dial Tone First — Prepay	No coin deposit required to dial	Collect or return as required

10.4 Postpay

A simplified schematic of a typical postpay instrument is shown in Fig. 10-2. It is electrically similar to a regular telephone instrument except for three things: a coin relay, coin collecting and counting mechanism, and coin signal transmitter (or equivalent). The central office line circuit is similar to a regular subscriber line circuit, too, except it uses reverse battery signaling.

The operation of a postpay coin line is simple. First, consider a chargeable call. When a user lifts the handset, a low resistance is connected across tip and ring of the loop, and the line circuit will return dial tone in the normal way. Normal loop polarity is tip grounded and ring at nominal –48 V. No initial rate deposit is required. The user dials (with a rotary dial, in the case of Fig. 10-2), and a connection is set up. When the called party answers and answer supervision is passed through the switching network, the line circuit immediately reverses the battery polarity applied to the loop giving –48 V on the tip, and ground on the ring.

The coin relay in the instrument is polarity sensitive. When it detects reverse battery answer supervision, it operates. This action:

1. Shorts out the transmitter, which prevents conversation by the calling party;
2. In older instruments, disables the receiver to prevent it from being used as a transmitter (newer instruments use a unidirectional amplifier connected to the receiver); and
3. Disables the tone dialing pad (if equipped) to prevent free transmission of coded information via DTMF signals.

When the initial rate is deposited, some of the coin relay contacts are released (coin shunt contacts in Fig. 10-2), which removes the transmission impairments. Normal conversation can now take place. Upon call completion (the parties go on-hook), the line circuit restores the loop to normal polarity, and it is ready for the next call.

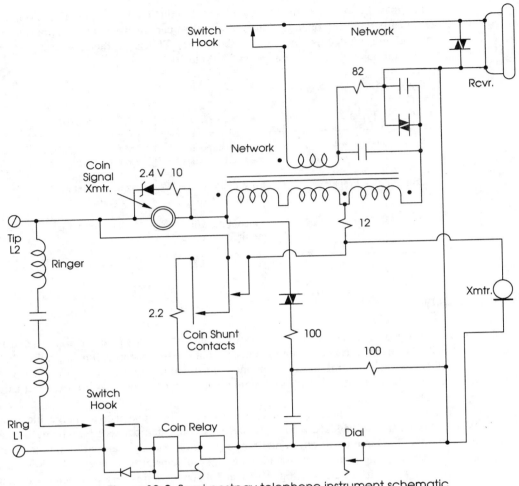

Figure 10-2 Semi-postpay telephone instrument schematic

Postpay paystations will always collect a coin as long as it is valid. Collection will take place even if the coin is deposited inadvertently, such as frequently happens when a user, accustomed to prepay instruments, attempts a call on a postpay instrument by depositing coins before dialing.

On free or abandoned calls, no further action is required to return coins since none were deposited.

The loops associated with postpay coin lines are designed in the normal way. Postpay lines are always loop start. The requirements for a typical postpay paystation installation are:

- Minimum off-hook voltage: 4.5 to 5.5 V
- Minimum loop current: 20 to 23 mA
- Maximum loop resistance: 1,600 Ω

The operation of coin lines may be upset by excessive longitudinal currents due to power line induction. If this is a problem, induction neutralizing transformers or noise chokes can be used to reduce interfering currents.

10.5 Prepay

Prepay instruments have the same physical appearance as postpay instruments, but they are considerably more complex internally. With this complexity comes much more flexibility and difficulty in making fraudulent calls. The two most common types of prepay options are discussed.

A prepay line circuit can be optioned for either "coin first" or "dial tone first" operation. With coin first, which is an older method, dial tone is provided to the user, but it cannot be broken until the initial rate is deposited.* The coin is returned on calls to free numbers. With dial tone first, dial tone can be broken without a coin deposit, and free calls can be made.

Dial tone first is the preferred option because calls can be made to emergency or free numbers without any coins. If a call is attempted to a chargeable number, however, and no initial rate deposit has been made, the caller will be routed to reorder tone or a recorded announcement. Calls requiring operator intervention and subsequent deposits, such as long distance toll calls, are under the operator's control.

A simplified schematic for a typical prepay instrument is shown in Fig. 10-3. As seen, a modern prepay instrument is considerably more complex than the postpay instrument previously described.† The typical prepay instrument contains the following:

- Coin relay
- Power supply
- Coin tone oscillator
- Rate register
- Coin pulse generator
- Initial rate controller
- Rate relay

The associated central office line is equipped with:

- Sources of ±130 V collect and refund potential
- Sources of ±48 V control and supervision potentials
- Coin control circuitry

Using these voltages, there is a variety of control signals that the line circuit can place on the loop. These are shown in Table 10-2. All voltages are with respect to ground; a prepay paystation instrument requires an earth ground to operate.‡

Assuming coin first operation, an off-hook will connect the instrument to the line circuit, which provides dial tone. Dial tone cannot be broken, however, because the dial is disabled by the released rate relay contacts. The central office line circuit is also arranged to prevent dialing until it detects an unbalanced current on the loop.

---

* Some instruments also will cut off the receiver so dial tone cannot be heard until the initial rate is deposited.

† With slight modification, many prepay instruments can be used as semi-postpay.

‡ Earth ground is required on all paystations for protection and safety. On postpay coin lines, however, the ground is not a functional requirement.

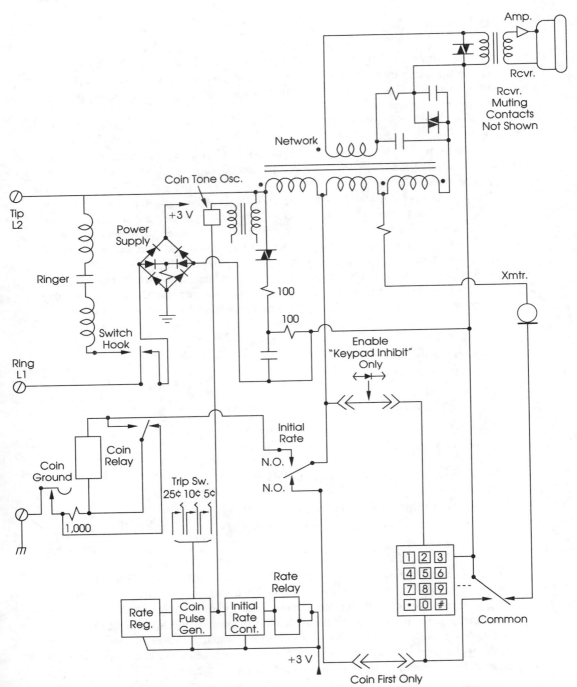

Figure 10-3 Prepay telephone instrument schematic, simplified

Table 10-2 Prepay Coin Line Control Signals

Signal	Action
Dial Tone First Idle	−48 V Ring/Ground Tip
Reverse Battery	−48 V Tip/Ground Ring
Coin First Idle	−48 V Ring/Open Tip
Keypad Inhibit	+48 V Ring/Ground Tip
Initial Rate Test	−48 V Tip/Open Ring
Stuck Coin Test	+48 V Tip/Open Ring
Coin Return	−130 V Tip/Open Ring
Coin Collect	+130 V Tip/Open Ring

The rate register counts (totalizes) the coins as they are deposited by the user. The first coin deposited by the caller will close the coin relay ground contact, which provides a 1,000 Ω ground to the normally open rate relay contacts. At the same time, the rate register pulses the initial rate control. When the initial rate has been deposited, the rate register enables the initial rate control, which, in turn, operates the rate relay.

Operation of the rate relay enables the dial (in Fig. 10-3, a pushbutton tone keypad or DTMF dial). At the same time, the 1,000 Ω coin relay ground unbalances the loop through the operated rate relay contacts. The central office makes an "initial rate test" (see Table 10-2) by momentarily opening the ring lead to detect this unbalance. The user is then allowed to break dial tone and make the call. Meanwhile, coins are held in suspense in the coin chute throughout the call.

A free call causes no further action until it is completed. If the call is free or abandoned, the central office line circuit will apply coin return voltage (−130 V) between the tip lead and ground when the user hangs up. If the call is connected, reverse battery supervision is returned by the line circuit. Some instruments will disable the keypad when this happens, but most instruments keep the keypad enabled so end-to-end signaling can be used.* If the call is chargeable, coin collect voltage (+130 V) is applied when the call is completed.

The collect and return voltages cause the coin relay to direct the coins to the proper place. If collect, the coins go into the coin box; if return, the coins go into the coin return hopper.

The coin relay is designed to operate completely on a 200 ms pulse, but the central office line circuit usually applies a pulse lasting about 500 ms to account for possible distortion by the loop. The relay has a slow release time to ensure proper disposal of the coins. In modern switching systems, the line circuit will automatically make a "stuck coin test" (see Table 10-2) to determine if coin disposal took place. A stuck coin is indicated by a persistent coin relay ground after the collect or return signal has been given. If disposal did not take place, a central office alarm is raised, and the coin line may be automatically taken out of service.

On calls requiring additional deposits (operator or ACTS), the initial call setup sequence is identical to above. In this case, however, the initial rate is refunded upon operator answer. The automatic return sequence can be a function of the line circuit or the trunk used to make the operator connection. The operator does not return answer supervision as such; the coin return sequence is only a consequence of operator answer.

---

* The process of using a DTMF keypad on an instrument at one end of a call to control equipment at the other end is called "end-to-end signaling."

Upon connection of the operator, an "operator attached" signal is sent to the central office. Similarly, when the operator disconnects, an "operator released" signal is sent. These signals are not specifically used by coin first lines but are used by dial tone first lines, as will be explained later.

With coin first, the keypad is disabled until the initial rate has been deposited as explained above. When the deposit is collected or returned (as would be the case on an operator call), the keypad is again disabled by control circuits in the paystation instrument. Since calling card service and end-to-end signaling requires the use of the DTMF keypad, it obviously must be enabled during the signaling interval. Therefore, the paystation instrument must be modified to enable the keypad on these types of calls. This modification is called "coin retention." Also, reverse battery answer supervision will be applied to the loop when the far end answers, which may prevent the keypad from functioning unless the instrument has further modifications to allow the keypad to operate normally regardless of loop polarity.

As additional coins are deposited, the coin pulse generator pulses the coin tone oscillator, which applies a coin denomination tone burst for each five cents deposited, as explained earlier. As the tones are sent, the transmitter and receiver in the paystation handset are muted (disabled). The receiver is muted to reduce the level of coin tones reaching the user's ear, and also to prevent the fraudulent use of these tones. The transmitter is muted to prevent the application of fraudulent coin tones on the loop and to reject ambient noise.

The operator or ACTS can collect or refund the coins as necessary by sending appropriate control signals to the central office.* The signals are converted to coin return or coin collect voltages by the line circuit and applied to the loop. Also, the operator has the ability to ring-back the calling party to collect additional fees, if necessary. Once the coins are collected (or returned as the case may be), the operator will extend the call and drop off the line. If the call requires yet additional deposits, the operator will come back on the line and collect more money. The sequence is the same as previously described.

The schematic for a typical dial tone first instrument is identical to Fig. 10-3 except for option settings. The basic operation of dial tone first is as explained for coin first, except dial tone can be broken before the initial rate has been deposited. The totalizer starts out in the local mode as before.

If the call is free or abandoned, no further action is required by the circuit. If the pre-pay call is chargeable and the proper coins have been deposited, the totalizer takes action by enabling the coin relay ground. The coin relay ground is detected by the initial rate test and the call is allowed to proceed. If no coins (or not enough coins) have been deposited, the coin relay ground will not be present when the initial rate test is made. In this case, the call will be routed to reorder tone or recorded announcement because the test failed. On successful calls, reverse battery answer supervision will be placed on the loop by the line circuit when the far end answers. As with coin first, this may disable the keypad unless the instrument has been modified.

* A variety of signaling methods is used between the operator and the central office. The three most common methods are *multi-wink, in-band signaling* and *expanded in-band signaling* (EIS). The first uses a series of winks (short on-hook transitions) to signal various states such as coin collect and return, ring-back and operator attached and operator released. The second uses tone combinations of 700 and 1,100 Hz for coin collect, 1,100 and 1,700 Hz for coin return and 700 and 1,700 Hz for ring-back. EIS uses a similar tone scheme but is expanded to provide tones for operator released, operator attached, etc.

Operator or ACTS calls are handled exactly as for coin first except the operator attached signal is converted by the central office line circuit to a "keypad inhibit" signal and applied to the loop. This is a positive polarity voltage rather than negative voltage as shown for "dial tone first idle" in Table 10-2.*

The keypad inhibit signal actually does more than its name implies: First, the positive voltage is sensed by the paystation instrument, which disables the pushbutton keypad to prevent its fraudulent use as previously described. Instruments used with ACTS do not require the keypad inhibit, and these may be modified to enable the keypad at all times. Second, the positive voltage changes the totalizer in the paystation instrument to the toll mode so coin deposits cause an immediate readout of the totalizer. The associated coin denomination tones are detected by the operator or ACTS equipment.

Upon collection or return of the coins, an "operator released" signal is sent to the central office by the operator. The line circuit removes the keypad inhibit signal (positive voltage) and reapplies the normal negative voltage to the loop. As before, reverse battery answer supervision will be applied when the far end answers.

Loops associated with prepay coin lines usually have the same basic requirements as postpay lines, but the prepay instrument requires a good earth ground. Without it, the paystation will not function. Most prepay paystations are loop start, but many can be optioned for ground start. The requirements for a typical prepay paystation installation are:

- Minimum central office voltage: 48 V
- Minimum off-hook voltage: 4.5 to 5.5 V
- Minimum loop current: 23 mA
- Minimum coin relay operate current: 41 mA
- Maximum loop resistance: 1,600 Ω
- Maximum ground resistance: 30 to 50 Ω
- Maximum earth potential: ±3 Vdc

REFERENCE

[1] *Notes on the BOC Intra-LATA Networks—1986*, Technical Reference TR-NPL-000275, April 1986. Available from BELLCORE Customer Service.

---

* The positive polarity (+48 V nominal) is not to be confused with reverse battery, which is the reversal of the battery and ground potentials on the tip and ring leads.

A

The Decibel

A sound increase from one power level to another heard by the human ear leaves an impression of increased loudness that is approximately proportional to the logarithm of the ratio of the two power levels. The original unit given to this phenomenon was the "bel." It, however, was not convenient to use and is not seen in practical problems. This gave rise to the *decibel* (dB), which is bel/10. A change in level of 1 dB is "barely perceptible to the ear," and a change of 2 dB is only "slightly apparent [1]."

The decibel is used in all forms of communications work to express the ratio of two powers according to the formula

$$dB = 10 \log \frac{P_2}{P_1}$$

where

P_2 and P_1 = the powers being compared

The sign resulting from the calculation indicates which power is greater. If the sign is positive, then $P_2 > P_1$; if negative, then $P_2 < P_1$.

The practical use of the decibel comes from its logarithmic nature, which permits the large power ranges used in communications work to be expressed and manipulated in convenient numbers as seen in Table A-1.

Strictly speaking, only power ratios can be measured using the decibel. It is customary, though, to express the ratio of two voltages or currents in dB also. This must be done with caution since the expression is only valid when the voltages (or currents) are measured across identical or conjugate impedances. If the impedances are not the same, correction factors must be used.

Table A-1 Use of the Decibel

dB	Power Ratio	
	Gain	Loss
0.0	1.00	1.000
0.1	1.02	0.977
0.5	1.12	0.891
1.0	1.26	0.794
2.0	1.58	0.631
3.0	1.99	0.501
6.0	3.98	0.251
10.0	10.0	0.100
20.0	100.0	0.050
30.0	1,000.0	0.001
60.0	1,000,000.0	0.000,001

The relationship between power and voltage is

$$P1 = V1^2 / Z1 \text{ and } P2 = V2^2 / Z2$$

where

$V1$ and $V2$ = the voltages across impedances $Z1$ and $Z2$
$P1$ and $P2$ = the resulting powers

Taking the ratio of P2 and P1, as above, and assuming the impedances are resistive

$$dB = 10 \log [P2 / P1] \quad \text{or}$$

$$dB = 10 \log \{ [V2^2 / R2] / [V1^2 / R1] \}$$

Splitting and reducing terms gives

$$dB = 20 \log [V2 / V1] + 10 \log [R1 / R2]$$

A similar expression can be developed for two currents. A frequent error is to ignore the second term containing the resistances. For example, consider the case where the resistances at the power measurement points are $R1 = 600$ and $R2 = 300\ \Omega$. The error is:

$$dB \text{ error} = 10 \log [600 / 300] = 3 \text{ dB}$$

This is a common error that occurs when a transmission test set double terminates a measurement point. That is, the set's internal impedance of 600 Ω is connected to a circuit already terminated in 600 Ω, giving a total parallel resistance of 300 Ω. The correct arrangement would be to switch the set to a high-impedance bridging connection such that the power is measured into the 600 Ω circuit impedance only.

Assuming the impedances are the same (R1 = R2)

$$dB = 20 \log [\, V2 \, / \, V1 \,]$$

The equation above is easily verified.

Many times power is measured in dBm or dBW. This is a comparison of the power in question to a standard value of 1 mW or 1 W, respectively. Therefore, –90 dBm is a power 90 dB below 1 mW, and +90 dBm is 90 dB above 1 mW. The power 0 dBm is equal to 1 mW. Similarly, 0 dBW is 1 W. Other references are used in power measurements besides the milliwatt or watt.

All telecommunication circuits have an input power level, output power level and circuit loss or gain. When decibels are used to characterize these quantities, the following equation is used

$$\text{Gain (dB)} = \text{Output Level (dBm)} - \text{Input Level (dBm)}$$

where

$$\text{Loss} = -\text{Gain}$$

Thus, simple addition and subtraction can be used to find the third quantity when any two are known. This greatly simplifies field work and speeds up testing and alignment.

Examples: A measurement of +3.0 dB means there is a gain (or the power has increased) by a factor of 2; –3.0 dB means there is a loss (or a decrease) by a factor of 0.5.

Consider a signal with level = –13 dBm injected into a loop with loss = 5.5 dB (or, stated another way, gain = –5.5 dB). The level at the other end can be easily found from –13 dBm –5.5 dB = –18.5 dBm. In terms of power ratios: an input level of –13 dBm corresponds to a power of 0.05 mW. The loop loss of 5.5 dB corresponds to a power ratio of 0.282. The output power is then 0.05 mW × 0.282 = 0.014 mW, which is –18.5 dBm.

REFERENCE

[1] Langford-Smith, F., ed. *Radiotron Designer's Handbook*. Harrison, New Jersey: RCA Electronic Components, 4th edition, 1953, p. 807.

B

Transmission Level Point

The *transmission level point* (TLP) concept is used throughout the telecommunication industry to specify the point in a circuit at which a certain test tone level is expected during testing. The basic relationship between the different units used with TLPs is

$$TLP = dBm - dBm0$$

where

dBm = absolute level with respect to 1 mW (this is the level measured by a transmission measuring set)

dBm0 = absolute level referred to the 0 TLP

TLP = the transmission level point (or reference) in question

Therefore, at the 0 TLP, TLP = 0 and the expected level is 0 dBm0 or (0 dBm absolute with a 0 dBm input). At a −2 TLP a measured level of 0 dBm would be +2 dBm0, and a level of −2 dBm0 would have an absolute level of −4 dBm. By convention, all levels are measured at 1,000 Hz*. TLPs may be established for other frequencies if desired.

The transmitting end of a two-wire circuit (such as a simple loop) is considered to be the 0 TLP. The TLP at the receiving end is established by the overall circuit loss. For example, consider a loop with 8 dB loss. Since the transmitting end is the 0 TLP, then the

---

* Actually, the exact frequency is 1,004 Hz to avoid interaction of the test tones with digital modulation schemes used in switching and transmission.

receiving end is a −8 TLP. A loop in this case is bidirectional and has the same loss in both directions, but the transmitting and receiving TLPs at a given end are different. This apparent ambiguity is not a problem with two-wire circuits as long as the directions and the 0 TLP has been established. It is also not a problem with four-wire circuits, because the transmitting and receiving TLPs for one direction of transmission are independent of the other direction. The concept of a simple loop is illustrated in Fig. B-1 for a two-wire circuit.

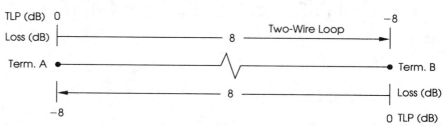

Figure B-1 Transmission level point of simple loop

The TLP concept can be applied to noise measurements in a similar manner. For example, a satisfactory voice circuit provides a 30 dB signal-to-noise ratio (S/N). Therefore, the noise at the 0 TLP must not exceed −30 dBm (−30 dBm0). For a noise measuring set reading in dBrnC, this is +60 dBrnC (+60 dBrnC0). At the −8 TLP, the measured noise should not exceed +52 dBrnC (+60 dBrnC0).

A simple end-office may be configured as shown in Fig. B-2. This circuit can be considered to consist of several tandem connections: station, loop, end-office switching system, carrier equipment, and four-wire toll switching system. TLPs can be established for the individual parts or the overall circuit.

Several conventions are used in this type of circuit to allow standardization. The transmitting direction on the two-wire side of the digital end-office line circuit is the 0 TLP. If the connection being considered is as shown (toll connecting trunk), the trunk circuit loss is prescribed as 3 dB. Since there is a 3 dB pad in the toll test board the total loss to the measurement point is 6 dB. Therefore, the test board is −6 TLP.* Thus, an absolute level of 0 dBm injected into the line circuit would be measured as −6 dBm at the test board. At both the input and output the level is 0 dBm0.

Similarly, the TLP in the receiving direction at the line circuit is −6 TLP since a 0 dBm signal injected at the test board is expected to be at −6 dBm when measured at the line circuit.

The intervening carrier equipment has standardized TLPs of −16 at the input and +7 at the output. This standardization allows properly adjusted carrier channels to be easily patched during testing or troubleshooting. At the modulating input (usually abbreviated "mod in") to the carrier, a level of 0 dBm0 would measure −16 dBm. At the other end of the carrier ("demod out"), the level is still 0 dBm0 but measures +7 dBm.

Further consideration of Fig. B-2 shows that if a test call is made at the station end of the loop, a level of +8 dBm must be injected at the station to give 0 dBm at the 0 TLP (and −6 dBm at the −6 TLP). It follows that the station is at a +8 TLP in the transmit direction.

It is not necessary to use a +8 TLP, however, when describing the station end of this loop. The input to the loop could be considered a 0 TLP and the output a −8 TLP, as

---

*   A digital pad is used in a digital switching system of this kind, which gives a decoded level that is reduced by 3 dB.

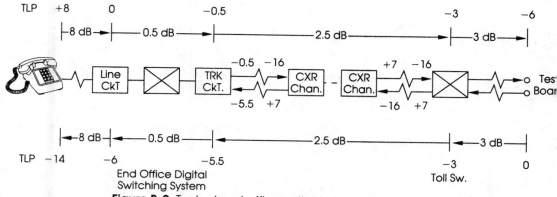

Figure B-2 Typical end office switching system TLP

before. Then, at the input to the line circuit, the TLP can be reset to 0 TLP (and this is usually done). Therefore, each part of the overall circuit can be considered to have its own 0 TLP. In many cases, the 0 TLP may be defined but may not physically exist.

One final set of calculations will round out this discussion. If a station-to-test board test is made with 0 dBm injected into the loop at the station end (for the purposes of this calculation, +8 TLP), what level will be measured at the test board? The levels with respect to the 0 TLP can be determined by using the relationship initially described above.

For the station end (transmit)

$$dBm0 = dBm - TLP = (0\ dBm) - (+8\ TLP) = -8\ dBm0$$

For the test board end (receive)

$$dBm = (-8\ dBm0) + (-6\ TLP) = -14\ dBm$$

C

Derivation of ABCD Functions for Transmission Line with Distributed Parameters

Let a transmission line, such as a twisted pair subscriber loop, be represented by complex distributed series impedances and shunt admittances as shown in Fig. C-1. The series impedance per unit length is $Z = R + j\omega L$, and the shunt admittance per unit length is $Y = G + j\omega C$. R, L, G and C are called the primary constants, and ω is the radian frequency ($2\pi \times$ frequency, where frequency is given in hertz).*

The following units apply to the impedance, admittance, and primary constants

Z= series impedance in ohms per unit length

Y= shunt admittance in siemens per unit length

R= series resistance in ohms per unit length

L= series inductance in henries per unit length

G= shunt conductance in siemens per unit length

C= shunt capacitance in farads per unit length

---

* The term primary "constants" implies that these parameters are constant under all conditions for any given cable construction. Actually, they are not; to some extent they depend on the frequency and temperature. The dependence is greater with some parameters than with others.

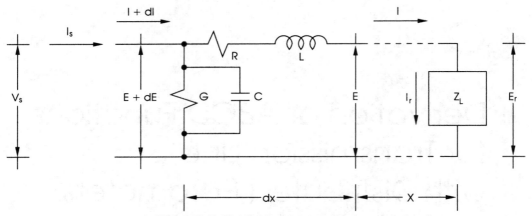

Figure C-1 Distributed parameter transmission line

where

     the length is in consistent units of miles, kilofeet, kilometers, etc.

If

     E = voltage across the line at distance x from the receiving end, and

     I = current in the line at distance x from the receiving end

then, in the short distance dx, the voltage changes an amount dE as a result of the voltage drop in the series impedance Zdx due to the line current I. Also, the current changes an amount dI as a result of current flow in the shunt admittance Ydx due to the voltage E across it. Therefore,

$$dE = IZdx$$

and

$$dI = EYdx$$

Rearranging gives

$$\frac{dE}{dx} = ZI$$

and

$$\frac{dI}{dx} = YE$$

Differentiating these expressions with respect to x yields

$$\frac{d^2E}{dx^2} = Z\frac{dI}{dx} = ZYE$$

and

$$\frac{d^2I}{dx^2} = Y\frac{dE}{dx} = ZYI$$

Let the quantity ρ be defined such that

$$\rho^2 = ZY \text{ or } \rho = (ZY)^{1/2}$$

Note that ρ is called the *propagation constant*. Substituting for Z and Y gives

$$\rho = [(R + j\omega L)(G + j\omega C)]^{1/2}$$

per unit length.

The term ρ is complex and can be rewritten as:

$$\rho = \alpha + j\beta$$

where

$$\alpha = \text{attenuation constant per unit length}$$

$$\beta = \text{phase constant per unit length}$$

Substituting ρ into the differential equations gives

$$\frac{d^2E}{dx^2} = \rho^2E$$

and

$$\frac{d^2I}{dx^2} = \rho^2I$$

These are the standard differential equations for wave propagation and have easily confirmed solutions of the form

$$E = E_1e^{\rho x} + E_2e^{-\rho x}$$

and

$$I = I_1e^{\rho x} + I_2e^{-\rho x}$$

where

$$e = \text{the fundamental numerical constant } (2.71828\ldots), \text{ and}$$

$$E_1, E_2, I_1 \text{ and } I_2 \text{ depend on the initial conditions}$$

Taking the first derivative with respect to x yields

$$\frac{dE}{dx} = E_1 \rho e^{\rho x} - E_2 \rho e^{-\rho x}$$

but

$$\frac{dE}{dx} = ZI$$

as previously found. Therefore

$$ZI = E_1 \rho e^{\rho x} - E_2 \rho e^{-\rho x}$$

or

$$I = \frac{E_1}{Z} \rho e^{\rho x} - \frac{E_2}{Z} \rho e^{-\rho x}$$

which, by comparison to the original solution, gives

$$I_1 = \frac{E_1}{Z} \rho$$

and

$$I_2 = \frac{E_2}{Z} \rho$$

Since $\rho = (ZY)^{1/2}$, then

$$I_1 = \frac{E_1}{(Z/Y)^{1/2}}$$

and

$$I_2 = \frac{E_2}{(Z/Y)^{1/2}}$$

The quantity $(Z/Y)^{1/2}$ is called the *characteristic impedance*, Z_0.* Substituting the primary constants gives

$$Z_0 = \left[\frac{(R + j\omega L)}{(G + j\omega C)} \right]^{1/2}$$

Z_0 is a complex quantity of the form $Z_0 = R + jX$, where R and X are the real and imaginary parts, respectively. Together, the characteristic impedance Z_0 and the propagation constant $\rho = \alpha + j\beta$ are known as the secondary parameters of a transmission line. Both are stated completely in terms of the primary constants R, L, G and C.

Z_0 is expressed in ohms and is independent of transmission line length but dependent on frequency. ρ has dimensions of per unit length and its real (α) and imaginary (β) parts are expressed in the following dimensions: The attenuation constant α is expressed in nepers per unit length (frequently converted to decibels per unit length as shown below); and the phase constant β is expressed in radians per unit length.

The attenuation constant is frequently used to express the insertion loss of a transmission line such as a subscriber loop. This is not strictly accurate, and it is important to note that α can be used to provide the actual insertion loss of the transmission line only when the line is terminated in its characteristic impedance Z_0. In this special case, the insertion loss of the line, in decibels, is

$$\text{Attenuation (dB)} = 20 \log \left[e^{\alpha(\text{nepers})} \right]$$

$$= 8.686 \, \alpha \, (\text{nepers})$$

The general case, for any terminating impedance, is developed in Appendix D.

The derivation given above for the secondary parameters can be used to solve transmission line problems in telecommunications and, specifically, for nonloaded telecommunication cables. The results, of course, are only as good as the values for the primary constants. In practice, the primary constants are difficult to measure directly, but the secondary parameters are comparatively easy to measure. The primary constants are then calculated from the secondary parameters.

To complete the derivation of the ABCD functions for a distributed parameter transmission line, it is necessary to find the quantities E_1, E_2, I_1 and I_2. These can be found by substituting initial conditions into the wave propagation equations. At distance $x = 0$, the initial conditions are

$$E(0) = E_1 + E_2$$

and

$$Z_0 I(0) = E_1 - E_2$$

Then

$$E(0) + Z_0 I(0) = 2E_1$$

---

* Z_0 for uniform lines is also called *iterative impedance* or *image impedance*.

and

$$E(0) - Z_0 I(0) = 2E_2$$

In general

$$E(x) = \tfrac{1}{2}\left\{ [E(0) + Z_0 I(0)]e^{\rho x} + [E(0) - Z_0 I(0)]e^{-\rho x} \right\}$$

and

$$I(x) = \tfrac{1}{2}\left\{ \left[\frac{E(0)}{Z_0} + I(0)\right]e^{\rho x} - \left[\frac{E(0)}{Z_0} - I(0)\right]e^{-\rho x} \right\}$$

Combining terms gives

$$E(x) = E(0)\left[\frac{e^{\rho x} + e^{-\rho x}}{2}\right] + Z_0 I(0)\left[\frac{e^{\rho x} - e^{-\rho x}}{2}\right]$$

$$I(x) = \frac{E(0)}{Z_0}\left[\frac{e^{\rho x} - e^{-\rho x}}{2}\right] + I(0)\left[\frac{e^{\rho x} + e^{-\rho x}}{2}\right]$$

Noting that

$$\left[\frac{e^{\rho x} + e^{-\rho x}}{2}\right] = \cosh(\rho x)$$

and

$$\left[\frac{e^{\rho x} - e^{-\rho x}}{2}\right] = \sinh(\rho x)$$

then

$$E(x) = E(0)\cosh(\rho x) + I(0)Z_0\sinh(\rho x)$$

and

$$I(x) = E(0)\frac{\sinh(\rho x)}{Z_0} + I(0)\cosh(\rho x)$$

Let the coefficients of $E(0)$ and $I(0)$ be called A, B, C and D such that

$$A = \cosh(\rho x)$$

$$B = Z_0 \sinh(\rho x)$$

$$C = \frac{\sinh(\rho x)}{Z_0}$$

$$D = \cosh(\rho x)$$

Since

$$E(0) = V(0) = E_r + V_r$$

and

$$I(0) = I_r$$

and

$$E(x) = V(x) = E_s = V_s$$

and

$$I(x) = I_s$$

then

$$V_s = AV_r + BI_r$$
$$I_s = CV_r + DI_r$$

Therefore, the relationship between the sending end voltage and current and the receiving end voltage and current is completely defined by the ABCD functions. The foregoing derivation gives those parameters for any transmission line with distributed series impedances and shunt admittances.

The above form of equations, using the ABCD functions, is well recognized in power transmission engineering work. The equations are quite useful in analyzing telecommunication transmission lines, such as the subscriber loop, as well. The ABCD functions are called by various other names, such as *transmission line parameters* and *matrix functions*.

The input impedance of a four-terminal network is

$$Z_{in} = \frac{V_s}{I_s} = \frac{AV_r + BI_r}{CV_r + DI_r}$$

The input impedance of a passive four-terminal network (two-port network) depends on what is connected to the output terminals. Since the output impedance is

$$Z_{out} = \frac{V_r}{I_r}$$

then

$$V_r = Z_{out} I_r$$

and noting that A = D for a distributed parameter transmission line

$$Z_{in} = \frac{AZ_{out} I_r + BI_r}{CZ_{out} I_r + AI_r} = \frac{AZ_{out} + B}{CZ_{out} + A}$$

In the case where $Z_{in} = Z_{out} = Z_0$

$$Z_0 = \frac{AZ_0 + B}{CZ_0 + A} = \left(\frac{B}{C}\right)^{1/2}$$

This relationship for Z_0 can be easily determined from the previous derivation where

$$B = Z_0 \sinh(\rho x)$$

$$C = \frac{1}{Z_0} \sinh(\rho x)$$

or

$$Z_0^2 = \frac{B}{C} \text{ and } Z_0 = \left(\frac{B}{C}\right)^{1/2}$$

as before.

Where the line is not terminated in its characteristic impedance, the expression for the input impedance is more complicated. Let the load impedance be given as Z_L, where $Z_{out} = Z_L$. Then, by substitution, the input impedance is given as

$$Z_{in} = \frac{Z_0 Z_L \cosh(\rho x) + Z_0^2 \sinh(\rho x)}{Z_L \sinh(\rho x) + Z_0 \cosh(\rho x)}$$

$$= Z_0 \left[\frac{Z_L + Z_0 \tanh(\rho x)}{Z_0 + Z_L \tanh(\rho x)}\right]$$

In the case of subscriber loops, the expressions for the ABCD functions can be used directly with nonloaded telecommunication cables. For loaded cables, however, the analysis is somewhat complicated by the addition of lumped series impedances at regular intervals to the distributed impedances.

One procedure for developing the secondary parameters for loaded cable uses the following concepts.

If the transmission line is considered to be a passive, four-terminal network, as shown in Fig. C-2, it has open circuit impedances Z_{11}, Z_{22} and Z_{12} ($= Z_{21}$).* Using these, the sending and receiving end voltages can be expressed as functions of sending-end and receiving-end currents for any four-terminal network, or

$$V_s = Z_{11}I_s - Z_{12}I_r$$
$$V_r = Z_{21}I_s - Z_{22}I_r$$

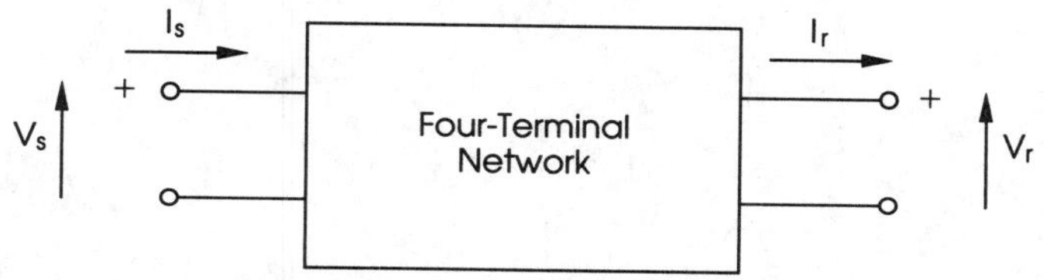

Figure C-2 Four-terminal network

With some manipulation, the following relationships can be found

$$A = \frac{Z_{11}}{Z_{21}}$$

$$B = \frac{Z_{11}Z_{22}}{Z_{21}} - Z_{12}$$

$$C = \frac{1}{Z_{21}}$$

$$D = \frac{Z_{22}}{Z_{21}}$$

The symmetrical T-network shown in Fig. C-3 is a four-terminal network; therefore, the following relationships apply

$$Z_{11} = Z_{22} = \frac{Z}{2} + \frac{1}{Y}$$

and

* For a description of the open circuit impedances and the derivation of the ABCD functions from them, see, for example, [1].

$$Z_{12} = Z_{21} = \frac{1}{Y}$$

Therefore

$$A = \frac{\left(\frac{Z}{2} + \frac{1}{Y}\right)}{\frac{1}{Y}} = \frac{ZY}{2} + 1$$

$$B = \frac{\left(\frac{Z}{2} + \frac{1}{Y}\right)\left(\frac{Z}{2} + \frac{1}{Y}\right)}{\frac{1}{Y}} - \frac{1}{Y} = Z\left(\frac{ZY}{4}\right) + 1$$

$$C = Y$$

$$D = \frac{\left(\frac{Z}{2} + \frac{1}{Y}\right)}{\frac{1}{Y}} = \frac{ZY}{2} + 1$$

Note that $A = D$ and $(A\,D) - (B\,C) = 1$. The above relationships will be used later.

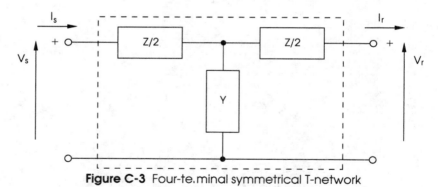

Figure C-3 Four-te.minal symmetrical T-network

When analyzing the characteristic impedance of a loaded cable, consideration of the actual application is necessary. Loaded cables are terminated in the central office through a half-section. (A full section has a length equal to the distance between load coils for the particular loading scheme; a half-section has half that length.) Now, consider a portion of a loaded cable as two half-sections with each half-section separated by a load coil as shown in Fig. C-4. These are simply three cascaded four-terminal networks. It is assumed that both outside ends of the networks shown are terminated in their characteristic impedance (whatever that might be; at this point the actual value is irrelevant).

This assumption is certainly valid for the half-section away from the central office; it is terminated in another identical network, which is terminated in another, and so on. At the very far end, the cable is then terminated in its characteristic impedance. A similar assumption is made for the central office end (although, in practice, this may not be exactly the case). Figure C-4 can be redrawn in terms of the ABCD functions as shown in Fig. C-5.

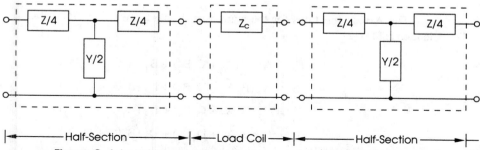

Figure C-4 Loaded cable as three symmetrical T-networks in series

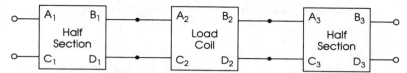

Figure C-5 Three four-terminal networks in terms of ABCD functions

The two outside networks are simply distributed parameter transmission lines for which the ABCD functions have already been derived. If a full section has length L, and the propagation constant for it is ρ_0, then the half-section has length L/2, and the propagation constant for it is $\rho_0/2$. From this point forward, the propagation constant (including α and β) is assumed to be for the length of cable in question, and the per-unit-length notation is dropped. Therefore

$$A_1 = A_3 = \cosh(\rho_0/2)$$
$$B_1 = B_3 = \sinh(\rho_0/2)$$
$$C_1 = C_3 = \frac{1}{Z_0} \sinh(\rho_0/2)$$
$$D_1 = D_3 = \cosh(\rho_0/2)$$

The ABCD functions for the load coil are given as [2]

$$A_2 = 1$$
$$B = Z_c$$
$$C_2 = 0$$
$$D = 1$$

where

$$Z_c = R_c + j\omega L_c$$

$$R_c = \text{load coil resistance in ohms}$$

$$L_c = \text{load coil inductance in henries}$$

The ABCD functions for the composite network are (where the subscript l denotes loaded cable) [2]

$$A_l = A_3 (A_1 A_2 + C_1 B_2) + B_3 (A_1 C_2 + C_1 D_2)$$

$$B_l = A_3 (B_1 A_2 + D_1 B_2) + B_3 (B_1 C_2 + D_1 D_2)$$

$$C_l = C_3 (A_1 A_2 + C_1 B_2) + D_3 (A_1 C_2 + C_1 D_2)$$

$$D_l = C_3 (B_1 A_2 + D_1 B_2) + D_3 (B_1 C_2 + D_1 D_2)$$

By substitution

$$A_l = \cosh^2(\rho_0/2) + \sinh^2(\rho_0/2) + \frac{Z_c}{Z_0} \sinh(\rho_0/2) \cosh(\rho_0/2)$$

$$= \cosh(\rho_0) + \frac{Z_c}{2Z_0} \sinh(\rho_0) = D_1$$

$$B_l = Z_0 \sinh(\rho_0/2) \cosh(\rho_0/2) + Z_0 \sinh(\rho_0/2) \cosh(\rho_0/2) + Z_c \cosh^2(\rho_0/2)$$

$$= 2 Z_0 \sinh(\rho_0/2) \cosh(\rho_0/2) + Z_c \cosh^2(\rho_0/2)$$

$$C_l = \frac{1}{Z_0} \sinh(\rho_0/2) \cosh(\rho_0/2) + \frac{1}{Z_0} \sinh(\rho_0/2) \cosh(\rho_0/2) + \frac{Z_c}{Z_0^2} \sinh^2(\rho_0/2)$$

$$= \frac{2}{Z_0} \sinh(\rho_0/2) \cosh(\rho_0/2) + \frac{Z_c}{Z_0^2} \sinh^2(\rho_0/2)$$

As previously shown, the characteristic impedance for any four-terminal network is

$$Z_0 = \left(\frac{B}{C}\right)^{1/2}$$

To avoid confusing the characteristic impedance of a purely distributed parameter transmission line with the impedance of a loaded line, let Z_l be the loaded line characteristic impedance. Therefore

$$Z_l = \left(\frac{B_l}{C_l}\right)^{1/2}$$

Substituting the appropriate expressions for B_l and C_l, and noting Z_0 and ρ_0 are the propagation constant and characteristic impedance, respectively, for the uniform cable sections (not considering the load coil), gives

$$Z_l = \left[\frac{2 Z_0 \sinh(\rho_0/2) \cosh(\rho_0/2) + Z_c \cosh^2(\rho_0/2)}{\dfrac{2}{Z_0} \sinh(\rho_0/2) \cosh(\rho_0/2) + \dfrac{Z_c}{Z_0^2} \sinh^2(\rho_0/2)} \right]^{1/2}$$

$$= Z_0 \left[\frac{Z_0 \sinh(\rho_0) + Z_c \cosh^2(\rho_0/2)}{Z_0 \sinh(\rho_0) + Z_c \sinh^2(\rho_0/2)} \right]^{1/2}$$

$$= Z_0 \left[\frac{Z_0 \sinh(\rho_0) + Z_c (1 + \sinh^2(\rho_0/2))}{Z_0 \sinh(\rho_0) + Z_c \sinh^2(\rho_0/2)} \right]^{1/2}$$

$$= Z_0 \left[\frac{Z_0 \sinh(\rho_0) + Z_c \sinh^2(\rho_0/2) + Z_c}{Z_0 \sinh(\rho_0) + Z_c \sinh^2(\rho_0/2)} \right]^{1/2}$$

$$= Z_0 \left[1 + \frac{Z_c}{Z_0 \sinh(\rho_0) + Z_c \sinh^2(\rho_0/2)} \right]^{1/2}$$

$$= Z_0 \left[1 + \frac{2 Z_c}{2 Z_0 \sinh(\rho_0) + Z_c (\cosh(\rho_0) - 1)} \right]^{1/2}$$

$$= Z_0 \left[\frac{2 Z_0 \sinh(\rho_0) + Z_c (\cosh(\rho_0) + 1)}{2 Z_0 \sinh(\rho_0) + Z_c (\cosh(\rho_0) - 1)} \right]^{1/2}$$

$$= Z_0 \left[\frac{2 Z_0 + Z_c \coth(\rho_0/2)}{2 Z_0 + Z_c \tanh(\rho_0/2)} \right]^{1/2}$$

The propagation constant ρ_l for one section of a loaded cable can be found as follows: A full load section is to be considered and, in this case, the full section is connected to a half-coil at each end as shown in Fig. C-6.

The ABCD functions for the half-coil are

$$A = 1$$

$$B = Z_c/2$$

$$C = 0$$

$$D = 1$$

The ABCD functions for the full-length nonloaded cable section connected between the half-coils are

$$A = \cosh(\rho_0)$$

$$B = Z_0 \sinh(\rho_0)$$

$$C = (1/Z_0) \sinh(\rho_0)$$

$$D = \cosh(\rho_0)$$

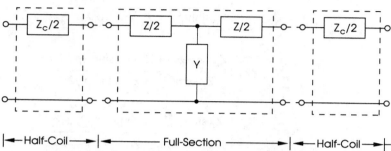

$\longmapsto$ Half-Coil $\longrightarrow$ | $\longleftarrow$ Full-Section $\longrightarrow$ | $\longleftarrow$ Half-Coil $\longrightarrow$ |

Figure C-6 Network for determining the loaded cable propagation constant

    The results are similar to the previous analysis except, instead of a cable half-section, a full section is used and, instead of a full coil, a half-coil is used. The same rationale is used for termination of the full section with half-coils; that is, the section in question is terminated in its characteristic impedance. Z_0 and P_0 are the characteristic impedance and propagation constant for the uniform cable section (not considering the load coil), as before.

    If the composite network is considered to be three cascaded four-terminal networks, the ABCD functions for the composite network are (as before)

$$A_l = A_3 (A_1 A_2 + C_1 B_2) + B_3 (A_1 C_2 + C_1 D_2)$$

$$B_l = A_3 (B_1 A_2 + D_1 B_2) + B_3 (B_1 C_2 + D_1 D_2)$$

$$C_l = C_3 (A_1 A_2 + C_1 B_2) + D_3 (A_1 C_2 + C_1 D_2)$$

$$D_l = C_3 (B_1 A_2 + D_1 B_2) + D_3 (B_1 C_2 + D_1 D_2)$$

In this case, however, subscripts 1 and 3 are used to denote the half-coil at each end, and subscript 2 is used to denote the uniform cable section. Since

$$A_1 = A_3$$

$$B_1 = B_3$$

$$C_1 = C_3$$

$$D_1 = D_3$$

then

$$A_l = A_1 + C_1 \frac{Z_c}{2}$$

$$B_l = B_1 + A_1 \frac{Z_c}{2} \; D_1 Z_c + C_1 \frac{Z_c^2}{2}$$

$$C_l = C_1$$

$$D_l = D_1 + C_1 \frac{Z_c}{2}$$

Substituting the appropriate values gives

$$A_l = \cosh(\rho_0) + \frac{Z_c}{2 Z_0} \sinh(\rho_0)$$

$$B_l = Z_0 \sinh(\rho_0) + Z_c \cosh(\rho_0) + \frac{Z_c^2}{4 Z_0} \sinh(\rho_0)$$

$$C_l = \frac{1}{Z_0} \sinh(\rho_0)$$

$$D_l = \cosh(\rho_0) + \frac{Z_c}{2 Z_0} \sinh(\rho_0)$$

The composite network can be considered to be a symmetrical T-network as shown in Fig. C-7. For any symmetrical T-network the ABCD functions were previously found to be (after substituting the proper subscripts)

$$A_l = 1 + \frac{ZY}{2}$$

$$B_l = Z\left(1 + \frac{ZY}{4}\right)$$

$$C_l = Y$$

$$D_l = 1 + \frac{ZY}{2}$$

where

Z and Y are the T-network impedance and admittance to be derived below.

Substituting for A_l gives

$$1 + \frac{ZY}{2} = \cosh(\rho_0) + \frac{Z_c}{2 Z_0} \sinh(\rho_0)$$

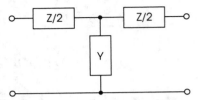

Figure C-7 Network for determining the loaded cable propagation constant

Therefore

$$Z = \frac{2 \, (\cosh(\rho_0) - 1)}{Y} + \frac{Z_c}{Z_0 Y} \sinh(\rho_0)$$

Since

$$C_l = Y = \frac{1}{Z_0} \sinh(\rho_0)$$

then

$$Z = 2 \, Z_0 \left[\frac{\cosh(\rho_0) - 1}{\sinh(\rho_0)} \right] + Z_c$$

Substituting the identity

$$\tanh(\rho_0/2) = \frac{\cosh(\rho_0) - 1}{\sinh(\rho_0)}$$

gives

$$Z = 2 \, Z_0 \tanh(\rho_0/2) + Z_c$$

For any particular set of conditions (section length, frequency, etc.), the ABCD functions for the equivalent T-network are equal to the ABCD functions for the generalized transmission line with distributed parameters. Therefore

$$A_l = 1 + \frac{ZY}{2} = \cosh(\rho_l)$$

where

ρ_l = propagation constant for the combination of a full cable section connected to half-coils at each end

Also, in general

$$\tanh(\rho_l/2) = \frac{\cosh(\rho_l) - 1}{\sinh(\rho_l)}$$

and

$$\sinh(\rho_l) = (A_l^2 - 1)$$

$$= \left[\left(1 + \frac{ZY}{2}\right)^2 - 1\right]$$

$$= \frac{Y}{2}\left(\frac{4Z}{Y} + Z^2\right)^{1/2}$$

It follows that

$$\tanh(\rho_l/2) = \left[\frac{\dfrac{ZY}{2}}{\dfrac{Y}{2}\left(\dfrac{4Z}{Y} + Z^2\right)^{1/2}}\right]$$

$$= \left(\frac{ZY}{ZY + 4}\right)^{1/2}$$

Therefore

$$(\rho_l/2) = \tanh^{-1}\left(\frac{ZY}{ZY + 4}\right)^{1/2}$$

or

$$(\rho_l/2) = \tanh^{-1}\left(\frac{ZY}{ZY + 4}\right)^{1/2}$$

where

$$Z = 2\,Z_0\tanh(\rho_0/2) + Z_c$$

and

$$Y = \sinh(\rho_0)/Z_0$$

as previously found.

Since

$$\rho_l = \alpha_l + j\beta_l$$

where

α_l = attenuation constant for loaded cable

β_l = phase constant for loaded cable

then

$$\alpha_l = RE\left[2\tanh^{-1}\left(\frac{ZY}{ZY+4}\right)^{1/2}\right]$$

and

$$\beta_l = IM\left[2\tanh^{-1}\left(\frac{ZY}{ZY+4}\right)^{1/2}\right]$$

where

$Z = 2\,Z_0\tanh(\rho_0/2) + Z_c$

$Y = \sinh(\rho_0)/Z_0$

ρ_0 = propagation constant for nonloaded cable section

Z_0 = characteristic impedance of nonloaded cable sections

Z_c = load coil impedance $(R_c + j\omega L_c)$

The values derived above for loaded cable are only valid for multiples of a section length. Since the end section nearest the central office is always a half-section, the assumption is that the subscriber (or load) is always located a half-section from the last load coil.

Subscribers are normally not placed on loaded cable unless they are more than 18,000 ft from the central office (15,000 ft for 26 gauge loaded cable). Therefore, with "H" loading (6,000 ft load coil spacing), at least two full sections (plus two half-sections) will always be used. With "D" loading (4,500 ft spacing), at least three full sections (and two half-sections) will be used.

Using the above derivation to determine the loaded cable attenuation for lengths other than exact multiples of load section length means some loss in accuracy. For most practical problems, however, the accuracy is acceptable.

Therefore, the attenuation of a loaded cable, per unit length, is taken to be

$$\text{Attenuation (dB/unit length)} = 8.686 \left(\frac{\alpha_l}{\text{section length}} \right)$$

where

the factor $8.686 = 20 \log(e)$ as previously shown

REFERENCES

[1] Skilling, H. H. *Electrical Engineering Circuits*. New York: John Wiley & Sons, Inc., second edition, 1965, Chapter 18.

[2] *Electrical Transmission and Distribution Reference Book*, Westinghouse Electric Corp., fourth edition, 1964, p. 327.

D

Insertion Loss
of the Subscriber Loop

The two-wire subscriber loop is a lossy transmission line inserted between the subscriber's terminal equipment and the central office. The actual value of its insertion loss depends on the propagation constant as well as the relationship between the loop's characteristic impedance (Z_0) and the terminating impedance at each end.*

If the loop is terminated in its characteristic impedance, it will be shown that the insertion loss equals the real part of the propagation constant expressed in dB, or:

$$\text{Insertion Loss IL} = \text{Re}(\rho) = 8.686\alpha \text{ dB}$$

where

α = attenuation constant in nepers per unit length

ρ = propagation constant

In practice, it is highly unlikely this ideal termination will ever be achieved throughout the frequency band of interest. Therefore, a more general case will be analyzed where the termination impedances can be any value.

---

* A similar term used to describe the loop loss is *transducer loss*. Transducer loss is a measure of the ratio of maximum power available from the generator to the output power available at the receiving end of the loop. In both insertion and transducer loss terms, the power is implied to be measured with real test equipment. With modern transmission test sets, there is no discernible difference between measured insertion loss and transducer loss, so the terms are considered to be equal for purposes of this discussion.

Initially, consider the case where a generator of impedance Z_G and voltage E is terminated directly in an impedance Z_L (no intervening loop) as shown in Fig. D-1. The generator can be the central office, and the load can be the terminal equipment connected directly at the central office.

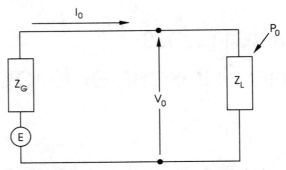

Figure D-1 Voltage generator connected directly to load

The voltage across the load is

$$V_0 = I_0 Z_L = E - I_0 Z_G$$

or

$$E = I_0(Z_G + Z_L)$$

where

$$Z_G \text{ and } Z_L = \text{generator and load impedances, respectively}$$

The power delivered to the load is

$$P_0 = V_0 I_0 = (I_0)^2 Z_L = EI_0 - (I_0)^2 Z_G$$

Next, a subscriber's loop is inserted between the generator and the load as shown in Fig. D-2. The loop can be considered a two-port network, and its insertion loss can be found by circuit analysis. The following equations apply to Fig. D-2

$$V_1 = AV_2 + BI_2$$
$$I_1 = CV_2 + DI_2$$
$$V_2 = I_2 Z_L$$

where

A,B,C and D = the familiar transmission line parameters (also called *ABCD functions*)*

* For an overview of the ABCD functions, see, for example, [1].

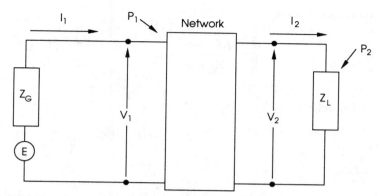

Figure D-2 Two-port network inserted between voltage generator and load

The power delivered to the load through the intervening two-port network (loop) is

$$P_2 = V_2 I_2 = (I_2)^2 Z_L$$

The input impedance of the loop is

$$Z_1 = \frac{V_1}{I_1}$$

Then

$$Z_1 = \frac{(AV_2 + BI_2)}{(CV_2 + DI_2)}$$

Substituting $I_2 Z_2$ for V_2 in this equation yields

$$Z_1 = \frac{(AZ_L + B)}{(CZ_L + D)}$$

Also, by inspection of Fig. D-2

$$V_1 = E - I_1 Z_G$$

Therefore

$$Z_1 = \frac{E}{I_1} - Z_G$$

or

$$\frac{E}{I_1} - Z_G = \frac{AZ_L + B}{CZ_L + D}$$

Solving for E/I_1 gives

$$\frac{E}{I_1} = \frac{AZ_L + B}{CZ_L + D} + Z_G = \frac{AZ_L + B + Z_G(CZ_L + D)}{CZ_L + D}$$

By substituting $I_1 = CV_2 + DI_2$ and $V_2 = I_2Z_L$

$$I_1 = I_2(CZ_L + D)$$

Also, since

$$E = I_0(Z_G + Z_L)$$

then

$$\frac{E}{I_1} = \frac{I_0(Z_G + Z_L)}{I_2(CZ_L + D)} = \frac{AZ_L + B + Z_G(CZ_L + D)}{CZ_L + D}$$

Solving for I_0/I_2 gives

$$\frac{I_0}{I_2} = \frac{AZ_L + B + Z_G(CZ_L + D)}{Z_G + Z_L}$$

The ratio of the power delivered to the load without the loop (P_0) to the power delivered with the loop (P_2) is

$$\frac{P_0}{P_2} = \frac{(I_0)^2 Z_L}{(I_2)^2 Z_L} = \frac{(I_0)^2}{(I_2)^2} = \left[\frac{AZ_L + B + Z_G(CZ_L + D)}{Z_G + Z_L} \right]^2$$

Therefore, the insertion loss of the loop, in dB per unit length, is

$$IL = 10 \log(P_0/P_2) = 10 \log\left| I_0/I_2 \right|^2 = 20 \log\left| I_0/I_2 \right|$$

Substituting gives

$$IL = 10 \log \left| \frac{AZ_L + B + Z_G(CZ_L + D)}{Z_G + Z_L} \right|^2$$

$$= 20 \log \left| \frac{AZ_L + B + Z_G(CZ_L + D)}{Z_G + Z_L} \right|$$

For a distributed parameter two-port network, such as a nonloaded loop, the transmission line parameters were found in Appendix C to be

$$A = \cosh(\rho)$$

$$B = Z_0 \sinh(\rho)$$

$$C = \sinh(\rho)/Z_0$$

$$D = \cosh(\rho)$$

where

$$\rho = \text{propagation constant, as previously defined}$$

$$Z_0 = \text{the characteristic impedance of the transmission line}$$

Substituting these values gives

$$\frac{I_0}{I_2} = \frac{Z_L \cosh(\rho) + Z_0 \sinh(\rho) + Z_G(Z_L \sinh(\rho)/Z_0) + Z_G \cosh(\rho)}{Z_L + Z_G}$$

Combining terms

$$\frac{I_0}{I_2} = \frac{Z_0 Z_L \cosh(\rho) + (Z_0)^2 \sinh(\rho) + Z_G Z_L \sinh(\rho) + Z_G Z_0 \cosh(\rho)}{Z_0(Z_L + Z_G)}$$

$$= \frac{(Z_0 Z_L + Z_0 Z_G)\cosh(\rho) + [(Z_0)^2 + Z_G Z_L]\sinh(\rho)}{Z_0(Z_L + Z_G)}$$

Noting that

$$\cosh(\rho) = (e^\rho + e^{-\rho})/2$$

and

$$\sinh(\rho) = (e^\rho - e^{-\rho})/2$$

then

$$\frac{I_0}{I_2} = \frac{(Z_0 Z_L + Z_0 Z_G)(e^\rho + e^{-\rho}) + [(Z_0)^2 + Z_G Z_L](e^\rho - e^{-\rho})}{2Z_0(Z_L + Z_G)}$$

$$= \frac{e^\rho(Z_0 + Z_G)(Z_0 + Z_L) - e^{-\rho}(Z_0 - Z_G)(Z_0 - Z_L)}{2Z_0(Z_L + Z_G)}$$

Multiplying by $\dfrac{e^{\rho}}{e^{-\rho}}$ gives

$$\frac{I_0}{I_2} = \frac{(Z_0 + Z_G)(Z_0 + Z_L) - e^{-2\rho}(Z_0 - Z_G)(Z_0 - Z_L)}{2Z_0 e^{-\rho}(Z_L + Z_G)}$$

$$= \frac{(Z_0 + Z_G)(Z_0 + Z_L)}{2Z_0 e^{-\rho}(Z_G + Z_L)}\left[1 - e^{-2\rho}\frac{(Z_0 - Z_G)(Z_0 - Z_L)}{(Z_0 + Z_G)(Z_0 + Z_L)}\right]$$

Therefore

$$IL = 10 \log\left|\frac{I_0}{I_2}\right|^2$$

$$= 20 \log\left|\frac{(Z_0 + Z_G)(Z_0 + Z_L)}{2Z_0 e^{-\rho}(Z_G + Z_L)}\left[1 - e^{-2\rho}\frac{(Z_0 - Z_G)(Z_0 - Z_L)}{(Z_0 + Z_G)(Z_0 + Z_L)}\right]\right|$$

Since this function requires the calculation of the magnitude of complex functions, the terms $e^{-\rho}$ and $e^{-2\rho}$ need to be replaced by $\text{Re}[e^{-\rho}]$ $(= e^{-\alpha})$ and $\text{Re}[e^{-2\rho}]$ $(= e^{-2\alpha})$, respectively. Also, α is given in nepers per unit length, so it must be evaluated at the appropriate loop length.

In the above form, the insertion loss equation has two distinct parts: The first part contains three terms that affect insertion loss: the first two terms (numerator) represent the reflection losses due to the mismatch between Z_0 and Z_G, Z_0 and Z_L, and the third (denominator) is the reflection loss due to the mismatch between Z_G and Z_L when the lossy loop is not present. The second part of the insertion loss equation results from the terminating impedances not matching the characteristic impedance of the transmission line; it is seen to be a second order effect and can be ignored for all loops except those with low loss (that is, short loops).

It is informative to evaluate the insertion loss equation for several situations where the loop is terminated in various impedances and compare these losses to a perfectly matched loop. These are

1. $Z_G = Z_L = Z_0$ (perfect match)
2. $Z_G = Z_L$ = complex conjugate Z_0 (conjugate match)
3. $Z_G = Z_L = 900\ \Omega$
4. $Z_G = Z_L = 600\ \Omega$
5. $Z_G = 600\ \Omega$; $Z_L = 900\ \Omega$
6. $Z_G = 900\ \Omega$; $Z_L =$ ("500" set impedance).

The above terminating impedances will be connected to three loops made up of 24 AWG conductors (air-core PIC, 55°F), as described in Chapter 5, with lengths of

$$L_1 = 500 \text{ ft}$$
$$L_2 = 5{,}000 \text{ ft}$$
$$L_3 = 15{,}000 \text{ ft}$$

For case (1), where $Z_G = Z_0 = Z_L$ at all frequencies, the insertion loss equation reduces to

$$IL = 20 \log \left| \frac{(2Z_0)(2Z_0)}{4(Z_0)^2 e^{-\rho}} \right| = 20 \log \left| e^\rho \right| = 20 \log(e^\alpha)$$

$$= 20 \, \alpha \log(e) = 8.686\alpha \text{ dB per unit length}$$

This result is expected; that is, the insertion loss equals the attenuation constant (α) converted to dB. Upon closer inspection of the insertion loss equation, it will be seen that this situation will arise if *either* Z_G or Z_L equals Z_0. In other words, both do not have to equal Z_0 for the insertion loss to equal 8.686α.

The attenuation constant at 1,000 Hz was found in Chapter 5 to be

$$\alpha = 2.26 \text{ dB/mi}$$

For the three loop lengths (perfectly matched), the insertion loss is

$$\left. \begin{array}{l} IL(500 \text{ ft}) = 0.21 \text{ dB} \\ IL(5{,}000 \text{ ft}) = 2.14 \text{ dB} \\ IL(15{,}000 \text{ ft}) = 6.42 \text{ dB} \end{array} \right\} \text{ Case (1)}$$

The situation of case (1), where the generator and load perfectly match the characteristic impedance of the loop at all frequencies, would almost never be encountered in practice without intentional impedance tuning. Nevertheless, the attenuation constant is used for loop loss calculations; it provides a conservative estimate for most practical problems, as will be seen. The more precise method, described in this appendix, would be too laborious to use on a daily basis without a computer program to speed up the calculations.*

Case (2) is another situation rarely encountered in practical problems. It is worth exploring, however, because it represents the case of maximum power transfer, which occurs when the terminating impedances have a value equal to the complex conjugate of the transmission line characteristic impedance.†

It is necessary to obtain Z_0 for the loop at the frequency of interest (noting that Z_0 is independent of length). Again, the insertion loss will be evaluated for the three loops.

* The calculations and plots in this appendix (and, for the most part, throughout this book) were made with a program called "MathCAD," which is available from MathSoft, Inc., One Kendall Square, Cambridge, MA 02139.

† The case of maximum power transfer can be confirmed by referring to any book on network analysis. An example is [2].

The value of Z_0 at 1,000 Hz was given in Chapter 5 as

$$Z_0 = 714\angle - 44.8°\Omega = 506.6 - j503.1\Omega$$

The complex conjugate

$$(Z_0) = 714\angle + 44.8°\Omega = 506.6 + j503.1\Omega$$

Therefore

$$Z_G = Z_L = 714\angle + 44.8° = 506.6 + j503.1\Omega$$

Substituting the foregoing values and appropriate loop lengths into the insertion loss equation gives insertion loss values of

$$\left.\begin{array}{l} \text{IL(500 ft)} = 0.004 \text{ dB} \\ \text{IL(5,000 ft)} = 0.275 \text{ dB} \\ \text{IL(15,000 ft)} = 2.22 \text{ dB} \end{array}\right\} \text{ Case (2)}$$

It is seen that the loss is less than in case (1), which is to be expected.

Case (3) represents a situation encountered in the field during testing when each end of the loop is terminated in a transmission test set with a 900 Ω (resistive) impedance ($Z_G = Z_L = 900 \Omega$). Substituting Z_0, Z_G and Z_L and the appropriate loop lengths into the insertion loss equation gives loss values of

$$\left.\begin{array}{l} \text{IL(500 ft)} = 0.16 \text{ dB} \\ \text{IL(5,000 ft)} = 1.67 \text{ dB} \\ \text{IL(15,000 ft)} = 5.48 \text{ dB} \end{array}\right\} \text{ Case (3)}$$

Comparing case (3) with case (1), it is seen that the loss of a perfectly terminated transmission line is greater than the loss of the same line terminated in the standard resistive impedance of 900 Ω. The difference is almost 1 dB for the long loop, around $\frac{1}{2}$ dB for the mid-length loop and negligible for the short loop. It is due to the reflection losses between the generator and load (as if the loop were not present) reducing the overall insertion loss. Stated another way, the perfectly matched transmission line does not provide maximum power transfer (minimum loss); the resistively matched line, in this case, does not either, but the power transfer is still greater (loss is less). The loss associated with practical terminations will not always be less than with perfect matching, as will be seen.

Since case (3) has practical application, it is carried further. Figure D-3 shows a plot of insertion loss error versus loop length for the four common cable pair gauges and 900 Ω terminations at each end. This plot can be used to estimate the error when testing loops and comparing the results with losses calculated from the attenuation constant.

Case (4) is similar to case (3) except a standard 600 Ω termination impedance is used at both ends instead of 900 Ω. The insertion loss for each of the three loop lengths is

$$\left.\begin{array}{l} \text{IL(500 ft)} = 0.16 \text{ dB} \\ \text{IL(5,000 ft)} = 1.66 \text{ dB} \\ \text{IL(15,000 ft)} = 5.44 \text{ dB} \end{array}\right\} \text{ Case (4)}$$

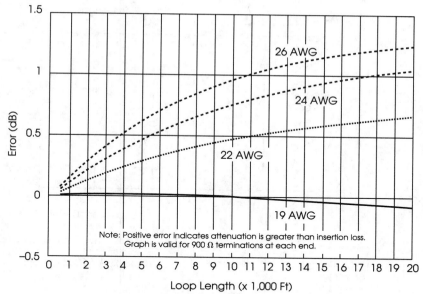

Figure D-3 Insertion loss error (air core PIC, 55°F)

For all practical purposes, case (4) provides the same results as case (3), and for the same reasons. It also illustrates that there is little practical difference in choosing between a 600 and 900 Ω terminating impedance when making nonloaded loop measurements.

Case (5) provides a slightly different twist. Here one test set provides a 900 Ω termination and the other a 600 Ω termination. This situation has practical significance in that it represents the case for measurements on switched loops. Evaluation proceeds as stated above and gives an insertion loss for each of the three loops of

$$\left.\begin{array}{l} \text{IL(500 ft)} = 0.15 \text{ dB} \\ \text{IL(5,000 ft)} = 1.61 \text{ dB} \\ \text{IL(15,000 ft)} = 5.33 \text{ dB} \end{array}\right\} \text{ Case (5)}$$

Case (6) can be considered another example of a real application in that the insertion loss is found when the central office end is terminated in a 900 Ω impedance, and the subscriber's end is terminated in a traditional "500" set. The impedance of a 500 set is a nonlinear function of the loop current, as seen in Fig. D-4.*

From the dc model, the following approximate loop currents (I_L) are found for the three loop lengths†

$$\text{IL(500 ft)} = 100 \text{mA}$$

$$\text{IL(5,000 ft)} = 70 \text{ mA}$$

$$\text{IL(15,000 ft)} = 40 \text{mA}$$

* Adapted from [3].

† This analysis assumes that the battery feed resistances in the central office line circuit total 400 Ω and there is no constant current source.

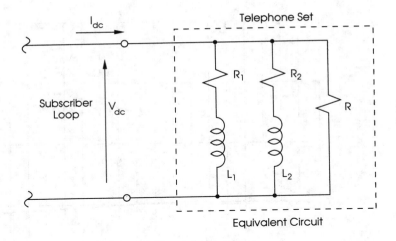

Figure D-4 Off-hook models for "500" set

These loop currents can then be entered into the ac model to find the ac load imped-ance (Z_L) as follows

$$Z_L(500 \text{ ft}) = 366.3\angle12.6°\Omega = 357.3 + j80.2\Omega$$
$$Z_L(5,000 \text{ ft}) = 477.6\angle16.6°\Omega = 457.7 + j136.3\Omega$$
$$Z_L(15,000 \text{ ft}) = 642.6\angle21.6°\Omega = 597.4 + j236.6\Omega$$

With a 900 Ω generator impedance and the above load impedances, the insertion loss for each of the three loops is

$$\left. \begin{array}{l} \text{IL}(500 \text{ ft}) = 0.13 \text{ dB} \\ \text{IL}(5,000 \text{ ft}) = 1.40 \text{ dB} \\ \text{IL}(15,000 \text{ ft}) = 4.83 \text{ dB} \end{array} \right\} \text{ Case (6)}$$

The insertion losses associated with loops terminated by other telephone sets will vary with the characteristics of the set. These characteristics can be quite variable among

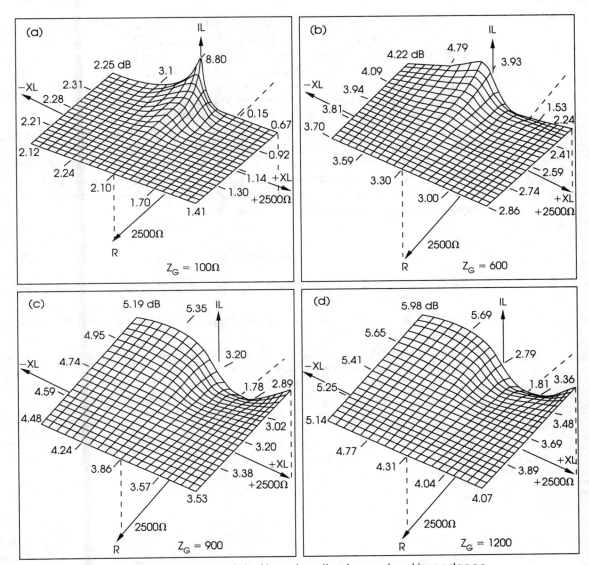

Figure D-5 Surface plot of loop insertion loss vs. load impedance, loop length = 10,000 ft, 24 AWG

different manufacturers and models, so no definite conclusions can be drawn from case (6) calculations that could be applied to other equipment. Also, it is important to note that, although the loop insertion loss is less when the loop is terminated in the 500 set, the overall *loudness loss* may not be.* In any case, the difference may not be discernible by the human ear on most loops unless the telephone instruments being used are poorly designed.

* Loudness loss is the loss in acoustic speech signal level across a connection (for example, a subscriber loop). It is a function of the transmitting and receiving acoustic conversion efficiencies, insertion loss of the loop and the efficiencies of any transmission or termination equipment in between.

As noted in each of the above practical cases, the insertion loss of the loop is less than the ideal case of a perfectly matched line at all frequencies. This effect is dependent on the actual impedances involved. That is, the difference magnitude and sign will vary with the termination impedances. For example, with $Z_G = 900 \ \Omega$ and $Z_L = 0 + j750 \ \Omega$ (a purely inductive load), the insertion loss of the loop with length equal to 5,000 ft is 0.24 dB, a difference of −1.90 dB. If $Z_L = 0 - j750$ (a purely capacitive load), then the insertion loss would be about 2.8 dB, a difference of +0.66 dB.

Figure D-5 shows a surface plot of loop insertion loss for a 24 AWG loop terminated in loads with resistive values that vary from 100 to 2,500 Ω and reactive values that vary from −2500 Ω to +2500 Ω. Four generator impedances are plotted: $Z_G = 100, 600, 900$ and 1,200 Ω. The shape of the surface plot will change if the generator impedance is not purely resistive as assumed here. For most practical applications, however, the generator impedance can be assumed to be purely resistive.

REFERENCES

[1] Skilling, H. H. *Electrical Engineering Circuits*. New York: John Wiley & Sons, Inc., second edition, 1965.

[2] *Van Valkenburg, M. E. Network Analysis*. Englewood Cliffs, New Jersey: Prentice Hall, second edition, 1965.

[3] *Transmission Systems for Communications*, Bell Telephone Laboratories, Inc., 1982. Available from AT&T Customer Information Center.

E

Reflection Loss Caused by a Bridged Tap

A *bridged tap* is any unused, open circuited, parallel connected cable pair on a subscriber's loop. It appears conceptually as shown in Fig. E-1. Electrically, the bridged tap appears as a shunting impedance at its point of connection to the loop. This shunt causes a reflection loss that depends on the tap pair's characteristics (gauge and length and, to a small extent, location of the connection point). It also depends somewhat on the characteristics of the loop to which it is connected.

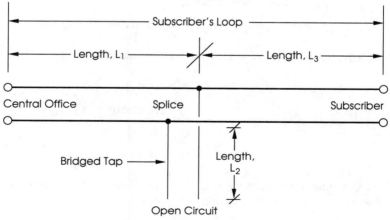

Figure E-1 Bridged tap connected to a subscriber's loop

The reflection loss can be analyzed by using the familiar transmission line parameters (ABCD functions). The ABCD functions for a nonloaded loop were derived in Appendix C. For purposes of the reflection loss analysis, the loop can be split into two sections as shown in Fig. E-2.

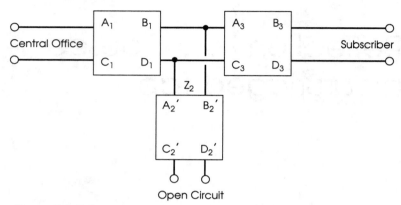

Figure E-2 Bridged tap connections in terms of two-port networks

The section connected to the central office has the following ABCD functions

$$A_1 = \cosh(\rho_1)$$
$$B_1 = Z_0 \sinh(\rho_1)$$
$$C_1 = \sinh(\rho_1)/Z_0$$
$$D_1 = \cosh(\rho_1)$$

where

Z_0 = characteristic impedance

ρ_1 = propagation constant* for the section of length L_1

Similarly, for the section connected to the terminal equipment

$$A_3 = \cosh(\rho_3)$$
$$B_3 = Z_0 \sinh(\rho_3)$$
$$C_3 = \sinh(\rho_3)/Z_0$$
$$D_3 = \cosh(\rho_3)$$

Assuming the bridged tap is made up of a cable with the same primary constants as the main cable, the ABCD functions for it are†

---

* It is understood throughout this analysis that the propagation constant ρ_1 is the propagation constant per unit length times the length of section 1.

† If the bridged tap cable is different, then the characteristic impedance and propagation constant per unit length associated with it will be different, and the analysis must be modified accordingly.

$$A_2' = \cosh(\rho_2)$$
$$B_2' = Z_0 \sinh(\rho_2)$$
$$C_2' = \sinh(\rho_2)/Z_0$$
$$D_2' = \cosh(\rho_2)$$

Further analysis of the bridged tap is needed. From Fig. E-3

$$V_S = A_2'V_L + B_2'I_L$$
$$I_S = C_2'V_L + D_2'I_L$$

Let $Z_2 = V_S/I_S$, then

$$Z_2 = \frac{A_2'V_L + B_2'I_L}{C_2'V_L + D_2'I_L}$$

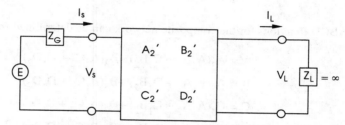

Figure E-3 Two-port representation of a bridged tap

Since the bridged tap is open circuited at the load end, the load current must be zero ($I_L = 0$). Then

$$Z_2 = \frac{A_2'}{C_2'}$$

Substituting gives

$$Z_2 = \frac{Z_0 \cosh(\rho_2)}{\sinh(\rho_2)} = \frac{Z_0}{\tanh(\rho_2)}$$

Figure E-4 shows an equivalent two-port network for the shunt impedance represented by Z_2.

The ABCD functions for a shunt impedance are given as [1]

$$A_2 = 1$$
$$B_2 = 0$$
$$C_2 = 1/Z_2 = \tanh(\rho_2)/Z_0$$
$$D_2 = 1$$

The three general two-port networks shown in Fig. E-2 can be combined into two-port networks as shown in Fig. E-5.

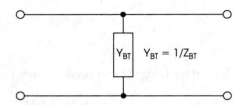

Figure E-4 Bridged tap represented as a shunt impedance

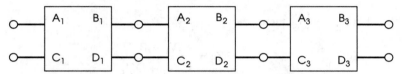

Figure E-5 Composite two-port network

The ABCD functions for the composite network can be determined from [1]

$$A = A_3(A_1A_2 + C_1B_2) + B_3(A_1C_2 + C_1D_2)$$
$$B = A_3(B_1A_2 + D_1B_2) + B_3(B_1C_2 + D_1D_2)$$
$$C = C_3(A_1A_2 + C_1B_2) + D_3(A_1C_2 + C_1D_2)$$
$$D = C_3(B_1A_2 + D_1B_2) + D_3(B_1C_2 + D_1D_2)$$

Substituting the values of the ABCD functions for each section gives

$$A = \cosh(\rho_3)\cosh(\rho_1) + Z_0 \sinh(\rho_3)\left[\frac{\cosh(\rho_1)\tanh(\rho_2) + \sinh(\rho_1)}{Z_0}\right]$$

$$B = Z_0 \cosh(\rho_3)\sinh(\rho_1) + Z_0 \sinh(\rho_3)[\sinh(\rho_1)\tanh(\rho_2) + \cosh(\rho_1)]$$

$$C = \left[\frac{\sinh(\rho_3)\cosh(\rho_1)}{Z_0}\right] + \cosh(\rho_3)\left[\frac{\cosh(\rho_1)\tanh(\rho_2) + \sinh(\rho_1)}{Z_0}\right]$$

$$D = \sinh(\rho_3)\sinh(\rho_1) + \cosh(\rho_3)[\sinh(\rho_1)\tanh(\rho_2) + \cosh(\rho_1)]$$

These ABCD functions can be inserted into the insertion loss equation derived in Appendix D, which is

$$IL = 20 \log\left\|\left[\frac{AZ_L + B + Z_G(CZ_L + D)}{Z_G + Z_L}\right]\right\|$$

The direct substitution gives

$$
IL = 20\log \left| \frac{
\begin{aligned}
& Z_L \cosh(\rho_3)\cosh(\rho_1) + Z_L \sinh(\rho_3)\sinh(\rho_1) + Z_L \sinh(\rho_3)\cosh(\rho_1)\tanh(\rho_2) \\
& + Z_0 \cosh(\rho_3)\sinh(\rho_1) + Z_0 \sinh(\rho_3)\cosh(\rho_1) + Z_0 \sinh(\rho_3)\sinh(\rho_1)\tanh(\rho_2) \\
& + \frac{Z_G Z_L}{Z_0}\sinh(\rho_3)\cosh(\rho_1) + \frac{Z_G Z_L}{Z_0}\cosh(\rho_3)\sinh(\rho_1) \\
& + \frac{Z_G Z_L}{Z_0}\cosh(\rho_3)\cosh(\rho_1)\tanh(\rho_2) + Z_G \sinh(\rho_3)\sinh(\rho_1) \\
& + Z_G \cosh(\rho_3)\cosh(\rho_1) + Z_G \cosh(\rho_3)\sinh(\rho_1)\tanh(\rho_2)
\end{aligned}
}{Z_G + Z_L} \right|
$$

The basic equation above can be reduced by using algebraic manipulation and a table of hyperbolic function identities found in any good mathematics handbook as follows [2]

$$
IL = 20\log \left| \frac{
\begin{aligned}
& Z_0(Z_G + Z_L)[\cosh(\rho_3)\cosh(\rho_1) + \sinh(\rho_3)\sinh(\rho_1)] \\
& + (Z_0^2 + Z_G Z_L)[\sinh(\rho_3)\cosh(\rho_1) + \cosh(\rho_3)\sinh(\rho_1)] \\
& + \tanh(\rho_2)\left[
\begin{aligned}
& Z_G Z_L \cosh(\rho_3)\cosh(\rho_1) + Z_0^2 \sinh(\rho_3)\sinh(\rho_1) \\
& + Z_0 Z_L \sinh(\rho_3)\cosh(\rho_1) + Z_0 Z_G \cosh(\rho_3)\sinh(\rho_1)
\end{aligned}
\right]
\end{aligned}
}{Z_0(Z_G + Z_L)} \right|
$$

$$IL = 20 \log \left| \frac{\begin{array}{l} Z_0(Z_G + Z_L)\cosh(\rho_3 + \rho_1) + (Z_0^2 + Z_GZ_L)\sinh(\rho_3 + \rho_1) + \tan(\rho_2) \\[6pt] \left[\dfrac{Z_GZ_L}{2}\cosh(\rho_3 + \rho_1) + \dfrac{Z_GZ_L}{2}\cosh(\rho_3 - \rho_1) \right. \\[10pt] + \dfrac{Z_0^2}{2}\cosh(\rho_3 + \rho_1) - \dfrac{Z_0^2}{2}\cosh(\rho_3 - \rho_1) + \dfrac{Z_0Z_L}{2}\sinh(\rho_3 + \rho_1) \\[10pt] \left. + \dfrac{Z_0Z_L}{2}\sinh(\rho_3 - \rho_1) + \dfrac{Z_0Z_G}{2}\sinh(\rho_3 + \rho_1) - \dfrac{Z_0Z_G}{2}\sinh(\rho_3 - \rho_1) \right] \end{array}}{Z_0(Z_G + Z_L)} \right|$$

At this point, it is convenient to use the identities

$$\cosh(X) = \frac{e^{(X)} + e^{-(X)}}{2} \text{ and } \sinh(X) = \frac{e^{(X)} - e^{-(X)}}{2}$$

With these and some additional manipulation, the insertion loss equation becomes

$$IL = 20 \log \left| \begin{array}{l} \left[\dfrac{(Z_0 + Z_G)(Z_0 + Z_L)e^{(\rho_3 + \rho_1)} - (Z_0 - Z_L)(Z_0 - Z_G)e^{-(\rho_3 + \rho_1)}}{2Z_0(Z_G + Z_L)} \right] \\[18pt] + \dfrac{\tanh(\rho_2) \left[\begin{array}{l} (Z_G + Z_0)(Z_L + Z_0)e^{(\rho_3 + \rho_1)} \\ + (Z_G - Z_0)(Z_L - Z_0)e^{-(\rho_3 + \rho_1)} \\ + (Z_G + Z_0)(Z_L - Z_0)e^{(\rho_3 - \rho_1)} \\ + (Z_G - Z_0)(Z_L + Z_0)e^{-(\rho_3 - \rho_1)} \end{array} \right]}{4Z_0(Z_G + Z_L)} \end{array} \right|$$

Multiplying the inside portion by

$$\frac{e^{-(\rho_3 + \rho_1)}}{e^{-(\rho_3 + \rho_1)}}$$

and grouping terms gives

$$
IL = 20 \log \left| \frac{\dfrac{(Z_0 + Z_G)(Z_0 + Z_L)}{2Z_0(Z_G + Z_L)e^{-(\rho_3 + \rho_1)}}\left[1 - \dfrac{(Z_0 - Z_L)(Z_0 - Z_G)}{(Z_0 + Z_G)(Z_0 + Z_L)}e^{-2(\rho_3 + \rho_1)}\right]}{+\dfrac{(Z_G + Z_0)(Z_L + Z_0)\tanh(\rho_2)}{4Z_0(Z_G + Z_L)e^{-(\rho_3 + \rho_1)}}\left[1 + \dfrac{(Z_G - Z_0)(Z_L - Z_0)}{(Z_G + Z_0)(Z_L + Z_0)}e^{-2(\rho_3 + \rho_1)} + \dfrac{(Z_L - Z_0)}{(Z_L + Z_0)}e^{-2\rho_1}\dfrac{(Z_G - Z_0)}{(Z_G + Z_0)}e^{-2\rho_3}\right]} \right|
$$

When considering the magnitude of the equation, only the real part of ρ is used (that is, α). The somewhat complex expression derived above for the insertion loss of a loop with a bridged tap has two basic parts. The first part is identical to the insertion loss equation found in Appendix D, where the propagation constant ρ in Appendix D equals the propagation constant $\rho_3 + \rho_1$ used here (that is, $\rho_3 + \rho_1$ is the propagation constant for the total length of the loop). This part can be called the *loop loss component* (LLC). The second part of the equation has similar form and includes additional loss due to the bridged tap with propagation constant ρ_2 and can be called the *bridged tap component* (BTC). Then, the insertion loss equation can be expressed as

$$IL = 20 \log|LLC + BTC|$$

where each component is as derived above for the general case.

If the bridged tap has zero length

$$\rho_2 = 0 \text{ and } \tanh(\rho_2) = 0$$

and the insertion loss equation reduces to the equation found in Appendix D, which is expected. If the bridged tap is connected at the central office (such as would be the case for an access line with an off-premises extension), then $\rho_1 = 0$ and

$$
IL = 20 \log \left| \left[LLC + \frac{(Z_G + Z_0)(Z_L + Z_0)\tanh(\rho_2)}{4Z_0(Z_G + Z_L)e^{-\rho_3}}\right] \times \left[\frac{2Z_L(Z_G + Z_0) + 2Z_L(Z_G - Z_0)}{(Z_G + Z_0)(Z_L + Z_0)}e^{-2\rho_3}\right] \right|
$$

Similarly, if the bridged tap is connected at the terminal equipment end, then $\rho_3 = 0$ and

$$IL = 20 \log \left| \begin{array}{c} LLC + \dfrac{(Z_G + Z_0)(Z_L + Z_0)\tanh(\rho_2)}{4Z_0(Z_G + Z_L)e^{-\rho_1}} \\[2em] \times \left[\dfrac{2Z_G(Z_L + Z_0) + 2Z_G(Z_L - Z_0)}{(Z_G + Z_0)(Z_L + Z_0)} e^{-2\rho_1} \right] \end{array} \right|$$

If the ideal condition exists where $Z_0 = Z_G = Z_L$, then

$$IL = 20 \log \left| e^{(\rho_3 + \rho_1)} \left[1 + \frac{\tanh(\rho_2)}{2Z_0} \right] \right|$$

In this case, the LLC is the same as found for a perfectly matched loop without a bridged tap; additional loss is added by the term for the bridged tap component, or

$$BTC = \frac{\tanh(\rho_2)}{2Z_0} e^{(\rho_3 + \rho_1)}$$

It is instructive to consider various cases for length and location of the bridged tap. First, consider the three situations shown in Fig. E-6, where a bridged tap is successively connected at three different locations.*

The table below summarizes the cases to be studied. The total loop length is 10,000 ft of 24 gauge, air-core PIC at 55°F in each case. The tap is the same type of cable as the main loop. Termination impedances are 900 Ω resistive at the central office end and 600 Ω resistive at the terminal equipment end.

Case (1) $\rho_1 = 2,500$ ft, $\rho_3 = 7,500$ ft, $\rho_2 = 1,000$ ft
Case (2) $\rho_1 = 5,000$ ft, $\rho_3 = 5,000$ ft, $\rho_2 = 1,000$ ft
Case (3) $\rho_1 = 7,500$ ft, $\rho_3 = 2,500$ ft, $\rho_2 = 1,000$ ft

Evaluating the insertion loss equation for each case yields:

Case	Insertion Loss with BT	Insertion Loss Without BT	Difference	Added Loss per 1,000 ft
(1)	3.62 dB	3.43 dB	0.19 dB	0.19 dB
(2)	3.63 dB	3.43 dB	0.20 dB	0.20 dB
(3)	3.63 dB	3.43 dB	0.21 dB	0.21 dB

* If these bridged taps were connected at the same time, the insertion loss equation would become quite complicated and would include terms that take into account the interaction of each tap with each section. For practical problems, however, the total loss for multiple taps can be taken as that for a single bridged tap with length equal to the sum of the individual taps.

If the tap length is increased in each case to 3,000 ft, then:

Case	Insertion Loss with BT	Insertion Loss Without BT	Difference	Added Loss per 1,000 ft
(1)	4.00 dB	3.43 dB	0.57 dB	0.19 dB
(2)	4.02 dB	3.43 dB	0.59 dB	0.20 dB
(3)	4.04 dB	3.43 dB	0.61 dB	0.21 dB

It can be seen from the above analyses that the location of the bridged tap on the main line has little effect on the resulting bridging loss.

The above bridging losses were determined only for 24 AWG cable pairs. Table E-1 shows the unit loss for all standard cable gauges in the case (2) configuration. No significant loss in accuracy results from using these values in general engineering practice.*

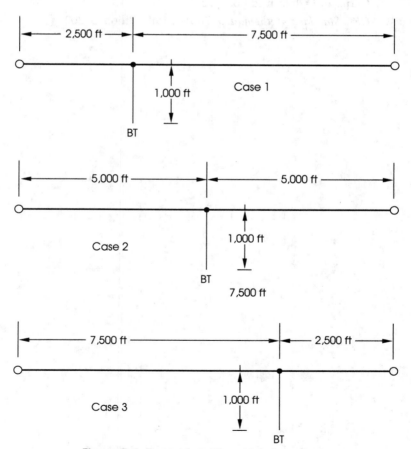

Figure E-6 Example bridged tap locations

* Bridged tap losses are usually quoted in prescription engineering literature as 0.25 dB/1,000 ft of tap length for all cable gauges. This value is conservative and will suffice for all practical problems.

Table E-1 Bridged tap loss

AWG	Loss (dB/1,000 ft.)
19	0.17
22	0.19
24	0.20
26	0.22

REFERENCES

[1] *Electrical Transmission and Distribution Reference Book.* Westinghouse Electric Corp., 1964, fourth edition, p. 327.

[2] *CRC Standard Mathematical Tables.* 19th edition, p. 202.

F

Availability Information
for References

References are shown in the text with a basic pointer to the company that can provide them as listed below. This appendix provides mailing addresses and telephone numbers (where available) for all available references except the well-known publishing houses such as McGraw-Hill Book Co., John Wiley & Sons, Inc. and others.

ABC Teletraining, Inc.
P.O. Box 537
Geneva, IL 60134
Tel. (312) 879-9000

American National Standards Institute
Sales Dept.
1430 Broadway
New York, NY 10018
Tel. (212) 642-4900
Fax (212) 302-1286

AT&T Corporate Mailings, Inc.
26 Parsippany Road
Whippany, NJ 07981
Tel. (800) 338-4038 or (201) 386-0349
Fax (201) 386-0735

AT&T Customer Information Center
2855 N. Franklin Road
Indianapolis, IN 46219
Tel. (800) 432-6600
Fax (317) 352-8484

BELLCORE Customer Service
60 New England Avenue
Piscataway, NJ 08854-4196
Tel. (800) 521-2673 or (201) 699-5800
Fax (201) 699-0936

BELLCORE Document Registrar
Information Exchange Management
P.O. Box 1910
445 South Street, Rm 2J-125
Morristown, NJ 07962-1910
Tel. (201) 829-5027 or (201) 829-4785
Fax (201) 699-0936

Electronic Industries Association
2001 Eye Street, N.W.
Washington, D.C. 20006
Tel. (202) 457-4966
Fax (202) 457-4985

GTE Practices Manager
Dept. 431, Tube Sta. C-1
400 North Wolf Road
Northlake, IL 60164
Tel. (312) 681-7483

IEEE Service Center
445 Hoes Lane
Piscataway, NJ 08855-1331
Tel. (800) 678-4333 or (908) 981-0060

Interference Control Technologies, Inc.
Route 625
Gainesville, VA 22065
Tel. (703) 347-0030

International Association of Electrical
Inspectors
930 Busse Highway
Park Ridge, IL 60068-2398
Tel. (312) 696-1455
Fax (312) 696-2510

National Fire Protection Association
Batterymarch Park
Quincy, MA 02269
Tel. (800) 344-3555

National Technical Information Service
5285 Port Royal Road
Springfield, VA 22161
Tel. (800) 336-4700

Naval Publications and Forms Center
Department of the Navy
5801 Tabor Avenue
Philadelphia, PA 19120-5099

Radio Publications, Inc.
P.O. Box 149
Wilton, CT 06897

Rural Electrification Administration
Administrative Services Division
USDA
Washington D.C. 20250-1500

Superintendent of Documents
Government Printing Office
Washington, D.C. 20402

Telephone Engineer and Management
233 N. Michigan Ave., 24th Floor
Chicago, IL 60601
Tel. (312) 938-2378
Fax (312) 938-4854

Telephony Publishing Corp.
P.O. Box 12901
Overland Park, KS 66212-0901
Tel. (913) 541-6633

Index